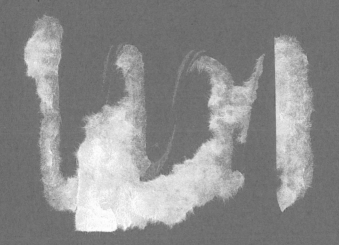

France

in the Age of the Scientific State

PUBLISHED FOR THE
CENTER OF INTERNATIONAL STUDIES,
PRINCETON UNIVERSITY.
A LIST OF OTHER CENTER PUBLICATIONS
APPEARS AT THE BACK OF THIS BOOK.

France

in the Age of the Scientific State

BY ROBERT GILPIN

PRINCETON, NEW JERSEY

PRINCETON UNIVERSITY PRESS

1968

354.44
G 42 f
64319
January 1969

DEDICATED TO MY PARENTS

Preface

Every book has a history of its own. This particular one began as a rather uncomplicated attempt to understand the changing relationship of science and state in France since the end of World War II. As a political scientist interested primarily in the contemporary interaction of scientific and political developments, I soon found myself forced to attempt to understand the long and complex history of scientific and political relations in France. Of no other country is it more proper to say that what is past is prologue and that the past maintains its tenacious hold over the present. Furthermore, I soon discovered that no issue of public life in France can ever be understood in its own terms, that each is intermeshed in a seamless web of subtle social and psychological relations which is exceedingly difficult to unravel, particularly for a non-Frenchman. It is precisely for this reason that the Frenchman reading this or any book about France written by a non-Frenchman is apt to say, "Yes! In the main you are correct, but it is essential that you *nuancez*." Unfortunately, Frenchmen, for their own part, do not provide us with many empirical and analytical examinations of French life. To explain this curious omission in French scholarship, one French social scientist suggested that it was due to the unwillingness of any Frenchman to confide in other Frenchmen, or to ask questions which would reveal an ignorance about how French society really operates.

In an age when science has become basic to economic life and military technology, I also learned that one cannot treat science in isolation as is the tendency of too many historians and sociologists of science. Therefore I found myself needing to come to terms with the growing literature on the economics of research and development, as well as forced to see the French scientific and technological effort in terms of the immense economic and political transformations taking place within the Atlantic basin and western Europe. Arriving in Paris in the summer of 1964 to do my "field" research, I encountered for the first time (and in its incipient stages) what has subsequently become the major source of conflict between the United States and western Europe: the so-called technology gap. As in the cases of the "dollar" and "missile" gaps, the upholders of proper grammar are no doubt offended. But the expression has taken its place in transatlantic debate as a shorthand expression for a whole series of developments distressing French and other European leaders—American superiority over Europe in science and technology; the brain drain of European scientists and engineers to the United States; and the historically unparalleled "invasion" of western Europe by large American corporations. Undoubtedly, too, the expression will also upset those persons who quite rightly point out that the gap is not really technological but one of management, education, and national attitudes.

As a result of these evolving issues and understandings, the subject of my study was transformed. From an effort to understand the change in relations between science and state in France in terms of social, political, and economic factors, it became an attempt to interpret (insofar as this is possible) contemporary economic and political events as a consequence of the new and revolutionary role of science and science-based technologies in human affairs. From this new perspective, while much of what is to be said in this book is unique to France, most of the generalizations and conclusions of the study have more general application for an age undergoing a profound scientific-technological revolution.

Though this study is organized around a central theme—the incompatibility of the traditional European nation-state with the new role of scientific technology in human affairs—different groups of readers will be interested in different chapters. The student of France, of science-state relations, or of modernization may find the middle eight chapters (four through eleven) of interest, while the student of international relations or of European affairs may find these chapters overly burdened with the details necessary for understanding internal French developments. For the latter, however, the three opening and two concluding chapters can be read as a unit, the primary concern of which is the impact of the technology gap on transatlantic and intra-European economic-political relations.

Throughout this study I have received the assistance of many kind and helpful critics. The difficulty in thanking them publicly is that many of the most helpful must remain anonymous. To identify only the others does not seem appropriate. Hopefully, each of them is aware how thankful I am for his time-consuming and thoughtful criticisms.

I would like to express appreciation here to the several organizations and individuals who made this work possible and who provided such excellent assistance. My research was supported initially by generous grants from the Rockefeller Foundation and the Social Science Research Council. It was supplemented by a term of leave provided by Princeton University and summer support from the Center of International Studies of Princeton University. The typing, and seemingly endless retyping, of the manuscript was patiently done by Anita D'Angelo, Mary Merrick, and Mary Leksa. At various points in the manuscript I was assisted in my research by three undergraduate research assistants: Michael Haroz, Richard Cass, and David Gardner. In preparing the manuscript for publication I have benefited from the excellent and patient editorial assistance of Roy Grisham of the Princeton University Press. Finally, my most demanding and helpful critic throughout has been my wife, Jean, to whom I am once again grateful.

Contents

Tables, Figures, Map

France

in the Age of the Scientific State

Chapter 1 · Scientific Research and National Independence: The French View

France throughout her existence has passed through periods in which the general process of evolution demanded a regeneration on her part, under penalty of decline and death. . . . This is certainly the case today, for the age in which we are living—marked as it is by the acceleration of scientific and technological progress, the need for social betterment, the emergence of a host of new states, the ideological rivalry between empires—demands a vast regeneration both within ourselves and in our relations with others. The problem is to accomplish this without France ceasing to be France.

—Charles de Gaulle, *February 5, 1962*

In late 1964 President Charles de Gaulle of France brought to the attention of the members of his Government a document warning that France, and indeed all of western Europe, must either adapt to the contemporary scientific-technological revolution or risk economic and political subjugation by the world's foremost scientific power, the United States.[1] This document, *Recherche Scientifique et Indépendance*, argued that the independence of France was being threatened by the scientific and technical imbalance between the United States and western Europe. It declared that unless France reformed her archaic scientific institutions and vastly expanded her support of scientific research and technologcal innovation, she would become

[1] The author was informed of this fact by a member of the staff of the General Delegation for Scientific and Technical Research—the French equivalent of the American President's Office of Science and Technology. The document was published in *Le Progrès Scientifique*, No. 76, Sept. 1, 1964. Its author was Pierre Cognard who probably should be credited with coining the expression, the technology gap.

an underdeveloped nation in a world dominated by scientific superpowers.

The basic issue raised by the statement of this French concern is the future of the nation-state in the age of scientific technology. The organization and dimensions of the traditional nation-state are inadequate for developing and managing the immense, complex technologies to which modern science is giving rise, technologies which provide the basis for military and economic power in the second half of the twentieth century. Just as the nation-state, with its superior organization and resources, supplanted the city-state and feudal society after 1500, so today the organization of political life is being transformed by the new role of science in human affairs. Increasingly international politics will be dominated by large-scale political entities with substantial scientific and technological resources at their disposal.

Science is playing much the same role in the evolution of the contemporary nation-state as did novel military requirements in the seventeenth century and industrialization in the nineteenth. The original institutions of the nation-state took shape in response to the international anarchy and violence of the sixteenth and seventeenth centuries. Then in the nineteenth and early twentieth centuries economic and political institutions made necessary by the first industrial revolution were grafted onto these institutions. In the contemporary world political life is once more undergoing change as science becomes the most critical single factor in military power, economic growth, and public welfare.

In the eyes of Frenchmen and increasing numbers of other Europeans the transformation of economic and political life wrought by modern science has caused the world to enter upon a new age of imperialism. The world, according to this view, is rapidly being divided into three types of so-

4

cieties.[2] On the lowest tier are the vast numbers of the under-developed societies of Asia, Africa, and Latin America, proletarian nations, scarcely able to feed themselves and dependent on the more developed nations for the technology and skills required for material progress. Next come the traditional industrial states of western Europe, as well as Japan, the United Kingdom, and several others. Many thoughtful Frenchmen believe these societies are now in danger of becoming overly dependent on the most powerful nation-states, the United States and the Soviet Union, for the technology required by a modern economy and military establishment.[3] In a world where science has become one of the vital sources of national power, only these two societies have the scientific and technological resources to enjoy full economic, military, and political independence.

Western Europe, according to this strong current of French thinking, is caught between the imperial rivalry of these two dominant scientific societies. For the period 1946-62 the threat to European independence came primarily from the Soviet Union and the overriding foreign policy task was the military containment of that power. Today the military containment of the Soviet Union, which loomed as so large a problem in Western foreign policy, has receded in importance as the United States has clearly, in the eyes of many Europeans, established its military superiority and as China has threatened Russia to the east. In the aftermath of the Cuban missile confrontation of 1962 and of the nuclear test ban treaty, a new set of priorities is believed to face France and the rest of western Europe.

Though Russia to the east remains a military menace for most western Europeans, the United States to the west is now viewed to be an increasing political and economic threat:

[2] Pierre Piganiol and Louis Villecourt, *Pour une Politique Scientifique*, Flammarion, 1963, p. 21.
[3] *Ibid.*

For France and western Europe, the military danger inherent in Stalinist postwar policy is now much attenuated. In contrast, the economic invasion by the United States is a clear and present danger. American economic power, the dynamic power of its big businesses and the size of their investments in Europe (even if in some cases they are merely pursuing on our side of the Atlantic their own competitive domestic practices) are the beginning of the colonization of our economy.[4]

Since the publication in 1964 of *Recherche Scientifique et Indépendance*, political leaders of other European countries have echoed its theme that the independence of Europe is threatened by the overwhelming scientific, technological, and economic power of the United States. In 1966 the Italian Foreign Minister, Amintore Fanfani, scored the problem of the technology gap and proposed a technological Marshall Plan for western Europe.[5] Only a little over a month later Prime Minister Harold Wilson of Great Britain warned the Council of Europe of "an industrial helotry under which we in Europe produce only the conventional apparatus of the modern economy, while becoming increasingly dependent on American business for the sophisticated apparatus which will call the industrial tune in the 70's and 80's." To avoid such a future Wilson proposed a European Technological Community including Great Britain, which might redress the balance on both sides of the Atlantic.[6] West German and Italian leaders have been vociferous in objecting to the Soviet-American treaty on the nonproliferation of nuclear weapons lest it enable these powers to have a monopoly of such advanced technologies as atomic

---

[4] Gaston Defferre, "De Gaulle and After," *Foreign Affairs*, LXIV, No. 3, Apr. 1966, pp. 440-41.

[5] *New York Times*, Oct. 7, 1966.

[6] *New York Times*, Nov. 15 and Dec. 1, 1966.

energy, space, and electronics.[7] In late 1966 the European Parliament devoted its full attention to the technology gap and to consideration of appropriate steps for Europe to take toward overcoming the problem.[8]

But it is the French who have been most concerned over the long-term consequences of the so-called technology gap and who have taken the lead among the European states in meeting the American challenge. Internally France is undergoing a revolution directed from the top by civil servants, scientists, and political leaders who seek to transform her into a science- and technology-centered society.[9] The creation of a nuclear striking force (*force de frappe*) and the founding of an ambitious space program are merely the most dramatic and outer manifestations of this concerted effort to make France into a scientific nation-state, after the image of the Soviet Union and, more especially, the United States. It is less well known but no less significant that France, under the Fourth Republic and at an accelerated pace under the Fifth, has begun the reform of her ancient and tradition-encrusted scientific and related institutions. The goal is to make science an instrument of French economic, military, and political objectives.

At the international level France is seeking to forge a system of scientific-technological alliances that could effectively balance American power. In a world where science and technology have scaled up the components of military and economic power, the French realize they must cooperate with other nations in scientific research and development. Contrary to general impressions, the French have taken the leadership

[7] Bryce Nelson, "Hornig Committee: Beginning of a Technological Marshall Plan?" *Science*, Vol. 144, No. 3,754, Dec. 9, 1966, 1,307.

[8] *European Community*, No. 98, Nov. 1966, pp. 10-13.

[9] Stanley Hoffmann and his coauthors have analyzed in depth the psychological revolution underlying the profound change which has taken place in contemporary France. *In Search of France,* Harvard University Press, 1963.

7

within Europe in both bilateral and regional, scientific and technological cooperation. Frenchmen are divided, however, over whether the purpose of these cooperative efforts is to create a united Europe, or to preserve France as an independent nation-state in a world of scientific giants.

Through an analysis of science and state in contemporary France this book aims not only to contribute to a more profound understanding of France in the latter half of the twentieth century, but to move toward new insights into the larger political implications of the modern scientific revolution. The growing importance of scientific research as the basis of national life poses a similar vast challenge to all nations. The internal problems France faces in modernizing her scientific and technological institutions are faced by traditional societies in western Europe and other parts of the world. For most if not all of these nations, changes in the nature of the scientific enterprise and in the role of science in technological innovation necessitate a reordering of educational, economic, and political institutions if they are to advance to the full of their capabilities. While other nations may not choose to follow the same strategy of modernization as France, the experience of France does provide an understanding of the challenges and problems involved in advancing from the status of a traditional to a scientific state.

The eventual success or failure of French efforts to modernize their scientific-technological institutions and to organize a cooperative effort with other nations which could balance American dominance in certain areas of advanced science and technology will have considerable significance for international politics. The degree of French success will greatly affect the balance of power within the emerging European political-economic community and the future of the Atlantic balance between the United States and western Europe. Beyond these concerns this study may provide an insight into the future position of Europe itself in an age of scientific nation-states.

The French were the first Europeans in the postwar period to appreciate the economic and political significance of the Atlantic imbalance in science and technology. This concern did not originate with the Fifth Republic, but arose from more fundamental features of contemporary France and international relations. De Gaulle, from this perspective, has been as much an instrument of these deeper economic, political, and psychological forces as he has been their master; his role has been primarily that of accelerating their effects and giving them direction.

The goal of French foreign policy since the end of the Second World War has been a European, Atlantic, and global balance of power which would insure the political independence of France and would enable her to enjoy primacy in western Europe and play a prominent role on the world scene.[10] The main obstacle to achieving this goal is increasingly believed to be the expansion of American power in the world and the penetration of western Europe by American economic influence. Contrary to prevailing American thinking that the influence of the United States is receding in western Europe, France sees an enveloping American hegemony which directly threatens French interests and which conceivably might eventually even destroy national independence.

The French regard many of their interests as conflicting with those of the United States. Though France and the

[10] Among the resources consulted on French foreign policy under de Gaulle are: Stanley Hoffmann, "De Gaulle, Europe, and the Atlantic Alliance," *International Organization*, xviii, No. 1, Winter 1964; David Calleo, *Europe's Future*, Horizon Press, 1965; André Fontaine, "What is French Policy?" *Foreign Affairs*, xlv, No. 1, Oct. 1966; Alfred Grosser, *French Foreign Policy under de Gaulle*, trans. Lois Ames Pattison, Little, Brown, 1965; and Grosser, *La IVe République et Sa Politique Extérieure*, Colin, 1961.

United States continue to share a common perspective with regard to the Russian threat to Western Europe, the divergence of interests has widened since the early 1960s. The clash within the North Atlantic Treaty Organization (NATO) between the American desire for integration of military forces and the French desire for nuclear independence is the most striking example and is too familiar to merit repetition here.[11] Less obvious are other political, economic, and even cultural matters where American and French interests are regarded by the French to be in conflict.

On the political level American and French interests are viewed as differing in almost every sphere of the globe, from Vietnam to the organization of Europe. The United States is a global power confronting antagonists on two widely separated fronts in Europe and Asia, while French security is tied intimately only to Europe. The issues of European unification and of Germany's place in Europe are important for the U. S. principally in terms of the power contest with the Soviet Union. The U. S. seeks a strong, federated Europe, but one joined with itself on important issues of world politics. West Germany, economically the third most powerful nation in the world, has, for the United States, a strong role to play in this balancing of Soviet power in Europe.

In contrast to the American theory of Atlantic partnership, the French desire a strong Europe which could exercise an independent role in the world. They do not deny that a "united" Europe, in terms of scientific-technical-economic matters, is emerging, but the important questions for the French are, who shall lead a united Europe and toward what political goals. Frenchmen recognize one issue as fundamental for France: Will Europe be shaped by one or both of the Great Powers in accordance with their interests? Will it be created

[11] The best treatment of the issue is Raymond Aron, *The Great Debate*, trans. Ernst Pawel, Doubleday, 1965.

by West Germany with the possibility of being converted into an instrument for forcing German reunification? Or will it be formed in accordance with French economic and political interests? The continued domination of European affairs by the United States conflicts with this French desire for the resolution of European diplomatic problems along lines conforming to French interests.

On the economic level, as well, important French and American interests clash. The economic evolution of France since the end of World War II has had the effect of making France more and more into an economic competitor of the United States in several important sectors. In agriculture, for example, a major goal of French planning has been to change France into a food-exporting nation and to make France the bread basket of the Common Market.[12] The success of this effort, though still limited in scope, has brought France into competition with the United States, the traditional external supplier of Europe's food needs.

And in the industrial realm the French ambition to become the scientific-technological leader of western Europe and of large areas of the non-Western world is bringing France and the United States into competition. In atomic energy, aviation, and other advanced technologies that depend on skills rather than the raw materials France lacks, the French see a chance to develop into an important industrial power.[13] Consequently the French have made a substantial investment to develop newer technologies which are being spun off by scientific advances. The success of this still weak effort to modernize French industry, the French believe, will depend ultimately on France's capacity to survive American competition and then to go on to capture European and world markets. Though

[12] Harry Johnson, *The World Economy at the Crossroads*, Oxford University Press, 1965, p. 54.

[13] Charles Morazé, *The French and the Republic*, trans. Jean-Jacques Demorest, Cornell University Press, 1958, p. 21.

the French are confident their industry will survive the opening of France to the competition of her fellow European nations, they doubt very much that France's highly dispersed and small-scale industries can survive the American onslaught they see in the offing.[14]

But the extraordinary vehemence with which the French attack the threat of American domination and economic "imperialism" cannot be explained solely in terms of a political and economic competition; this is a concern which is shared, though in lesser degree, by many other Europeans. What is involved in the French case is something deeper. It can be explained only in part by a desire to assert a crushed nationalism.[15] But it is more than this, and even more than what is indicated in de Gaulle's statement that "for a great people, to possess freedom of action is a categorical imperative."[16] The French Minister for Science got to the heart of the matter when he explained why France or any nation had to be strong in science and technology. In the balance, he exclaimed, "was the ability of a nation to maintain itself in the world without renouncing its unique spirit."[17]

This capacity to express French genius in the world (*le besoin de rayonnement*) is believed to be threatened by the expansion of American power and influence throughout the world. It is feared that slowly French traditions and values will be suffocated by the more aggressive and dynamic American civilization and that French culture will cease to exist as the Western world becomes one mass society with a common set of values imposed by the United States.[18] It is this type of con-

[14] *Le Monde*, Sept. 23, 1966.

[15] Henry Kissinger, "For a New Atlantic Alliance," *The Reporter*, July 14, 1966, p. 19.

[16] Press Conference, Jan. 14, 1963.

[17] *Nouvelle Frontière*, No. 8, Oct.-Nov. 1964.

[18] Jacques Gervais, *La France Face aux Investissements Étrangers*, Éditions de l'Entreprise Moderne, 1963, p. 189; Alfred Grosser, "Les

cern that explains the overly sensitive insistence of de Gaulle and the French Academy of Sciences that French scientists use their native French rather than English at international scientific conventions! Fear of the inundation of French culture by the American was also the basis for the refusal of the French to permit the translation of the journal *Scientific American* into French; France, the Government argued, should have its own journal for the popularization of French scientific achievements.

This theme of the antithesis between French and American civilization is an old one for France. It is encountered in Alexis de Tocqueville's *Democracy in America*, where stress is given to American emphasis on quantity in contrast to Europe's emphasis on quality.[19] More bitterly Georges Duhamel in the 1930s wrote of the United States as embodying those features of future technological civilization which France must resist.[20] Duhamel saw France threatened by scientific and technological advances spreading from America to the Old World. Even more recently Pierre Massé, the head of the French Planning Commission, expressed this theme in stating that the purpose of the national plan is to modernize France but to do so without developing the materialism of American culture. In place of the callous competition and Babel of modern materialism which Frenchmen identify with business-dominated American society, the plan is considered to be an essential instrument by means of which the state can guide economic and social modernization while preserving the integrity of French civilization.[21] In short, a strong and independent

---

Commodités de l'Anti-Americanisme," *Le Monde*, Nov. 25, 1965.

[19] De Tocqueville, *Democracy in America*, trans. Henry Reeve, D. Appleton, 1904.

[20] Duhamel, *Scènes de la Vie Future*, Mercure, 1930.

[21] Henry Ehrmann, *Organized Business in France*, Princeton University Press, 1957, p. 284. For Massé's comments see Michel Drancourt, *Les Clés du Pouvoir*, Fayard, 1964, pp. 141-42.

economy is essential if French civilization is to survive and radiate throughout the world.

> In the present-day world and in the world to come, if a country is to count on the plane of ideas, of politics, of civilization, it must depend on large instruments of production. It would be vain to hope to exercise a real influence without a sufficient base of large enterprises depending on its own modern technologies. The audience of the *philosophe* is in large measure tied to technical and economic forces.[22]

For Frenchmen of nearly all political opinions American civilization has achieved a preponderance of technical and economic power. Though there was a brief fascination with Russian scientific and technological achievement in the period following the first Sputnik flight (October 4, 1957), it has waned and been displaced by the conviction that the United States reigns almost alone as the world's foremost technological, economic, and military power. As one French writer put it, Frenchmen should not be misled by Russia's thermonuclear arsenal and Luniks; the fundamental reality is that there is only one Super-Grand, the United States.[23] According to Maurice Duverger, a well-known French political scientist, there is no longer a bipolarity of power in the world but an American monopoly.[24] "What is important," a leading French economist has written, "is the fact that under present-day conditions, the U.S.S.R. has no chance of winning the battle of economic growth. Consequently, and unless the United States makes some serious mistakes, the U.S.S.R. cannot hope for victory either in the competition for military power or living standards."[25]

[22] *Ibid.*, p. 218.
[23] *Le Monde*, Oct. 27, 1965.
[24] *Le Monde*, Nov. 7-8, 1965.
[25] Jean Marczewsky, "Can Russia Outgrow America?" *Réalités*, No.

In the face of this overwhelming threat French leaders believe France must take up once again the defense of the traditional values of western European civilization against the encroachment of an alien civilization. They point out that other Europeans are regrettably unwilling or powerless to act. The West Germans are too dependent on America for their military security; the British are considered to be an American satellite, and the rest of western Europe is too weak or too anxious for the things America has to offer. Even the Russians are helpless because of their problems and particularly because of the Chinese challenge to the east. As André Fontaine, *Le Monde*'s distinguished writer on foreign affairs, wrote in an article with the arresting title, "Face à la Nouvelle Rome," "but, for the moment there are only three countries which contest American power, each of which is symbolized by one man: France of de Gaulle; China of Mao; and North Vietnam of Ho Chi Minh."[26]

In a world where scientific research has become a primary determinant of national power, the three goals of French foreign policy—the continued military deterrence of the Soviet Union, the economic and political containment of the United States, and the establishment of French primacy in western Europe—are greatly dependent on the state of French science and technology. For this reason, as well as that of the general welfare, the advancement of scientific research has become a dominant concern of the leadership of contemporary France. More than any other European nation France is making a determined effort to increase her supply of scientists and engineers, to raise the level of financial support for science, and to

---

179, Oct. 1965, p. 25. Curiously, few Americans share these views. In fact, there is growing concern among a sizeable number of Americans that Russian power will surpass American by the late 1970s. This possibility however, does not affect present French concerns.

[26] *Le Monde*, Sept. 28, 1966.

15

reform her ancient scientific and technological institutions. In short, France is seeking to transform herself into a scientific nation-state after the model of the Soviet Union and, particularly, the United States.[27]

The effort to achieve this goal poses for France two dilemmas which provide the major concerns for this book. The first dilemma arises from the clash between traditional France and the imperatives facing a society which wishes to foster the rapid expansion and utilization of scientific knowledge. The problem for France inherent in this situation, as de Gaulle himself acknowledges, is to bring about this vast internal transformation without France ceasing to be France. The second dilemma is that the degree of European cooperation required to meet the American challenge appears to necessitate a considerable diminution of that independence and autonomy which the French are trying so very hard to preserve.

[27] As the concern of this study is primarily the relationship between science and national power, relatively little attention will be given to such important topics as medical research and social welfare.

Chapter 2 · The Atlantic Imbalance in Science and Technology

Most important of all, the Europeans, once they began to compete directly with the United States, discovered what everyone is now aware of: the tremendous discrepancy in size between American and European business. They have also discovered that, to the extent that research and development play an ever-growing role, America's potential is incomparably greater than Europe's. It is certain that in twenty-five years, even if the European standard of living is closer to the American standard of living than it is today, the world's most advanced and powerful economy will probably be that of the United States.

—RAYMOND ARON, *1965*

Whatever one chooses to label it—the "science gap," the "technology gap," the "educational gap," or as Americans tend to prefer, the "managerial gap"—the discrepancy between American and European capabilities in science and technology has become a major preoccupation of the French and other Europeans. They are particularly distressed over the U.S. superiority in those "strategic" technologies such as computers, aerospace, and atomic energy that are being spun off by scientific advance and are basic to industrial-military power in the contemporary world. These technologies not only constitute the growth sectors of the modern industrial economy and the foremost expressions of military power, but are altering the very dimensions of social life. "The computer," Christopher Layton has written, "is comparable in its significance for the age of automation to steam-power in the nineteenth century, a force that changes the whole way economic life is run. Yet the know-how is esoteric and easily kept within the magic circle of the firms involved."[1] Having already alluded to the fact that Europe is increasingly dependent on International Business Machines (IBM) and other American companies for its computers and automation know-how, Layton asked a question which the French and other Europeans have asked themselves about the need for a strong indigenous computer industry: "Can Europe afford to do without it? Ultimately, the decision is political. If it is held, politically, that Europe should be a power with a voice of its own in world affairs, one can argue with force that it should also have within its borders a center of power in this key industry that is transforming society."[2]

In practically all areas of advanced scientific technology the French and other Europeans believe the United States possesses a predominant position which it is seeking to preserve and exploit.[3] IBM controls over two-thirds of the world computer market and dominates the multibillion-dollar European market which is growing at the rate of 25 percent a year.[4] At a time when nuclear power generation is in rapid expansion the European atomic energy industry (with the exception of Great Britain and France) is based largely on American nuclear reactors. In aviation the position of the European industry has become extremely shaky and its future is uncertain, even though the aircraft market is expanding at the rate of 13 percent a year.[5] With respect to space technology, the futility of the European situation is evidenced by the fact that European-built satellites of any consequence must ride into space on American rocket boosters. Of much greater im-

[1] Christopher Layton, *Trans-Atlantic Investment*, The Atlantic Institute, 1966, p. 99.

[2] *Ibid.*

[3] W. W. Kulski, *De Gaulle and the World*, Syracuse University Press, 1966, p. 137.

[4] Layton, *Trans-Atlantic Investment*, p. 98.

[5] *Ibid.*

portance, the multi-billion dollar, and rapidly growing, field of global communications by satellite will undoubtedly be dominated by the American Communications Satellite Corporation (*Comsat*), the manager of the International Communications Satellite Corporation (*Intelsat*). And, of course, in the military exploitation of these advanced technologies the U.S. is far advanced over the other nations of the West.

What disturbs the Europeans, however, is not merely the present imbalance of technological power between the United States and western Europe, but the long-term consequences of America's over-all and commanding lead in those basic and applied sciences which are constantly producing new technologies of economic and military importance. France, in particular, has been sensitive to this situation. Faced with the American scientific-technological colossus France as late as 1963 found herself on the seventh rung in per capita expenditure of funds for scientific research.[6] In an era when technological innovation is increasingly the fruit of scientific research the French fear that this "science gap" will lead ultimately to the permanent dependence of Europe on the United States for the technologies required for economic growth, public health, and national security. To appreciate this fear, one must understand the changed relationship between science and technology in the contemporary world.

The New Relationship between Science and Technology

Western society is presently entering the third phase of the industrial revolution. The first phase was associated with the application of the *method* of science to mechanical invention in the eighteenth century and with the political rise of Great Britain. The second phase originated in late nineteenth-century Germany with the application of scientific *theory* to in-

---

[6] Assemblée Nationale, Séance du 29 Octobre 1960, *Journal Officiel*, p. 6,016.

dustrial processes and technological invention. The present phase is due to the narrowing lead time between a scientific discovery and its technological application; this period is characterized by the integration of science as an *institution* for the discovery of knowledge with those other institutions which utilize this knowledge. This latest phase is associated with the political rise of the United States and, to a lesser extent, the Soviet Union.

The essence of the first phase of the industrial revolution lay in the application of the new experimental method of science to an understanding and improvement of industrial processes and techniques. As Mantoux, Ashton, and Gillispie, among others, have shown, abstract and theoretical concepts played little part in the changes in industrial practice.[7] It was rather the spirit and example of their scientific acquaintances which guided the English entrepreneurs who began the first industrial revolution. The theoretical advances in natural history, chemistry, and mechanics of the eighteenth century were not important in themselves for the vast changes which began to take place in the textile, chemical, and power industries.[8] The evidence suggests, for example, that James Watt's pivotal invention of the separate-condenser steam engine in 1769 owed little to work on thermodynamic theory such as that by Watt's friend, Joseph Black, on the concept of latent heat.[9] Black's work did, however, infuse Watt with the "new spirit of in-

[7] Paul Mantoux, *The Industrial Revolution in the Eighteenth Century*, Harper and Row, 1961, p. 475; T. S. Ashton, *The Industrial Revolution, 1760-1830*, Oxford University Press, 1961; Charles Gillispie, "The Natural History of Industry," *Isis*, Vol. 48, Part 1, Mar. 1957, 398-407; and Charles Gillispie, *The Edge of Objectivity*, Princeton University Press, 1960, pp. 173-74.

[8] For the case of the chemical industry see Charles Gillispie, "The Discovery of the Le Blanc Process," *Isis*, Vol. 48, Part 2, No. 152, June 1957, 152-70.

[9] Sir Eric Ashby, for example, among many others, makes this point. *Technology and the Academics*, Macmillan, 1958, p. 5.

quiry."[10] In Watt's own words, Black, by revealing the "correct modes of reasoning and of making experiments of which he set me the example, certainly conduced very much to facilitate the progress of my inventions."[11] It was only much later in the nineteenth century that a true scientific understanding was obtained of just exactly why Watt's steam engine actually worked.

In the latter part of the nineteenth century the gap between scientific understanding and technological innovation began to close. Prior to this time scientific theory and its elaboration had simply not progressed sufficiently to be of much utility in the solution of industrial problems. A great deal of "normal" science,[12] to use Thomas Kuhn's phrase, had had to transpire between the great theoretical discoveries of the late eighteenth and early nineteenth centuries in chemistry and electricity before these theories could become the foundation of the modern chemical and electrical industries.[13] Furthermore, scientific theory could not be of assistance to technology until the latter had reached the high level of development which it did attain in the latter part of the nineteenth century. In short, science and technology had developed in separate and relatively autonomous spheres until around 1870 when they reached a point in their respective evolutions where scientific theory and technological innovation could become closely intertwined.

This critically important marriage between science and technology took place in Germany. Though industrial research had existed previously, the Germans were the first to under-

[10] Carl Condit, "Comment: Stages in the Relationships between Science and Technology," *Technology and Culture*, vi, No. 4, Fall 1965, 590.

[11] Quoted in Donald Fleming, "Latent Heat and the Invention of the Watt Engine," *Isis*, Vol. 41, Part 1, No. 131, Apr. 1952, 5.

[12] Thomas Kuhn, *The Structure of Scientific Revolutions*, University of Chicago Press, 1962.

[13] John Beer, "The Historical Relations of Science and Technology," *Technology and Culture*, vi, No. 4, Fall 1965, 549.

take the systematic application of the theoretical results of research to technological invention.[14] The achievement essential to this development was the transfer to industry of the laboratory organization and exact techniques of scientific research developed in the German university.[15] This "invention of the method of invention," which Alfred North Whitehead called the greatest invention of the nineteenth century,[16] took place in the German electrical and synthetic organic chemical industries.[17] While the older methods of empirical innovation did not cease to be important, scientific concepts and scientists themselves for the first time began to play a much larger role in technological innovation.

Prior to the second phase of the industrial revolution science had little to do with the political and economic fortunes of nations. The past hegemonies of Spain, France, and England were entirely unrelated to the strength or weakness of their respective sciences, though technology, of course, played an increasingly important part, especially in the political rise of Great Britain after 1560. But the technologies of gunpowder, iron, and ship-building, which provided a base for national power, had little to do with scientific understanding. On the contrary, as Thomas Kuhn has suggested, until the latter part of the nineteenth century science and technology were not only separate enterprises but "the cultural matrix that has supported a flourishing scientific enterprise has not usually supported a progressive technology and vice versa."[18]

Germany was the first nation whose meteoric political rise

---

[14] A. C. Crombie, ed., *Scientific Change*, Basic Books, 1963, p. 671.
[15] *Ibid.*, p. 676.
[16] Whitehead, *Science and the Modern World*, Mentor, 1952, p. 98.
[17] John Beer, "The Emergence of the German Dye Industry," *Illinois Studies in the Social Sciences*, XLIV, 1959, 70.
[18] "Comment on Scientific Discovery and the Rate of Invention," in National Bureau of Economic Research, *The Rate and Direction of Inventive Activity: Economic and Social Factors*, Princeton University Press, 1962, pp. 452-53.

is attributable in large measure directly to science. Before the twentieth century it was "the only nation that . . . achieved simultaneous eminence in both science and technology . . . from about 1860 to 1930."[19] Especially through the systematic advancement and exploitation of chemical theory the Germans were able, in a relatively short period of time, to transform a backward society into the technically most progressive nation on the continent—a change of no mean consequence for the European balance of power.

Unfortunately we lack any term which denotes this new alliance between science and technology. Yet, the need for some appropriate expression is obvious and such awkward phrases as "science and technology" or "research and development" are employed to cover a vast and continuous spectrum of activities which runs from fundamental scientific research at one end through applied research to technological innovation and prototype development at the other. The boundaries separating one activity from another are rarely distinct in terms of either the motives of the individuals involved or the consequences that flow from their work. Perhaps, however, the term "scientific technology," in contrast to the "empirical technologies" of the past, conveys best this notion of the increasing dependence of technological innovation on scientific theory today.

Currently the Western world is passing through a third phase of the industrial revolution because of the rapidly decreasing lead time between scientific discovery and its technological application (see TABLE 1). Scientific knowledge is not only advancing at an exponential rate—with a doubling time of less than 10 years—but scientific and technical advance increasingly go hand-in-hand. The discovery of the laser and the transistor, for example, were scientific as well as technological achievements, for which both Nobel Prizes and patents

[19] *Ibid.*, p. 453.

23

TABLE I.[a]

Decreasing Lead Time Between Discovery and Application

Telephone	56 years (1820-76)
Radio	35 years (1867-1902)
Television	14 years (1922-36)
Radar	14 years (1926-40)
Atom Bomb	6 years (1939-45)
Transistor	5 years (1948-53)
Laser	5 years (1956-61)

[a] Pierre Lelong, "L'Évolution de la Science et la Planification de la Recherche," *Revue Économique*, No. 1, Jan. 1964, p. 19.

were awarded. As a consequence, man's power over nature and over his fellow man is advancing in abrupt jumps rather than through the accumulation of many slow incremental advances.

If one inspects the spectrum of technology running from the most empirical to the most scientific, he discovers that in the contemporary world the technologies of greatest importance for national prestige and military power—electronics, aerospace, and atomic energy—are found at the scientific end of the spectrum where the lead time between discovery and application is frequently very short. It is essentially for this reason that basic scientific research has become an important factor of national power. This fact alone sets apart our age.

The essential aspect of the third phase of the industrial revolution is the transformation of scientific, industrial, and political institutions in order to accelerate the advancement of basic scientific knowledge and the exploitation of this knowledge for the innovation of novel and powerful technologies. This development began in Great Britain just before World War Two when natural scientists were taken into government to work on such technical problems as radar. But its full manifestations were not to be seen until during the war itself when the United States mobilized its entire scientific population and institutions for the successful exploitation of science for the military effort. The result was a change in the quality of scientific organization and in the role of science in society.

Today Great Power status accrues only to those nations which are leaders in all phases of basic research and which possess the financial and managerial means to convert new knowledge into advanced technologies. In the case of the two superpowers, eminence in science and in technology go hand-in-hand, and it appears most unlikely that any nation or group of nations can ever again aspire to a dominant role in international politics without possessing a strong, indigenous scientific and technological capability. International politics has passed from the era of traditional, industrial nation-states to one dominated by the scientific nation-states.

In an address to the European Parliament on the need for greater European scientific-technical cooperation, Robert Marjolin, then Vice President of the Commission of the European Economic Community, underscored the significance of the transformation that is taking place:

> The capacity for invention and its corollary, the capacity to exploit invention, now play a part similar to the possession of mineral deposits and sources of energy in the past. To be in the front rank of nations, it is not enough now to possess the equipment for mass production; you have to be able to remold your production and techniques at a pace which there is every reason to believe will grow faster in the future.[20]

The Science Gap

If one accepts the validity of Marjolin's statement on the importance of scientific research and development for the modern economy, then the Europeans have genuine cause for concern when they compare themselves with the United States. For

[20] European Economic Community, Press Release, Oct. 19, 1966, p. 1.

example, in 1962 the U.S. spent about four times as much, at official exchange rates, as did western Europe for research and development. Because of differences in research costs the effective expenditure differential is smaller but still striking. Utilizing a "research exchange rate" the United States in 1962 spent about two and a half times as much as western Europe, and about 20 percent more than the Soviet Union. Of greatest political significance is the fact that about 60 percent of this American expenditure was for military and space research, compared with about 33 percent in western Europe for the same purpose. As a consequence, the U.S. leads western Europe by a factor of four at the "research exchange rate" in the militarily significant areas such as atomic energy, aerospace, and electronics, although in nonmilitary research (and politically less significant areas) the American lead is only 1½ to 1 at the "research exchange rate."[21]

Whereas the United States has been expending three percent of its gross national product (GNP) on research and development, the Europeans have been devoting only two percent of a much smaller base. In absolute terms the U.S. is spending about $20 billion per year on research and development, as opposed to about $5 billion for all of Europe (see TABLE 2). This is an immense gap if one compares it to the period of the early 1930s when expenditures on both sides of the Atlantic were approximately equal, between $50 and $80 million.[22]

Perhaps the most reliable index of scientific-technical power is the number of engineers and scientists employed in research and development, because in the long run the supply of skilled manpower is the primary factor limiting the growth of re-

[21] C. Freeman and A. Young, *The Research and Development Effort in Western Europe, North America, and the Soviet Union*, Paris, Organization for Economic Cooperation and Development (OECD), 1965, p. 11. This is the most authoritative study of the subject.

[22] Layton, *Trans-Atlantic Investment*, p. 91.

TABLE 2.

Estimated Gross Expenditure on R and D (GERD) *and
Gross National Product* (GNP), *1962[a]*

	Millions U.S. dollars, off. ex. rate	pop. (millions)	R & D expenditure per capita, U.S. dollars, off. ex. rate	GERD as percent GNP at market price
United States	17,531	187	93.7	3.1
Western Europe[b]	4,360	176	24.8	
Belgium	133	9	14.8	1.0
France	1,108	47	23.6	1.5
West Germany	1,105	55	20.1	1.3
Netherlands	239	12	20.3	1.8
United Kingdom	1,775	53	33.5	2.2

[a] Adapted from Freeman and Young, *The R and D Effort in Western Europe, North America, and the Soviet Union*, Paris, Organization for Economic Cooperation and Development (OECD), 1965, p. 71. This is the most authoritative study of the subject.

[b] Belgium, France, West Germany, the Netherlands, United Kingdom.

search and development activities. While definitions of "scientists and engineers" differ, there were in 1962 approximately 436,000 "full-time equivalent" scientists and engineers in the United States, 415,000 in the Soviet Union, and only 148,000 in all of western Europe (see TABLE 3).[23] Thus, even though the total population of the United States and western Europe is approximately the same, the former has almost three times as many scientists and engineers.[24]

Of even greater significance, this discrepancy will not only continue to exist for the indefinite future but it will undoubtedly increase because of the greater output of the American system of higher education. "Even if Western European

[23] Freeman and Young, *R and D Effort*, p. 12.
[24] *Ibid.*, p. 72.

TABLE 3.

Estimated Manpower Engaged in R and D, 1962[a]

	Scientists & Engineers engaged in R & D (thousands full-time equivalent)	Other personnel engaged in R & D (thousands full-time equivalent)	Tot. personnel engaged in R & D (thousands full-time equivalent)	Tot. pop. (millions)	Tot. working pop. (age 15-64) (millions)	R & D personnel per 1,000 pop.	R & D personnel per 1,000 working pop.
U.S.	435.6	723.9	1,159.5	186.6	111.2	6.2	10.4
Western Europe[b]	147.5	370.8	518.3	176.1	113.9	2.9	4.6
Belgium	8.1	12.9	21.0	9.2	6.0	2.3	3.5
France	28.0	83.2	111.2	47.0	29.1	2.4	3.8
West Germany	40.1	102.1	142.2	54.7	36.7	2.6	3.9
Netherlands	12.6	20.2	32.8	11.8	7.3	2.8	4.5
U.K.	58.7	152.4	211.1	53.4	34.8	4.0	6.1
U.S.S.R.	416.0[c]	623.0	1,039.0	220.0	142.0	4.7	7.3
	487.0[d]	985.0	1,472.0			6.7	10.4

[a] Adapted from Freeman and Young, *R and D Effort*, p. 72.
[b] Belgium, France, West Germany, the Netherlands, United Kingdom.
[c] "Conservative" estimates.
[d] "Project" assumptions.

28

countries' ambitious programmes for the expansion of higher education facilities are all realised, the output of scientists and engineers in the United States in 1970 will probably still be much larger, and the relative size of her total stock will be greater still."[25] Even in qualitative terms it is feared that the Europeans will be farther behind in 1970 than in 1950.[26]

In addition, a significant proportion of this European production of scientists and engineers will migrate to the United States. Between 1956 and 1963 some 1,500 scientists and engineers (5½ percent of the European annual output) migrated *per year* from western Europe to the U.S.; and these migrants tend to be the better scientists and engineers, or at least of higher than average quality.[27] There is no reason at the moment to believe that this "brain drain" will cease (see TABLE 4).

Raw statistics on research expenditures and scientific-technical manpower, however, are not indicative of scientific achievement. Of this there are no satisfactory quantitative measurements, but there are nevertheless some crude indices one can employ. Perhaps the nearest thing to an international scoreboard for science is provided by the Nobel Prizes for science in the areas of chemistry, physics, and medicine (TABLE 5). These figures reveal a steady rise in American scientific achievement and a relative decline in western European science. France, especially, has fallen behind with respect to its past performance and in relation to that of other major European countries. Between 1935 and 1965 France, for

[25] OECD, "Resources in Research and Development," Paper prepared for the Ministerial Meeting on Science, Jan. 12-13, 1966, p. 2.

[26] This is the conclusion of one French expert on the basis of an exhaustive survey of European education from the elementary to the university level. Raymond Poignant, *L'Enseignement Dans les Pays du Marché Commun*, Paris, Institut Pédagogique National, 1965.

[27] OECD, "Resources in Research and Development," p. 4. For a detailed analysis of the "brain drain" see "L'Émigration des Scientifiques et des Ingénieurs vers Les États-Unis," *Le Progrès Scientifique*, No. 93, Feb. 1966, pp. 38-53.

TABLE 4.[a]

Migration of Scientists and Engineers to the U.S.

Last permanent residence	Immigration into U.S. (ann. av. 1956-61)			Immigrants as ratio of 1959 output of science & engineering graduates (in percent)		
	Scientists	Engineers	Scientists and Engineers	Scientists	Engineers	Scientists and Engineers
France	26	56	82	0.5	1.2	0.9
Germany	124	301	425	6.0	9.8	8.2
Netherlands	34	102	136	7.9	21.8	15.1
U.K.	155	507	661	2.6	17.2	7.4
Total "western Europe"	339	966	1,304	2.5	8.7	5.4
Austria	23	43	67	——	10.9	7.0[b]
Greece	14	50	64	3.6	20.7	10.2
Ireland	13	32	45	4.7	15.4	9.3
Italy	29	42	71	0.9	1.7	1.3
Norway	6	72	78	3.4	23.8	16.2
Sweden	8	97	106	1.3	16.3	8.8
Switzerland	38	96	134	10.6	22.4	17.0
All Europe (including others)	549	1,684	2,233	——	——	——
Canada	212	1,027	1,240	12.5	48.0	32.3
All countries	1,114	3,755	4,868	——	——	——

[a] Adapted from Freeman and Young, *R and D Effort*, p. 76.

[b] SOURCES: *Scientific Manpower from Abroad*, NSF 62-24, *Washington, D.C.*; and *Resources of Scientific and Technical Personnel in the OECD Area*, OECD, 3rd International Survey, Paris, 1963.

example, received no Nobel Prizes for science. In 1965 the award for medicine was shared by three French biologists at the Pasteur Institute, André Lwoff, François Jacob, and Jacques Monod; in 1966 the award in physics went to Alfred Kastler at the *École Normale Supérieure*.

In mathematics, on the other hand, France has been more successful in maintaining its traditionally strong position. In 1950, 1954, and 1958 French mathematicians won the

TABLE 5.

Nobel Prize Awards for Science, 1901-63

	France	U.K.	West Germany	U.S.	Russia	Italy
Physics						
1901-11[a]	4	2	3	1		1
1911-21	1	3	4	–	–	–
1921-31	2	2	3	2	–	–
1931-41		3	1	4	–	1
1941-51		3	–	3		
1951-63		3	3	15	4	–
Chemistry						
1901-11	1	2	5	–	–	
1911-21	3	–	3	1	–	–
1921-31	–	3	4	–	–	–
1931-41	2	1	4	3	–	–
1941-51	–	1	3	4	–	–
1951-63	–	6	2	5	1	1
Medicine and Physiology						
1901-11	1	1	4	–	2	1
1911-21	1	–	–	1	–	–
1921-31	1	2	1	–	–	–
1931-41	–	3	3	5	–	–
1941-51	–	3	–	8	–	–
1951-63	–	6	1	14	–	–

[a] The years are those for which the prize was awarded, not necessarily those in which the prizes were announced. The awards for certain countries such as Japan have not been included.

coveted Fields Medal, the equivalent of the Nobel Prize in mathematics.[28] But even here there is growing evidence that the French preeminence in mathematics is now being seriously challenged by Americans.[29]

Turning to another index of scientific productivity—the publication of scientific papers—here again the U.S. enjoys a

[28] Louis Dollot, *La France Dans le Monde Actuel*, Presses Universitaires de France, 1964, p. 59.
[29] *Le Monde*, Sept. 15, 1966.

significant lead over all other nations. As Derek de Solla Price has been able to show, although the number of scientific workers in the United States and the Soviet Union is approximately the same, American scientific productivity in physics and chemistry is twice that of the Soviet Union (TABLE 6). In fact, American scientists produce about one-third of the world's scientific output, in terms of research papers published, while their nearest competitors—the Russians—account for only one-sixth.

The Technology Gap

But the Atlantic imbalance is not merely a matter of scientific research. If it were, the French and many other Europeans would not be so concerned. In addition to this scientific lead, and in large measure because of it, the United States enjoys a commanding lead over western Europe in the innovation of advanced scientific technologies. As in the case of scientific research, there are no adequate quantitative measures of relative technological position, yet rough and meaningful comparisons are possible. One measure advanced by the Europeans (much to the distaste of American officials and economists) to gauge a nation's technological standing is the quasi-mercantile notion of the "technological balance of payments."[30]

A nation's technological balance of payments compares its payments abroad for technical know-how, i.e., the purchase of licenses, with its receipts from the sale of licenses. Using this measure, most knowledgeable Europeans accept as valid the conclusion that there can be no serious doubt that the United States has a very large and growing "favourable balance," while the principal western European countries have a large "unfavourable balance."[31] Most significant of all, this unfavorable balance (TABLE 7) arises mainly from the heavy and

[30] Freeman and Young, *Research and Development Effort*, pp. 51-55.
[31] *Ibid.*, p. 51.

TABLE 6.

World Production of Scientific Papers[a]

Country	Share of GNP 1964	Share of phys. abstr. 1961	Share of chem. abstr. 1965	Share of pop. 1964
U.S.	32.8	31.6	28.5	5.9
U.S.S.R.	15.6	15.6	20.7	7.0
W. Germany	5.2	} 6.2	6.3	1.8
E. Germany	0.8		2.2	0.5
U.K.	4.8	13.6[b]	6.7	1.6
France	4.5	6.3	4.5	1.4
Japan	3.6	7.8	7.3	2.9
Italy	2.6	3.4	2.7	1.5
Canada	2.2	1.1	2.0	0.6
India	2.2	1.8	2.2	14.4
Poland	1.6	1.5	2.9	0.9
Australia	1.1	0.5	1.2	0.3
Rumania	1.0	0.6	0.9	0.5
Spain	0.9	0.2	0.4	1.0
Sweden	0.9	0.7	0.9	0.2
Netherlands	0.9	5.2	0.8	0.4
Belgium	0.8	0.3	0.6	0.3
Czechoslovakia	0.7	0.9	1.6	0.4
Switzerland	0.7	1.0	1.0	0.2
Hungary	0.5	0.5	1.0	0.3
Austria	0.4	0.2	0.5	0.2
Bulgaria	0.4	0.2	0.5	0.2
All other countries	15.8	0.8	4.6	57.5

[a] Private communication. The reader's attention is invited to Price's interesting statistical studies of science. See especially his *Little Science, Big Science*, Columbia University Press, 1963.

[b] Note: Data known to be swollen because of one or more large international journals published from this nation.

growing deficit of these European countries to the U.S.; two-thirds of the total French deficit and half that of Germany is with the United States.[32]

[32] *Ibid.*, p. 53.

TABLE 7.

Estimated "Technological Balance of Payments"[a]
(in millions of dollars at off. ex. rates)

	Receipts	Payments	Balance	Ratio of payments to receipts
Transactions with all countries, all industries				
U.S., 1961[b]	577	63	+514	0.1
France, 1962	40	107	− 67	2.7
West Germany, 1963	50	135	− 85	2.7
Transactions with U.S. only, all industries				
France, 1962	11	53	− 42	4.8
West Germany, 1963	10	52	− 42	5.2
U.K., 1961	17	86	− 69	5.1
Western Europe (including others), 1961	45	251	−206	5.6
Transactions of particular industries with all countries				
West Germany (1963)				
chemicals[e]	19.3	33.8	− 14.5	1.7
electrical mach.	10.7	29.0	− 18.3	2.7
steel, mach., vehicles	14.2	45.2	− 31.0	3.2
France (1960)				
chemicals[e]	10.3	14.0	− 3.7	1.4
electrical mach.	1.7	12.6	− 10.9	7.4
mach.	0.2	4.1	− 3.9	17.2
U.S. (1956)				
chemicals[e]	34.1	10.7	+ 23.4	0.31
electrical mach.	21.0	0.7	+ 20.3	0.03
mach.	28.2	1.3	+ 26.9	0.05
vehicles	16.6	2.3	+ 14.3	0.14
Transactions of particular industries with U.S. only				
West Germany (1963)				
chemicals[e]	7.5	13.5	− 6.0	1.8
electrical mach.	0.9	13.5	− 12.6	14.9
steel, mach., vehicles	2.5	16.2	− 14.1	7.1

[a] Adapted from Freeman and Young, *R and D Effort*, p. 74. It should

be remembered that only a part of the total flow of technical know-how can be measured.

 ᵇ The unadjusted 1961 figures were $707 million (receipts) and $81 million (payments). These figures include some nontechnical payments. On the unadjusted basis the 1962 figures were $807 million (receipts) and $104 million (payments).

 ᶜ Including petroleum products.

In addition to the technological balance of payments situation, Europeans lag behind the United States in a second measure of inventive activity—patents. This is of course a much less reliable measure, because while the purchasing of licenses gives some indications of value, it is very difficult to assess the significance of patents, which can differ greatly in quality. Nevertheless, patent-filing does constitute another rough measure of technological innovation.

The American share of total European patents has averaged about 17 percent from 1957 to 1963 and is much higher than the combined western European share of total American patents (about 10 percent).[33] In the specific case of France, while French patents in the U.S. amounted to only two per-cent of the number of domestic patents in 1961, U.S. patents in France were equivalent to 45 percent of the number of domes-tic patents.[34]

But what has been most disconcerting to the French about the state of affairs is not merely the magnitude of their own deficit, with respect to patents and the technological balance of payments, but the rate of growth. In 1930 France was sec-ond in the world after the United States in the export of pat-ents. By 1938 she had dropped to fourth place, trailing after the U.S., Great Britain, and Germany. In the postwar world she was no longer an exporter but had become an importer of new technologies.[35]

[33] *Ibid.*, p. 54.   [34] *Ibid.*
[35] "55% des Brevets Exploités en France Sont Étrangers," *Entreprise*, No. 185, Mar. 21, 1959, pp. 51-53.

The deterioration of the French technological situation became cause for alarm after 1959. Between 1952 and 1958 the number of American patents taken out in France increased by 80 percent.[36] Between 1959 and 1962 the French deficit in technological payments doubled to 335 million francs and the number of foreign patents per hundred national patents had increased several times that of any other European countries (TABLE 8).[37] By 1963 the French were spending abroad 380

TABLE 8.

Number of Foreign Patents Per Hundred National Patents[a]

	1951	1960
West Germany	21	57
U.S.	22	26
France	44	170
U.K.	67	67

[a] Adapted from OECD, *Reviews of National Science Policy—France*, p. 80.

million francs more for licenses than they earned in return, and "none of the major industries in France were able to balance their license accounts in 1963."[38] (see TABLE 9.)

In 1964 the French deficit in technological payments had risen to 400-500 million francs per year and the indications were that this amount *would continue to grow.*[39] As one report pointed out, the available figures on the current state of Europe's technological balance of payments reflect the United States' research lead that existed in the 1950s. The continuing American research and development lead, the Europeans fear, will be reflected in patent and "technological payments" mainly in the latter part of the 1960s and the 1970s.[40]

[36] "La Recherche Scientifique en France et Dans les Grands Pays Étrangers," *Problèmes Économiques*, No. 809, July 2, 1963, p. 12.

[37] OECD, *Reviews of National Science Policy—France*, Paris, 1966, p. 80.

[38] *Ibid.*   [39] *Le Monde*, Feb. 7-8, 1965.

[40] Freeman and Young, *R and D Effort*, p. 54. The implications of

TABLE 9.

French Balance of Licenses and Patents by Industrial Sector, 1963[a]
(in millions of francs)

	Income	Expenditure
Oil and fuels	1.2	11.5
Foundry, heavy engineering	6.3	42.2
Automobiles	16.7	27.5
Elec. engineering and electronics	9.5	118.8
Precision engineering, clock and watchmaking, optics	0.9	52.6
Glass	1.5	4.4
Chemicals	80.8	123.9
Dairy	0.6	25.2

[a] Adapted from OECD, *Reviews of National Science Policy—France*, p. 80.

In surveying the Atlantic imbalance in science and technology in terms of its dimensions and dynamics, Frenchmen and other Europeans see little prospect that it can be overcome in the immediate or even distant future. A similar pessimism was expressed of course about the "dollar gap" of the early postwar years, and that soon developed into a "dollar glut."[41] But Europeans, and especially the French, believe the present situation to be one of an entirely new and different order. The problem posed for Europe is not just that of the present size of the gap, but the fact that the American advantages create their own momentum, forcing Europe into a vicious cycle from which it cannot easily escape.

Frenchmen fear that the consequence of the U.S.-western

American scientific leadership for the future have been nicely spelled out by Antonie Knoppers, *The Role of Science and Technology in Atlantic Economic Relations*, The Atlantic Institute, 1967.

[41] Actually the United States continues to enjoy a very favorable balance of trade. The American balance of payments difficulties are due principally to nontrade factors such as American investments abroad, expenditures by American tourists, and the costs of maintaining American troops abroad and fighting the Vietnam war.

Europe imbalance in science and technology could be the permanent economic subjugation and political domination of Europe by the United States. The rapid American advance in both spheres has added for the French a new dimension to the problem of U.S. hegemony in the Western world. By creating a *force de frappe* and departing from NATO the French have sought to lessen their military dependence on the United States and to enhance their own freedom of action in western Europe. Now, however, they find themselves faced by a new and—from their perspective—even more ominous challenge, for the technology gap has added a new dimension to the problem of American power. The technological superiority of the U.S. and the over-dependence of Europe on American technology, the French fear, increases American political influence in Europe and threatens Europe with United States economic domination.

Chapter 3 · The Dimensions of the American Challenge

It is clear that it is necessary to produce always more and always better, to save and to invest constantly and, even more, to push relentlessly our technical and scientific research, in order to avoid sinking into a bitter mediocrity and being colonized by the activities, inventions, and capacities of other countries.

—CHARLES DE GAULLE, *Address to the French Nation, 1964*

Underlying French apprehension over the technology gap is the fact that the international economy of the West has entered upon a momentous transformation with profound consequences for the positions of France and western Europe in the world. At the same time an immense common market of over a hundred million people is forming in western Europe, a true Atlantic economy composed of North America and western Europe is evolving because of recent technical advances in transportation and communication.[1] The jet airplane, the communications satellite, and the declining costs of oceanic transportation have moved the United States and western Europe ever closer together and made one united Western economy a technical possibility. The success of the Kennedy Round of tariff liberalization will make the prospect into a reality.

In response to this development the corporate giants of the United States and western Europe are girding themselves for

[1] Harry Johnson, *The World Economy at the Crossroads,* Oxford University Press, 1965; Charles Kindleberger, "Public Policy and the International Corporation" in U.S. Senate, Committee on the Judiciary, Subcommittee on Antitrust and Monopoly, *Hearings on International Aspects of Antitrust,* 89th Cong., 2nd Sess., Part 1, 1966, p. 162.

39

sustained battle. The stakes are tremendously high, both in terms of rewards for the victor and consequences for the vanquished. While there can be little doubt that the ultimate outcome will be a more productive and rationalized Western economic system, many groups, hundreds of businesses, and perhaps even whole nations will suffer during the period of transition.

Alluding to the era of intense economic competition into which France is moving, President de Gaulle warned the French people in late 1964 that they faced the danger of a new imperialism. Obviously in de Gaulle's mind the imperial power the French must fear is the United States. In this conviction de Gaulle is not alone in present-day France nor in western Europe in general. On the contrary, he has been condemned by his opponents for doing too little to meet the threat of American economic expansionism. The debate in the National Assembly in December 1964 over the proposed five-year plan, for example, was filled with recriminations against the Government on this point. It was Gaston Defferre, at that time de Gaulle's foremost opponent, who charged that the failure of the French Government to assist industrial research and production was leading to the "colonization of France by the United States." The Gaullists, he complained, are taking France not "to the independence of which they speak so much but to economic enslavement and finally political enslavement."[2] The Socialists, Defferre claimed, were better equipped to meet the American economic and political threat because they were not reluctant to place the necessary demands on French business.[3]

Until the 1960s the U.S. was seen to pose no serious economic threat to Europe. Though aware of the discrepancy between

[2] Assemblée Nationale, Séance du 24 Novembre 1964, *Journal Officiel*, p. 5,588.
[3] *Ibid.*

American and European economic power, Europeans had been preoccupied with reconstruction of their economies and had assumed that with recovery would come economic equality. In terms of such factors of economic competition as population, energy, and raw materials, the American economy has had no decided advantage over the European. While the United States has always had a greater facility in taking advantage of new inventions of whatever origin, in general the technologies underlying economic competition and growth were products of the first quarter of the twentieth century when the scientific effort was equal on both sides of the Atlantic, if not actually to the European advantage. Of course, this was also a period when scientific research was of little consequence for international economic competition.[4]

However, in the 1960s, at the very moment a unified Atlantic economy appeared to be coming into existence and when science had become a major factor in the innovation of radically novel technologies with immense economic importance, the U.S. was leaping ahead of Europe in science and advanced technologies. As a consequence, the French feared the Atlantic economic "balance" would be destroyed as America increased her scientific and technological lead over western Europe. France and Europe would doubtless become less able to compete effectively against the United States in those technologies resulting from the scientific advance.

Underlying the concern of the French was the belief that economics was rapidly being transformed by the new role of scientific research in technological innovation and the importance of technology for economic growth and competition. In the words of *Recherche Scientifique et Indépendance*, "the battles of price, conforming to the classical competition for the conquest of markets will be increasingly displaced by the

---

[4] Délégation Générale à la Recherche Scientifique et Technique, "Recherche Scientifique et Indépendance," *Le Progrès Scientifique*, No. 76, Sept. 1, 1964, p. 4.

battles for innovation [*batailles pour l'innovation*]."[5] Predictions to the effect that by 1975 40 percent of industrial turnover will concern products not known in 1965, raise for Frenchmen and others the spectre of being left far behind in the race for world markets.[6]

Again, in the words of *Recherche Scientifique et Indépendance*, "a new industrial revolution is commencing, fruit of an intensive collaboration between science and the great potential of American industry."[7] The document then warns that this "alliance and the financial base which supports it, constitutes a direct menace for all the classical economies and the autonomy of the firms who do not possess the same means."[8] In the future, "he who has technical superiority is master."[9]

According to such a view of international economics the industrial corporations of the world are seen as necessarily dividing into "pioneers" and "followers." The former, basing their competitive position on large research and development programs, will increasingly dominate the economic scene nationally and internationally. Corporations lacking significant research and development programs will become followers and dependent on the pioneers for the required technology. Forced to expend increasingly greater funds for foreign licenses and weakened by a brain drain to the centers of original research, these followers, the French fear, become vulnerable to takeover by innovative pioneering firms. This danger, the French Minister for Science told the National Assembly in October 1963, was a risk being run by too many French industries. "For

[5] *Ibid.*, p. 10.

[6] United Kingdom Council of the European Movement, *European Cooperation in Advanced Technology, Report of a Conference*, London, July 1965, p. 6.

[7] Délégation Générale, "Recherche Scientifique," *Le Progrès Scientifique*, p. 13.

[8] *Ibid.*   [9] *Ibid.*, p. 12.

reasons which are often very understandable, industry hesitates to advance the cost of research that is often expensive and hazardous. It seems more attractive in the short run to use foreign licenses, even if in the long run this may compromise the chances and even the very independence of the firm."[10]

The Spectre of American Imperialism

Many Frenchmen believe the subjugation of French firms and the French economy by American corporations was well underway in the mid-1960s. This "imperialism," in the French view, was rapidly advancing on several fronts. In the first place, as we have already seen, the "technological balance of payments" revealed that Europe had become highly dependent on the United States for its technologies. In the second place, American corporations were believed to be acquiring a strategic position in the emerging European Common Market which would enable them because of their financial, technological, and managerial superiority to dominate the French and even the entire European economy. Third, the U.S. had established for itself a dominant position with respect to those "strategic," science-based technologies on which industrial society and military power would increasingly be based.

The movement into western Europe of powerful American corporations has been viewed by the French as a grave threat to their long-term independence. As of January 1965 over 1,900 American corporations either had established subsidiaries in western Europe or had purchased a strong interest in existing European firms.[11] Between 1960 and 1966 the total American direct investment in western Europe increased from approximately 6.7 to 16.2 billion dollars.[12] As a consequence, by

[10] Quoted in OECD, *Reviews of National Science Policy—France*, Paris, 1966, p. 81.

[11] *New York Times*, Jan. 14, 1965.

[12] Walther Lederer and Frederick Cutler, "International Investments of the United States in 1966," *Survey of Current Business*, Vol. 47, No. 9, Sept. 1967, p. 45.

43

the time of President Johnson's freeze on capital exports (January 1, 1968)—a measure intended to improve America's balance of payments—most interested American corporations had established themselves in Europe. Furthermore, they could continue to grow (though at a more limited pace) through reinvestment of profits earned abroad and borrowing on the European capital market.[13]

Though the movement of American corporations into France has not been as great as that into West Germany or Great Britain, its rate of growth after 1957 alarmed the French (FIGURE 1).[14] By 1963 approximately 400 American corporations of consequence were well established in France, and a substantial number were among the largest companies in the country.[15] Parenthetically, many of the corporate invaders of France are older European firms (created prior to 1940) such as Shell or Philips, but the large U.S. company is the primary French concern.

It should be understood that the French have not been disturbed by portfolio investment but by direct investment, which entails managerial control by American corporations possessing worldwide interests, corporations whose investment in Europe is only part of a global corporate strategy.[16] Of this

[13] Max Peyrard, "American Investments in Europe Grow and Grow—Voluntary Restraints Do Not Cramp Giants," *European Community*, No. 96, Sept. 1966, p. 7.

[14] Allan Johnstone, *United States Direct Investment in France: An Investigation of the French Charges*, MIT Press, 1965, pp. 43-44.

[15] Gilles Y. Bertin, *L'Investissement des Firmes Étrangères en France*, Presses Universitaires de France, 1963, p. 246. The different statistical bases used to evaluate American investment in Europe make it difficult to obtain a clear picture. British and German estimates, for example, of American investments in France are half as high as that of the U.S. Department of Commerce. The French estimate is twice that of Commerce.

[16] Charles Kindleberger, *Europe and the Dollar*, The MIT Press, 1966, p. 30; C. E. Karsten, "Should Europe Restrict United States Investments?" *Harvard Business Review*, XLIII, No. 5, Sept.-Oct. 1965, 53-61.

Figure 1

VALUE OF U. S. DIRECT INVESTMENTS IN FRANCE, 1929-65
(IN MILLIONS OF DOLLARS)[a]

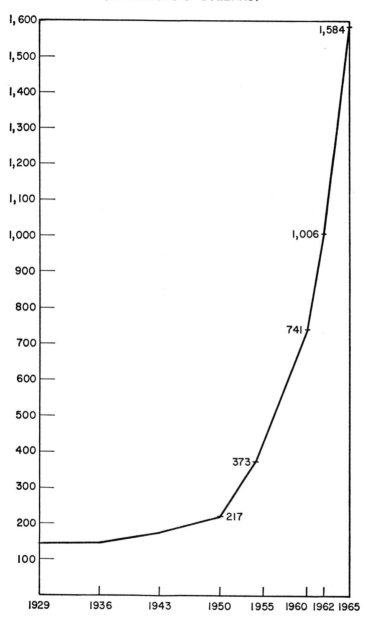

[a]Figures available from U. S. Department of Commerce, *Survey of Current Business.*

direct investment, about 80 percent is accounted for by the formation of subsidiaries, and 20 percent has involved the purchase of controlling interest in European companies. In contrast, though of an equivalent magnitude, European investment in the U.S. has generally not involved the transfer to Europe of managerial control.[17]

In the opinion of French and European observers there are several advantages American corporations have over their European rivals.[18] First, American corporations have access to a huge and fluid capital market, in contrast to the small, slow moving, and nationally oriented capital markets of western Europe. Second, American firms enjoy immense "economies of scale" and have had decades of experience dealing with a large, mass market. Finally, American management and labor are equipped by attitude and experience to accept and promote rapid technological change; from product innovation through production and marketing, the American businessman is freer of traditional restraints and can employ techniques and methods which enhance his competitive position.

Two advantages of American corporations have been stressed by the French. The first is the size of American corporations, relative to European firms, and the consequent resources they can devote to scientific research and development. In 1964, among the first 25 industrial firms of Europe (based on gross activity) only three were French: Électricité de France (9th), Charbonnages de France (11th), and Shell Française (20th).[19] If one makes the comparison with American and British corporations, Électricité de France, the largest French firm, would be in 57th place and only nine French companies—as against 114 American—were shown to have a

[17] Peyrard, "American Investments in Europe," p. 7. For a non-alarmist evaluation of American investment in Europe see *The Economist*, Dec. 17, 1966, pp. 1,254-55.

[18] Michel Drancourt, *Les Clés du Pouvoir*, Fayard, 1964.

[19] Assemblée Nationale, *Séance du 25 Novembre 1964, Journal Officiel*, p. 5,625.

yearly turnover of more than $500 million.[20] Most dramatically, one French report put the matter this way: the gross income of the first twenty American corporations is equivalent to the gross national product of West Germany; that of the first five is equivalent to the Italian; and that of General Motors alone ($14.6 billion in 1964) is greater by 10% than the gross national product of the Low Countries.[21]

In terms of gross statistics, one French writer has pointed out that although the American population is only four times that of France (200 to 50 million), the American GNP is approximately 14 times greater than the French and the investment capacity of American firms is approximately 25 times greater than that of French firms.[22] Over-all, the quantitative difference between average American and French corporations is estimated by one prominent French authority to be on the scale of 50 to 1.[23] Regardless of what these comparisons may actually mean in practical economic terms, they do give the French and other Europeans considerable cause for alarm.

The second, and even greater, advantage in the eyes of many Europeans is the subsidization of domestic corporate research and development by the American government under the auspices of its space and military programs.[24] In the 1960s 70 percent of private industrial research in the U.S. was being subsidized by the state, and nearly 80 percent of these funds was allocated to the advanced sectors related to defense and space—aviation, electronics, and atomic energy—giving American corporations a world lead in these areas. Consequently,

[20] "Face à la Concurrence Américaine les Entreprises Européennes Devront Souvent Concentrer leurs Moyens," *Patronat Français*, Sept. 1964.

[21] "La Concurrence Américaine et l'Avenir de l'Industrie Européenne," *Problèmes Économiques*, No. 869, Aug. 25, 1964, p. 8.

[22] *Atlas*, Dec. 1966, p. 36.

[23] *Le Monde*, Sept. 21, 1966.

[24] "Situation de la Recherche Scientifique Américaine," *Le Progrès Scientifique*, No. 70, Apr. 1, 1964, p. 10.

47

according to one French estimate, American corporations spend of their own and government-provided funds 25 times more on research and development than do French firms.[25]

The magnitude of the difference between American and French industrial research and development is illustrated by a comparison from the field of electronics that is frequently repeated in France. The gross revenue in 1962 of one of France's leading electronics companies was 1.7 billion francs; that of its American equivalent was 23 billion francs or a ratio of 1 to 13.5. The research budget of the French firm was 80 million francs; the American firm spent two billion francs, for a ratio of 1 to 25. Most significant, whereas the French firm received only 16 million francs in state support, the American firm received 1.2 billion francs, a ratio of 1 to 90.[26] Thus in this vital field of modern technology the French find themselves fifth in the world (see TABLE 10),[27] and dwarfed by American

TABLE 10.[a]

Size of Electronics Industries

Country	Annual turnover (millions of new francs)	Personnel
France	3,335	70,000
Great Britain	8,500	225,000
West Germany	6,000	135,000
Japan	5,500	160,000
U.S.	51,000	700,000

[a] Adapted from "L'Électronique Française est an Outsider Possible sur le Plan Mondial," *Entreprise*, May 27, 1961, pp. 14-15.

[25] "La Concurrence Américaine," *Problèmes Économiques*, No. 869, Aug. 25, 1964, p. 9.
[26] Assemblée Nationale, Séance du 9 Novembre 1964, *Journal Officiel*, p. 5,190.
[27] "L'Électronique Française est un Outsider Possible sur le Plan Mondial," *Entreprise*, May 27, 1961, pp. 14-15.

giants benefitting from huge government research and development contracts.

The situation, as the French view it, was well summarized by *Recherche Scientifique et Indépendance*: "When one sees besides that 50 billion francs of the American government's research and development contracts benefit 200 or 250 firms, of which a large part already have scientific and industrial potential 10 to 20 times ours, it is correct to fear some difficulties in the future for the new or advanced industries: electronics, computers, spatial telecommunications, new materials, rockets, biochemistry and chemical industries, and precision materials and precision optics—that is to say, all those industries whose origins and subsequent survival are intimately affected by a concentration of scientific effort and a very important innovative power."[28]

The consequences of this *inégalité de puissance scientifique*,[29] to use Raymond Aron's phrase, between American and French corporations regarding the areas of advanced scientific technologies was dramatized for the French in 1964 by what has become a classic case, one that symbolizes the problem faced by France and the other west European countries. The French had set great hopes on the prospect that the Compagnie des Machines Bull might capture a sizable portion of the vast multibillion-dollar computer market opening up in western Europe. After IBM it was the largest computer manufacturer in western Europe, and there was confidence in France that Bull could at least hold its own against the American giant. Bull, however, did not hold its own and was in fact going bankrupt. Against the 12 or so computer models IBM had on the European market, Bull had one, *Gamma 30*, and it was an adaptation of an American computer, the *RCA 301*, which

[28] Délégation Générale, "Recherche Scientifique et Indépendance," *Le Progrès Scientifique*, p. 8.
[29] Raymond Aron, "Les Pionniers et les Suiveurs," *Le Figaro*, Nov. 4, 1965.

Bull was manufacturing under license. Nor did Bull have the financial or research capabilities to develop new and more competitive models and the necessary "software." A massive transfusion of computer know-how and risk capital was required. And to obtain both, the firm desired to form an "alliance" with IBM's American competitor, General Electric.[30]

Initially the French Government strongly resisted GE's late 1962 bid to buy 20 percent of Bull's shares. The potential role of Bull in national defense and in the development of the independent French nuclear deterrent was deemed too great. Resistance to the proposed affiliation was strengthened also because the U.S. Government had just refused to permit IBM's French subsidiary to sell France a large computer for its nuclear weapons program. As a consequence, the French Government was determined to maintain full control over its single remaining, important source of computers. Nevertheless, the search for a French—even a European—solution to Bull's ills came to naught, and in July 1964 the French Government accepted a 50-50 arrangement between the American and French companies, an arrangement which took the French Government's "preoccupations" into account.[31]

The *affaire Bull* had a profound impact on the Franco-European attitude toward the economic significance of the technology gap. A strong current of European opinion was summarized by one writer in the following words:

In the short run, "a policy of licenses," a conference of European Science Ministers in late 1965 is reported to have agreed, "may be more effective than heavy spending on re-

[30] For Bull's problems before and after its merger with G.E. see G. H. Wierzynski, "G.E.'s $200-million Ticket to France," *Fortune*, June 1, 1967, pp. 92-95ff.
[31] Johnstone, *United States Investment in France*, pp. 25-26. The French approached Siemens of West Germany and Olivetti of Italy. They also tried to have the French firms combine into one large firm.

search. . . . But in the long run the cost to an industry of buying needed technical information may rise so high that the firms are faced with the choice of spending large sums on research and development or selling out. It appears that the French computer firm of Machines Bull found [itself] . . . in this position.[32]

Although the French economy benefits from this injection of American know-how and capital and the level of American investment is judged even by the French Government to be far from excessive, the French concern stems from the apparent pattern of this investment and possible long-term effects of over-dependence on American know-how.[33] American firms "control" only five to seven percent of the French economy, but "the most menaced industries are naturally the ones most necessary for our independence, liberty, power and future as a great nation"—such as electronics, new materials, and chemicals.[34] Thus, whether or not it has been planned that way, American corporations appear to be gaining control of the growth industries of the French economy and of the strategic technological areas most essential to national defense.

French officials fear that if American corporations dominate the key sectors of the French economy France would be vulnerable to American economic pressure. While the French do not doubt the sincerity of American businessmen and their denials of any political purpose in the pattern of their investment, the threat is seen to be there if the U.S. Government should choose to take advantage of it.[35] Lesser concerns of the French are

[32] Victor McElheny, "Technologically, the Atlantic Community Exists," *Science*, Vol. 149, No. 3,688, Sept. 3, 1965, 1,081.

[33] In July 1965 the Ministry of Industry issued a report on foreign (*i.e.*, American) investments in France, which stands as the best document on the subject. *Le Monde*, July 15, 1965.

[34] Assemblée Nationale, Séance du 25 Novembre 1964, *Journal Officiel*, p. 5,625.

[35] For a sample of the type of debate taking place in France over the

that foreign controlled firms will not respect the French national plan and that any research conducted in France by these subsidiaries will be on relatively insignificant problems; the important research and development work is expected to be reserved for the parent firm.[36] In addition, the parent firm through its network of subsidiaries is in a position to acquire the knowledge of French scientists and engineers.[37] And as such—the French fear—the subsidiaries may fail to be of aid in training European scientists, reversing the "brain drain," and advancing indigenous French scientific-technological capabilities. "The French," as Charles Kindleberger put it, "want a French and not an international technology, just as they want a French and not an international deterrent."[38]

Because direct foreign investment does indeed bring important resources into France, along with foreign influence, the French attitude toward it has been mixed and has undergone several reversals over a period of years. Valéry Giscard d'Estaing as French Finance Minister, for example, pursued a rather restrictive policy. His replacement, Michel Debré commenced a more permissive policy. Foreign investment was to be encouraged, provided it could meet a number of immigration tests. Investment is discouraged, for example, in areas

---

economic and political aspects of American investment, see "Pour ou Contre les Investissements Américains en France," *Entreprise*, Sept. 26, 1964, pp. 41-51.

[36] *Le Monde*, Nov. 2, 1965. Apparently only a few American firms in Europe do their important research in European laboratories. A survey by the Stanford Research Institute of 200 large American corporations based in Europe revealed that only half were engaged in research *in Europe* and that this activity represented only four percent of their total budgets for research and development. *Long-Range Planning, Research and Devolopment in Europe*, Report No. 198, 1965.

[37] Délégation Générale, "Recherche Scientifique et Indépendance," *Le Progrès Scientifique*, p. 11.

[38] *Europe and the Dollar*, p. 36.

related to national defense (which is somewhat broadly defined in France) or where the "French character" of a firm might be jeopardized. Such investment must also be consistent with the objectives of the national plan and the firm's research must be conducted as much as possible in France.[39] Despite these restrictions, however, the economic threat posed by American investment in France and elsewhere in Europe remains a real one for Frenchmen, who see the prospect of Europe being converted into a Latin America subjugated by powerful American corporations and subjected to the diplomacy of the dollar. One French writer has dramatized the situation by stating that the third industrial power of the world after the U.S. and USSR in 15 years will be not Europe but U.S. firms in Europe.[40]

The United States, the French point out, has already attempted on many occasions to use its scientific, technological, and economic power to punish France for challenging American leadership and to force American foreign policy objectives on the French. French officials note that France has been denied nuclear technology and information which the United States has made available to Great Britain.[41] For a long time

[39] For a discussion of French policy with respect to foreign investments see Christopher Layton, *Trans-Atlantic Investment*, The Atlantic Institute, 1966, Chap. 2.

[40] Jean-Jacques Servan-Schreiber, *Le Défi Américain*, Denoël, 1967. This book on the American challenge was on the bestseller list in France. It should be noted that the liberalization of French policy on foreign investment was greeted with accusations, even by moderates, that de Gaulle was selling out to the Americans. (*New York Times*, Jan. 15, 1967.) For a more European view, which has gained currency in France and elsewhere, see Alessandro Silj, *L'Industrie Européenne Face à la Concurrence Internationale*, Lausanne, Centre de Recherches Européennes, 1966; and see the review in *Le Monde*, Sept. 22, 1966.

[41] *New York Times*, Apr. 20, 1966. On the other hand, the U.S. has also refused to sell Great Britain communications satellite technology that might weaken the American hold on this field. *The Economist*, June 11, 1966, p. 1,167.

53

the U.S. refused to sell France certain types of computers for fear they would be employed in the construction of France's nuclear striking force.[42] The French also point out that American firms have been prevented by the U.S. Government from cooperating with French firms in missile development.[43] The U.S., they argue, also reneged on agreements to supply France with the enriched uranium needed to develop a submarine propulsion reactor.[44]

From the perspective of the United States its actions could be justified in terms of its goal of arresting nuclear proliferation. But from the French perspective, these incidents clearly illustrate both the dangers of over-dependence on the U.S. for advanced technologies and the willingness of America to press her advantage. Perhaps more than anything else, the refusal of the United States to share nuclear and related information and technology with France that it does share with Great Britain has poisoned American-French relations. This discrimination has weighed heavily on the minds of de Gaulle and other French leaders. It is a key to an appreciation of French concerns over American domination and, parenthetically, de Gaulle's refusal to let Britain into Europe.

A statement by Gaston Defferre that appeared in the American journal, *Foreign Affairs*, summarizes the growing and intense French concern about American domination:

---

[42] The U.S. finally agreed to sell France computers, provided France first agreed not to use them in the construction of her nuclear weapons program. (*Le Monde*, Oct. 22, 1966.) The basis for the original American refusal was the nuclear test ban treaty, which forbids the signatories from assisting a nonnuclear power to obtain nuclear weapons.

[43] Aerojet General Corporation, the leading American firm in solid fuel rocket technology, was negotiating a deal with two French groups (SEREB and SNECMA) when the United States Government in September 1959 sent out an order forbidding cooperation on missile projects. Cf. Leonard Beaton and John Maddox, *The Spread of Nuclear Weapons*, Praeger, 1962, p. 94.

[44] *New York Times*, Apr. 17, 20, 1966.

The relative economic power of the United States is shown by the fact that its national income is eight times that of France; the annual increment alone is half the total French national income. A single American corporation, General Motors, has a budget nearly equivalent to that of France. The largest French enterprise would rank fiftieth among American firms, which are scaled to a continent of nearly 200,000,000 people. Clearly, French firms are unable to fight these competitors from across the sea. As a result, American investments are becoming more and more numerous in France and in Europe, particularly in fields of most rapid growth. The Bull concern, the only large French maker of electronic computers, is both a crushing example of this phenomenon and an illustration of how the Gaullist government meets it. When Bull was in difficult straits, the French Government helped it to avoid bankruptcy; then it allowed the majority holdings to pass into the hands of General Electric, which competes on the world market with another American firm, IBM. Thenceforth, the centers of decision in a vital sector, not only in the economics sense but for the national defense, were no longer in France but in the United States.

Thus it can be said that General de Gaulle's nationalist policy is not only carrying us back to a bygone era, but is leading—under an appearance of independence—to the colonization of the French economy by the United States. Some say that this is neither wished for nor welcomed by the U.S. Government, that it foils its efforts to maintain the stability of the dollar and that unfavorable reactions to it hamper American diplomacy. It none the less remains a dangerous and unacceptable fact. Colonization always leads sooner or later to decolonization—after trouble, suffering and sometimes war.[45]

[45] "De Gaulle and After," *Foreign Affairs*, LXIV, No. 3, Apr. 1966, 441-42.

The Foundation of French Fears

Underlying French concern about the political and economic implications of the technology gap are a number of assumptions. Since they impinge on this study throughout, they should be made explicit, evaluated, and placed in the perspective of the over-all study.

First, the French position assumes that in this age of scientific technology leadership in basic research gives a nation and its industries the edge in the innovation of novel technologies. Basic research is not viewed as a public good equally available to all nations; instead a strong *indigenous* capability in basic research conveys a number of advantages in the competition to innovate new products and industrial processes. In an age when the lead time between new science and new technology has become so short, the French believe that it is no longer sufficient to draw on the world's common pool of knowledge, but that a nation must itself be at the frontier of knowledge.[46]

The second French assumption is that there is a direct relationship between corporate size and inventiveness.[47] Size in itself is believed to impart an overwhelming advantage to a firm because of the magnitude of the research and development effort it can support. In competition with the great American corporations entering western Europe, the French fear that their small firms have little prospect of innovating and financing technologies that will outsell American counterparts.

[46] Pierre Piganiol and Louis Villecourt, *Pour une Politique Scientifique*, Flammarion, 1963, p. 54.

[47] Another assumption related to size, which we will not discuss, is that the United States enjoys the advantage of a large, homogeneous market. An excellent analysis of alleged American strengths vis-à-vis European weaknesses is James Quinn, "Technological Competition: Europe Versus United States," *Harvard Business Review*, July-Aug. 1966, pp. 113-30.

The third assumption of the French and other Europeans is that the multinational corporations, largely of American character, establishing themselves in western Europe constitute a potential economic and political danger. Contrary to the prevalent view of neoclassical economics, indeed, of the American government, that the interests of these corporations and the host countries are identical, the French are afraid these large corporations will establish monopolies in strategic fields and thus dominate the European economy.

The fourth French assumption is that priority of technological innovation constitutes a decisive and self-perpetuating advantage in economic competition. Given the American lead in such advanced technologies as electronics and pharmaceuticals, the French fear they will virtually never be able to compete in these and other important areas of scientific technology. As a consequence the growth sectors of the French economy will become increasingly dominated by American firms, and France, as well as the rest of western Europe, will be totally dependent on American technical know-how in those economic areas that really matter.

A proper assessment of these assumptions would necessitate an inquiry which goes beyond the scope of this study. Each is a mixture of truth and fiction. But in the present state of economic knowledge no definite conclusions can be asserted that conclusively support or refute the French position. As one study on the economics of research and development has put it, "one simple proof of the present rudimentary state of knowledge is that practically any statement can be made without fear of decisive contradiction."[48] Without attempting to do anything more than to suggest the direction in which the truth may lie, let us look at each assumption in turn.

[48] John Jewkes, David Sawers, and Richard Stillerman, *The Sources of Invention*, Macmillan, 1961, p. 5.

The Dimensions of the American Challenge

Though traditional laissez-faire economists are reluctant to admit it, there is much truth in the French position that leadership in basic research strengthens a nation's or firm's innovative competence. Carl Kaysen, Director of the Institute for Advanced Study, has distinguished four kinds of benefits to a nation that flow from basic research: (1) basic research is "a major input to the advance of applied science and technology"; (2) "there is the intimate relation between the conduct of research and the provision of higher education in science and technology," for the scientists and technicians needed "to operate the apparatus of society in defense, industry, and health, as well as to continue the stream of improvements in that apparatus that we have experienced in the past and expect in the future"; (3) "experience shows that an applied research and development effort, undertaken with the purpose of solving specific practical problems, benefits from a close relation with basic research"; and (4) "the corps of scientists working on basic research represent an important reserve of capability in applied research and development that can be drawn upon when national needs dictate."[49]

The essential reason for a corporation and even a nation having a strong capability today was expressed by Hendrik Bode, Vice President of Bell Telephone Laboratories, in reply to a question put to him by this writer on the relationship of basic research and technological innovation:

[49] Carl Kaysen, "Federal Support of Basic Research," in *Basic Research and National Goals,* A Report to the Committee on Science and Astronautics, U.S. House of Representatives, by The National Academy of Sciences, Mar. 1965, pp. 149-50. A normal career in many large American corporations is to start out in basic research and as one's research develops practical implications the researcher moves over into development and administration. The writer is indebted to Thornton Read of the Bell Telephone Laboratories for this observation.

So far as I am aware, there are very few real facts on which one might base a reliable statement. I can only express a few cautious opinions. Briefly, then, the economists' view that the results of basic research are an international resource rather than a purely national asset has clearly been true in the past. I believe it is still true for many industries, but the desirability of a relatively close coupling between basic research and an indigenous technology becomes more and more obvious as one goes into areas of more sophisticated technology or areas where very short time scales are important. These might exist in either military areas or very competitive civilian areas.

The commonest fallacy which most laymen make in discussing the relation between basic research and industrial application is to assume that if one simply reads the scientific papers he will come across a series of recipes which can be applied in a reasonably straightforward manner. This is hardly ever true. The application of science, particularly in a trail-blazing way, is much more likely to be a subtle and demanding occupation. To understand the basic research at all one frequently needs to be working in the field himself. Many of the research areas in industrial laboratories are maintained primarily with this end in view, rather than because they will themselves contribute a great deal to the total stock of relevant knowledge. Their basic mission, in other words, is simply to "keep in touch."[50]

In short, according to this position, scientific research is a national resource which conveys important advantages of a direct and indirect nature. It is, however, a very mobile resource which seeks out the locale "where the action is." If a nation does not have an active and advanced scientific and technical program, it runs the serious risk of seeing its best

[50] Letter to the author, dated Nov. 8, 1965.

minds migrate abroad. Experience supports the argument that France and Europe must have ambitious research programs in basic research if they are to retain their scientific-technical personnel and to innovate the technologies of the future.

There is, however, support for the opposite position. Harry Johnson, a distinguished economist, has argued that "there is no necessary connection between leadership in basic science and leadership in the application of science. . . ."[51] In his words, "American leadership has rested primarily on two elements: the capacity to put science and technology to work in the service of raising the standard of living of the masses, and the capacity to mobilize science and technology on a massive scale in the development of superior armament."[52] What has been important has been the economic and managerial capacity "to pay for and organize scientific and technical progress . . . rather than the scientific leadership that has established the capacity to perform the projects."[53]

In support of this position it is pointed out that for a long time the American advantage over western Europe definitely lay primarily in its managerial and engineering capacity to outpace Europe in converting new knowledge into new technology; it was the Europeans who were the leaders in basic research and the inventors of many of the new technologies, e.g., television or jet propulsion, which U.S. industry has exploited. Even today the lead time between discovery and application is still sufficiently long in most areas that new basic knowledge of whatever origin is available for anyone to exploit. The Dutch and the Japanese, for example, have made important technological advances recently without distinguishing themselves in the related sciences. This is Johnson's position:

[51] "Federal Support of Basic Research: Some Economic Issues," in *Basic Research and National Goals*, p. 127.

[52] *Ibid.*, p. 130.

[53] *Ibid.*

Given the international character of science, which makes scientific discoveries in one country available to scientists in all, and the fact that the value of a scientific discovery may not be apparent for a long time and is frequently contingent on other discoveries of an unpredictable nature, there is no reason to assume that leadership in basic scientific research and leadership in technology and applications of science are necessarily connected. A nation could achieve leadership in applications by drawing on knowledge provided by the basic research conducted by the scientists of other countries, confining its own participation in basic science to the minimum required to keep in touch with developments elsewhere and "fill in the holes" where necessary. Conversely, a position of leadership in basic research might benefit a nation almost exclusively in terms of the intangible prestige of scientific accomplishment, the concrete benefits of the application of scientific findings being reaped mainly by other nations. In that case, the expenditure of public money on the support of basic scientific research would serve mainly to save other countries the cost of basic research and enable them to concentrate on development and application; and the "leadership" so obtained might be largely leadership in the eyes of a relatively small group of scientists in other countries, plus those members of the general public who are interested in scientific achievement in the same sort of way as others are interested in international sporting competitions.[54]

The conclusion this argument suggests is that basic research is increasingly a necessary but not a sufficient prerequisite for leadership in technology. While a certain level of basic research is necessary to stay abreast of advances elsewhere, even of greater importance is corporate management's willingness and skill to exploit new knowledge. In the present era, as in the past, it is the possession of these psychological and administra-

[54] *Ibid.*, pp. 128-29.

tive strengths which have provided American corporations with a certain advantage over their European competitors in the innovation of new technologies.

RELATION OF CORPORATE SIZE
TO TECHNOLOGICAL INVENTION

It is not easy to obtain a clear answer to the French assertion that there is a positive correlation between corporate size and technological inventiveness.[55] At the most, there appears to be no direct relationship between size and innovation. Small firms may lack risk capital for research and development, but the management of large firms may have a greater tendency to become stolid and conservative. The Route 128 phenomenon around Boston, for example, reveals that small firms with dynamic managements and good ideas can excel in the highly competitive realm of advanced technology.[56] But even here the French appear to be at a disadvantage because so many factors —conservative business practices, the absence of venture capital, and the snobbish attitude of French scientists toward business—mitigate against the development of dynamic research industries.

On balance the available evidence suggests that "medium sized" firms in a competitive situation are optimum for rapid technological innovation since they have both the necessary resources and the incentive to innovate. As one leading American authority summarized available research findings, "giant

[55] There are of course other claims for the advantages of size in economic efficiency and competition.

[56] A frequently cited example is that of Control Data Corporation, which started with eight engineers and less than one million dollars and was able to challenge IBM's technical leadership in computers. ("Small, Smart, Sharp," *Business Week*, May 25, 1963.) One recent study showed that the individual with a new idea is still the key to new invention, but the development of the idea into a useful innovation increasingly involved huge funds and team of researchers. Jewkes, Sawers, and Stillerman, *Sources of Invention*.

size is no prerequisite for the most vigorous inventive and innovative activity. There may be a size threshold below which firms have a disadvantage because they cannot reap all R and D economies, spread risks, or tap sufficiently large markets in exploiting their research results."[57] Even so, what gives so many American firms of all sizes a decisive advantage over their European competitors is the fact that American corporate management appreciates the importance of innovation in economic competition.[58]

Rightly or wrongly, the French are convinced that their industries are below the necessary "threshold" for effectiveness and that corporate size is the key to economic power in the modern scientific age.[59] Certainly the archaic structure of the French economy with its many relatively small firms is regarded by the French Government as a major cause of France's technological and economic backwardness. For example, the size of French corporations is held to be responsible for the fact that "the percentage of development expenditures (the most expensive scientific activities) to total industrial research is lower in France than anywhere else."[60]

The correlation between corporate size and technological development does appear to be highest in those areas of scientific technology which are themselves the growth sectors of the modern economy and are also most relevant for military power. As Hendrik Bode has pointed out, science-based indus-

[57] F. M. Scherer, statement before the U.S. Senate, Committee on the Judiciary, Subcommittee on Antitrust and Monopoly, *Hearings on Economic Concentration*, 89th Cong., 1st Sess., Part III, May 25, 1965, p. 25.

[58] *Le Monde*, Sept. 22, 1966.

[59] Drancourt, *Les Clés du Pouvoir*. For a detailed analytical study of French industrial structure see Joe Bain, *International Differences in Industrial Structure*, Yale University Press, 1966.

[60] OECD, *Reviews of National Science Policy—France*, p. 78. One rule of thumb is that in any project, for every dollar spent on research, 10 must be devoted to prototype construction and 100 for development.

tries tend to differ from traditional mass production industries in that emphasis is placed on an increase in the size, complexity, or some other quality of the product, such as speed in computers or aircraft rather than on the production of large quantities.[61] Therefore, as relatively more engineering hours must be invested to produce a dwindling number of products, the "cost relation between production and engineering development moves farther and farther from the proportions that were obtained historically."[62] For example, research and development costs, considered as a percentage of sales, are 24.2 for aerospace, 10.4 for communications, 4.6 for chemicals, and only 2.9 for motor vehicles.[63] Moreover, the "total development bill must be paid before even one unit is available" and "the success of [the] . . . project . . . depends on the existence of a full storehouse of interrelated techniques on which to draw."[64]

What this analysis seems to suggest is that in the contemporary world of complex and extremely costly science-based technology, there is a "critical mass" of scientific, technical, and financial resources which a corporation or nation must possess if it is to innovate, earn from selling know-how, and make the most of the know-how purchased from others.[65] Only large corporations, and perhaps even only relatively large nations, have the great variety of competences and risk capital for in-

[61] "Reflections on the Relationship of Science and Technology," in *Basic Research and National Goals*, pp. 66-67.

[62] *Ibid.*, pp. 70-71.   [63] *Ibid.*, p. 61.   [64] *Ibid.*, p. 71.

[65] Unfortunately there is very little available evidence on the relation of national size and economic performance. (Cf. E. A. G. Robinson, ed., *Economic Consequences of the Size of Nations*, Macmillan, 1960; Harold Sprout, "Geopolitical Hypotheses in Technological Perspective," *World Politics*, xv, No. 2, January 1963, 204-206.) One empirical study by the British National Institute of Social and Economic Research estimated that a minimum research and development budget of four million pounds was required to develop a commercial computer and 40 million pounds was required to develop a simple space satellite. "Research and Development in Electronic Capital Goods," *National Institute Quarterly Review*, Nov. 1963.

venting and developing such advanced technologies as computers, supersonic aircraft, and spacecraft.

From this perspective it is sobering for France or Great Britain to realize, for example, that IBM's annual research budget is greater than the annual sales of Britain's largest computer firm (International Computers and Tabulators),[66] and that IBM invested the approximate amount ($5 billion) to develop its all-purpose model, the *360*, that France plans to spend on her nuclear force during the military law-program (1965-70). It was in appreciation of this relationship between size and technological dominance that Prime Minister Wilson proposed a European Technological Community:

> America's technological dominance in so many parts of the world derives from the original opportunities presented by her own wide, dynamic markets. It derives too from the fact that her industries are sufficiently developed and massive, sufficiently free from undue fragmentation, to enable her to reap the advantage of a large scale production which modern technology demands, and will in increasing measure demand.[67]

Consequently, although size may not generally be an important prerequisite for technical invention, economies of scale are extremely important in certain areas of "big technology" if a corporation is to have the financial and technical resources to develop new ideas and concepts into useful innovations. As Bode concludes: "The depth and adequacy of the supporting technology are what count. In this respect, the communications satellite, or the supersonic transport, are at least broadly akin to the atomic bomb and the transistor. . . ." in terms of the "critical mass" of scientific, technical, and managerial resources required for their development.[68]

[66] Layton, *Trans-Atlantic Investment*, p. 95.
[67] Quotation from *Science*, Vol. 154, No. 3,754, Dec. 9, 1966, 1,309.
[68] Bode, "Reflections on Science and Technology," pp. 71-72.

The economic sectors most affected are those science-based industries where the percentage of research and development expenditures relative to total sales is the greatest. These areas, of course, are the ones most closely related to national power and international prestige, as well as being highly competitive civilian areas. In the realm of sophisticated technology the big company with a large R and D budget does most often predominate. Thus while it is impossible for American corporations to have a comparative advantage in all aspects of economic competition, the Europeans, with good reason, fear the United States does have and will continue to have an absolute advantage in those advanced technologies that affect national power and prestige. Moreover, even in the realm of nonmilitary technologies "one cannot dismiss the argument . . . ," Bela Balassa has written, "that in industries characterized by rapid technological progress, the disadvantages of European firms in regard to the availability and cost of financing, and the ability to engage in research and development, would adversely affect their competitiveness vis-à-vis the U.S. subsidiaries."[69]

MULTINATIONAL CORPORATIONS: A POLITICAL AND ECONOMIC THREAT TO THE HOST COUNTRY?

The third French assumption is that the invasion of Europe by large American corporations brings with it dangers of foreign, monopolistic control and that conflicts of interest can exist between these multinational corporations and the host country. Here there is actually very little one can say on the basis of economic theory and experience. Stephen Hymer attests to the state of our knowledge: ". . . when one considers the enormous importance of international firms in the flow of goods, capital and technology between countries, it is surprising how little is known about why direct investment in foreign

[69] "American Direct Investments in the Common Market," Banca Nazionale Del Lavoro, *Quarterly Review*, No. 77, June 1966, p. 144.

branch plants and subsidiaries occurs, and what, if anything, should be done about it."[70]

What the available evidence does suggest is that direct investment by large corporations in foreign manufacturing is a relatively new phenomenon not adequately covered by neoclassical views of international trade. Both the motivations for, the magnitude of, and the possible consequences of this type of investment differ from the traditional free trade doctrine which holds that "capital flows toward higher interest rates, and has generally beneficial effects."[71]

The novelty in the situation is due to the fact that direct investment involving consequent managerial control is "associated with a small number of large firms in oligopolistic industries."[72] As in any oligopolistic situation these firms frequently enjoy market power and free choice rather than being "controlled" by the forces of the competitive market. Furthermore, the acquisition of a foreign subsidiary, as Kindleberger has suggested, is part of a global corporate strategy by which the parent corporation seeks to exploit certain advantages such as a technological lead and thereby to maximize its profits.

As several authorities have suggested, what is good for the multinational firm or its homeland may not be good for the country in which a particular subsidiary is located.[73] Rightly or wrongly, one French fear, for example, is that the multina-

[70] "Direct Foreign Investment and International Oligopoly," Economic Growth Center, Yale University, mimeo., June 1965, p. 1.

[71] *Ibid.*, p. 29.

[72] Stephen Hymer, "The Impact of the International Firm," Economic Growth Center, Yale University, mimeo., May 17, 1966, p. 2.

[73] This point is made by both Hymer and Kindleberger in their previously mentioned writings. See also Jacques Houssiaux, "La Grande Entreprise Multinationale," *Économie Appliquée*, xvii, April-Sept. 1964. For a wide-ranging discussion of the role of the international corporation today see U.S. Senate, Committee on the Judiciary, Subcommittee on Antitrust and Monopoly, *Hearings on International Aspects of Antitrust*. A study of American corporations in Canada does not bear out

tional corporation might conceivably operate its subsidiary at a loss to destroy local competition. Or the U.S. might impose policies on these firms which would harm France. Certainly the second *affaire Bull* of 1966, in which General Electric cut back its computer lines in France, reinforced the French Government's concern,[74] as did the U.S. decision of January 1, 1968, that those firms repatriate a fixed percentage of their profits to the U.S. But as French reaction to U.S. restrictions on American investment in Europe revealed, these long-term fears are subordinate to France's present need for American capital and technology.

THE ECONOMIC ADVANTAGES
OF TECHNOLOGICAL LEADERSHIP

The fourth French assumption and, that of many other Europeans is that technological inventiveness has become a major factor in economic competition. Defending the French nuclear striking force because of its scientific and technical "fallout," one French writer expressed the logic of this position:

> Scientific research . . . has during recent years become one of the basic means of competition and tends increasingly to be organized into a veritable "industry of discovery." More

---

the French fear. A. E. Safarian, *Foreign Ownership of Canadian Industry*, McGraw-Hill, 1967.

[74] *New York Times*, Jan. 4, 1967. It also raised the spectre of a French Castroism, i.e., the demand for nationalization of Bull and elimination of absentee ownership. (*Le Monde*, Jan. 3, 1967.) In this connection it should be appreciated that "multinational corporation" refers to the scope of operation and not the control of the corporation. If the boards of directors were truly international in character and managerial control did not rest in a foreign country the French attitude might be different. Furthermore, it should be noted that a French firm would probably have acted no differently than G.E. under the circumstances and that in general the multinational firms have been more responsive to the French government's plans, especially that of regional development than have been indigenous firms.

exactly, it is indispensable to emphasize that, in a prospective view of international commerce, in which industries can henceforth supply themselves with raw materials at practically equal prices and in which wage scales progressively tend to equalize in all countries, advantages in competition can be achieved only by constant technical improvements, that is to say, by an intense and continuous development of research in every field.[75]

According to this view, international trade in a significant number of goods is determined by the technological gap between countries rather than by relative cost or other traditional factors of competition.[76] The relative importance of research-intensive goods in American international trade, for example, is cited to bear out this contention.[77] Furthermore, it is argued, once a lead is established in an advanced technology it is usually maintained.[78] As Andrew Shonfield has stated it, "the point is simply that the breakthrough which leads to the production of a new chemical, for example, is only the beginning of an extended process of innovation. The firm which

[75] Albert Boyer, "Aspects Scientifiques et Économiques de la Construction d'un Armement Nucléaire par la France," *Revue De Défense Nationale*, Oct. 1963, p. 1,545.

[76] G. C. Hufbauer, "Synthetic Materials in International Trade," unpub. thesis, Cambridge University, quoted in Andrew Shonfield, *Modern Capitalism*, Oxford University Press, 1965, p. 430. See also Christopher Freeman, "The Plastics Industry: A Comparative Study of Research and Innovation," *National Institute Economic Review*, No. 26, Nov. 1963.

[77] Harvey Brooks, "Future Needs for the Support of Basic Research," *Basic Research and National Goals*, p. 79. Cf. Donald Keesing, "Research, Development and Trade: Does the United States Specialize in New Products?" preliminary draft, Nov. 23, 1965. The U.S. has 60 percent of world exports of electronic capital goods, compared with 20 percent for world exports of all types. "The U.S. Electronics Industry in International Trade," *National Institute Economic Review*, No. 34, Nov. 1965, pp. 92-97. Cf. M. V. Posner, "International Trade and Technical Change," *Oxford Economic Papers*, XIII, 1961.

[78] G. Teeling-Smith, ed., *Science, Industry and the State*, Pergamon Press, 1965, pp. 35-52.

gets ahead initially tends to go on making improvements both in the quality of the products and in the process of production."[79]

In essence this position argues that the contemporary technological revolution has modified to some extent the relative advantages of "forwardness" and "backwardness" in development and that Europe will suffer the consequences:

> ... there are some strong reasons for supposing that in a period of accelerated technological change the advantages of "forwardness" may be very great indeed. If the opportunities for raising productivity by means of new techniques continue to multiply and if they result in radical changes in the quality, or even the identity, of a large number of products, the big prizes, for example in export markets, will go to those who are habitually first. ... The transient monopolistic element in the new products may produce advantages for the innovator, both by shifting the terms of trade in his favour and by enlarging his export market opportunities. ...
>
> In sum, it is likely to be the habit of rapid and continuous innovation which will produce the greatest rewards, in an age in which scientific discovery is communicated faster and the opportunities for its exploitation in productive processes are uncovered more rapidly than in the past. ... There is nothing so far to show that the Americans will be less flexible in this regard than their European competitors, and some evidence which suggests that with their vast budgets of research and development, their more sophisticated institutions for the management of innovation, and the underlying cultural bias in favour of rapid change, the conditions for accelerated economic growth in the second half of the twentieth century may be especially in their favour.[80]

[79] Shonfield, *Modern Capitalism*, 1965, p. 60.
[80] *Ibid.*, pp. 59-60.

On the other hand, a view does exist which minimizes the economic importance of technological leadership. It is noted that it is virtually impossible that any one country or corporation have an advantage with respect to every factor of economic competition and every product; the effort to exploit most efficiently one factor of production or the emphasis placed on one product necessarily leads to relative weakness with respect to other factors or products. Second, technological leadership provides a temporary advantage at best and there is a decided advantage in "backwardness." The industrial or technological leader pays the price of research and development costs which the follower does not have to pay. The follower, in fact, can learn from the mistakes of the leader and through the purchase of licenses (provided the patent holder is willing to sell) can reap equal or greater benefit. The higher growth rate of western Europe as compared with the United States over the past several decades is frequently cited as evidence in support of this position. On the other hand, most production processes and frequently products are not available through licensing.

American critics of the technology gap thesis point to the fact that the technological lead of the United States over western Europe has actually existed for over a century and a half and that in many areas it has begun to slip during recent decades. Two factors in particular account for this: (1) European industry has become more research-minded; and (2) technology is diffused today with ever greater rapidity from one country to another. Europeans, it is argued, have been misled by American success in the spectacular technologies associated with space and national defense to assume an American lead exists in all areas. There is in fact a concern among many writers in the United States that before many decades the technology gap will reverse itself because the U.S. has squandered its resources on "spectaculars"[81] such as manned space flight

[81] Seymour Melman, *Our Depleted Society*, Holt, 1965; "Science,

while neglecting vital areas of basic or applied research which would benefit more vital national needs.[82]

As a result of these developments some have argued that American businessmen who once enjoyed a 10- to 15-year monopoly of a new product now complain that European or Japanese competitors can cut this lead to a matter of a few years or even months.[83] For example, even though the transistor was an American discovery one-half of all transistor radios sold in the United States in 1959 were imports.[84] Obviously, through the purchasing of licenses the "backward" Japanese were able to catch up with and even surpass American industry with little difficulty. In short, the U.S. paid for the R and D while the Japanese reaped many of the benefits.

The Japanese experience has led some Europeans to suggest that the science and technology gap is really to their advantage. To meet the needs of American industry and the military services for advanced technologies, the U.S. *must* support a high volume of research and development, the results of which are available to Europe at a fraction of the cost. Given this fact, European countries should do just enough research to remain informed of advances abroad and to enable them to take advantage of American discoveries and inventions.

The basic issue involved is the relationship between the rate

---

Technology and the Gold Drain," *Science*, Vol. 147, No. 3,661, Feb. 26, 1965, 987. As Simon Kuznets has pointed out, economists know very little about the relative advantages of backwardness and forwardness. *Modern Economic Growth*, Yale, 1966, p. 291. See also Alexander Gerschenkron, *Economic Backwardness in Historical Perspective*, Cambridge University Press, 1962.

[82] Richard Tybout, ed., *The Economics of Research and Development*, Ohio State University Press, 1965.

[83] Hal Lary, *Problems of the United States as World Trader and Banker*, National Bureau of Economic Research, 1963, p. 53.

[84] Richard Cooper, *American Competition in World Markets, 1953-1960*, doc. diss., Harvard University, 1961, pp. 110-11. Cooper points out (p. 109) that empirical testing of hypotheses on the relationship of technical innovation and trade is very difficult because one has no adequate measures of product innovation.

of innovation of new technology and the rate of diffusion of technical knowledge. If a firm can innovate new technologies and improvements at a faster rate than its competitors can imitate its existing products and processes, then the technology gap undoubtedly has important economic significance. Speaking of the American balance of payments deficit Richard Cooper put the problem this way:

> If the delays in international transmission of new production techniques exceed the delays in making use of them domestically and of marketing new products abroad, then it is quite possible that a country unable to balance its payments at existing external and internal prices in a long-run static equilibrium could nevertheless export new products and introduce new techniques at a sufficiently rapid pace to keep its payments in balance at all times. This is a dynamic equilibrium in which one must run rapidly in order to stay even.[85]

The importance of this relationship between rate of technological advance and rate of diffusion of new knowledge provides the key to an understanding of the fundamental paradox which has pervaded this discussion of the consequences of the technology gap for international competition. The paradox is that although the rate of technical advance in the United States is unprecedented and much greater than that of western Europe, the U.S.'s traditional technological lead over western Europe has actually diminished in numerous areas because of the greater rate and speed of diffusion today. As Cooper has pointed out, unless one takes both of these rates into consideration, as well as costs and exchange rates, it is impossible to come to any significant conclusion with respect to the consequences of the technology gap.[86]

[85] *Ibid.*, p. 107.

[86] The status of economic thinking about the relationship of technology and trade is summarized by Richard Cooper in U.S. Department of Commerce, *Technology and World Trade*, 1967, pp. 15-21.

The ratio of the rates of innovation and of diffusion actually prevailing at any given moment can only be determined through empirical investigations for particular products and industrial processes. Unfortunately, as this discussion has already indicated, such empirical studies are practically nonexistent, and those which do exist are not adequate for assessing the true significance of any technology gap that may exist. However, with respect to certain advanced technologies such as atomic energy, electronics, and aerospace, there are several reasons for Frenchmen and other Europeans believing that the rate of diffusion will be much slower than the rate of innovation and that the technology gap and the competitive advantages it confers on American corporations will be a permanent and growing feature of international trade. This belief rests on the notion that the European states will be barred from competing with the U.S. in many of these technologies because they seem unable to commit the considerable financial, scientific, and technical resources necessary to enter the competition. Also, the diffusion of knowledge with respect to these technologies is frequently restricted for national security reasons and by international agreement. For example, the diffusion of technical data about certain types of atomic, electronic, and space technology to third countries is proscribed by the Anglo-American Agreement on Atomic Cooperation of 1943, the Nuclear Test Ban Agreement of 1963, and the Anglo-American Nassau Agreement of 1962. Finally, the complexity of these technologies and the esoteric knowledge involved limits the rate of diffusion; the recipient industry cannot always merely buy a license and obtain technical assistance; it must have the managerial and technical competence to master the new technology.[87] In the meantime, it is pointed out, American innovators have moved ahead into an even more advanced and com-

---

[87] This is one explanation of the fact that the Russians, backward in many areas of advanced technology, especially electronics, have joined the international patent pool. It is no longer possible to "pirate" West-

74

plex scientific-technical realm, leaving Europe behind and dependent on the U.S. for these technologies of military, and frequently great economic, significance.

There is a strong disposition among American economists accustomed to the tradition of free trade, and among American officials and businessmen, to scorn the Franco-European position that the technology gap poses a clear and present danger to the autonomy of their industries and economies. These European fears are frequently discounted as merely the self-serving propaganda of European interests who want more government support or protection against American competition. Frequently, too, European apprehensions are brushed aside on the ground that the American lead in certain advanced technologies is altogether appropriate for such a highly technical and industrialized economy as that of the United States. It is also pointed out that in many scientific and technical areas such as metallurgy, chemicals, and shipbuilding the Europeans actually lead the United States. All these points are no doubt valid but their truth makes no less real the fundamental concern of Europeans about their future because of the preponderance of the U.S. in so many areas of advanced scientific technology, and in particular in those technologies which affect Europe's military-diplomatic position.

Moreover, even if one were to dismiss the existence of any technology gap outside certain militarily relevant areas and to discount the commercial significance of the gap that may exist, vital considerations still remain. What is important to remember is the political meaning of the technology gap for the French and Europe. In politics the most important factors are frequently what people *think* is true and the assumptions on which they act, even though the truth of the matter may be something else entirely.

---

ern technology. In addition, of course, the Russians have technical ideas of their own to sell.

In the present case the belief on which the French are acting has been identified by Raymond Aron:

> Of primary concern to Europeans is the theory that the American superiority in research and development tends to be cumulative. It builds on itself, and tends to increase because the mass of the resources which can be devoted to research is greater as the over-all national and corporate resources are greater. Therefore, the nation which has the research leadership has a good chance to retain it, and to increase it even further.

Whether the theory of U.S. cumulative superiority is true is uncertain. What is important is that at least many Europeans fear that it is true. And many are obsessed by the thought that in 10 or 20 years, the majority of large European firms will be dominated by multinational companies with American predominance.[88]

What the foregoing analysis suggests is that the technology gap is less an economic issue than a political one. First, whether or not the Atlantic imbalance in science and technology has importance for the competition of American and European firms, the important point is that the Europeans believe it does and, as will be shown in Chapter 12, they are taking steps to counter the alleged American threat. Second— and of greatest importance—what is at issue for France and Europe is their political position vis-à-vis the great powers and their capacity for long-term national independence. Whereas, beginning in the latter part of the nineteenth century, control over petroleum resources became essential once naval ships shifted from sail to diesel, so today an independent aerospace and electronics industry, along with the supporting sciences, has become crucial for a nation to enjoy diplomatic and military freedom of action.

[88] *The General Electric Forum*, IX, No. 2, Apr.-June 1966, p. 16.

Chapter 4 · The Heritage of the Napoleonic System

Take interest, I beseech you, in those sacred institutions which we designate under the expressive name of laboratories. Demand that they be multiplied and adorned; they are the temples of wealth and of the future. There it is that humanity grows, becomes stronger and better. There it learns to read in the works of nature, symbols of progress and of universal harmony, whereas the works of mankind are too often those of fanaticism and destruction.

—LOUIS PASTEUR, *1871*

The task of adapting themselves to the contemporary scientific-technological revolution poses a similar set of problems for all European nations. In these countries of long traditions and honored institutions change can be introduced only very slowly into the organizations on which the vigor of science and technology depends. The character of the European university system, for example, has a tenacity that persists through war, political revolution, and social upheaval. Even in Communist eastern Europe the structure of the university remains essentially what it was long before the change in political system. As the report of a 1966 conference at the University of Caen observed, the university is the last refuge of feudalism in western Europe.[1]

While it is true that the problems faced by France are also familiar to other European nations, the French state is making a signal effort to overcome them. But the magnitude of the task is an immense one. French society in general and French scientific institutions in particular are exceedingly resistant to

[1] *Le Monde*, Nov. 15, 1966. Though this characterization may not be technically correct it conveys the notion of institutional rigidity and isolation from the demands of modern economic life.

the emergence of an efficient scientific enterprise which could feed rapid technological advance. In order, therefore, to appreciate the problems facing the leadership of present-day France in its attempts to adjust to the new role of science in society, one must understand the scientific heritage which has been shaped by French society and history.

But first a word of caution. The following discussion is not intended to present either a sociology or a history of French scientific institutions. The intention here is rather to establish certain generalizations about the relationship of science and society in France and to describe the traditional institutional structure of French science in order to supply the necessary background for the rest of this study.

Social Context of French Science

An understanding of French scientific institutions in the context of French society is difficult to achieve. There is hardly a sociology of French science, though the historians of French science have provided excellent studies relating French science to its social context. Indeed, the complexity of French society in general, which is accompanied by insufficient knowledge of how it really functions, is discouraging. As Laurence Wylie has commented, "the social organization of France, like the value system which it represents, has never been described and undoubtedly never can be, for quite obviously it is a complicated mass of constantly changing and often conflicting elements. . . . To define completely the organization of even a limited part of the French social structure . . . is a formidable task. . . ."[2] Nevertheless, several important features of French society can be isolated as having had a profound influence on the development of French scientific institutions.

The first essential feature of French society affecting the

[2] "Social Change at the Grass Roots," in Stanley Hoffmann, ed., *In Search of France*, Harvard University Press, 1963, p. 215.

welfare of science is the existence of a centralized structure of authority which does not tolerate the establishment of intermediate, corporate entities between the state and the citizen.[3] In American or British society the national government is only one, though by far the most important, of a number of bodies which possess authority. French society, on the other hand, places all political authority in the national government; the result is an administrative and political centralization that limits all initiative to Paris and the higher echelons of the ministries. A major administrative consequence has been the fragmentation of the French bureaucracy. The lines of communication in France tend to run vertically within the separate ministries, producing a cleavage (*cloisonnement*) among institutions which is a barrier to the type of extensive communication and cooperation required in a modern industrial society. Horizontal coordination and communication within the government take place primarily in Paris, at the highest policy-making levels, and decisions filter down to the operating levels. In addition, there is little opportunity under such a system for local authorities to take initiative or to coordinate programs among ministries at the working levels.

Related to administrative centralization is a fierce personal individualism suspicious of everyone and resistant to change. In the absence of intermediate levels of authority to provide a balance to the power of the state and to protect the citizen, the isolated Frenchman resists the state at the same time that he looks to it for protection against anyone who might threaten him. Resistance to change endemic to any society is intensified in France as Frenchmen seek to resist aggrandizement of state power and to preserve their acquired rights (*droits acquis*).[4]

[3] Stanley Hoffmann, "Paradoxes of the French Political Community," in *In Search of France*, ed. Hoffmann, pp. 9-12.
[4] Wylie, "Social Change," p. 223.

The French theory of authority and its counterpart, fierce individualism, are reinforced by the strong desire of the French to avoid face-to-face conflict,[5] to be free of dependence on other individuals,[6] and to preserve an equalitarianism which holds that the law must be equally binding on all in a particular status.[7] Fear of the undefined, of one's neighbor, of organization, and of arbitrary action, run deep in the French character and contribute to the French tendency to codify all rules of behavior. "Every function, attribute, responsibility, right, or relationship of the individual has been spelled out in either legal or official terms, or in tacit but clearly understood codes."[8] Consequently there is little room for play in the tightly interwoven French social and political system. Gradual piecemeal adjustment to change and limited social experimentation are difficult to achieve in such a system. The Frenchman, believing everyone must be dealt with equally according to clearly defined rules, suspiciously inspects each change or proposal for reform to be certain it does not give advantage to groups other than his own.

The French system of higher education and scientific research, considered as an example of these tendencies, may be viewed as a product of the conflict in France between the tendency toward administrative centralization and the opposed tendency of individualism. Throughout much French history the recurring desire of the state to adapt education to accommodate new fields of learning has been frustrated by resistance

[5] This thesis is developed by Michel Crozier in his brilliant study, *The Bureaucratic Phenomenon*, University of Chicago Press, 1964.

[6] Jesse Pitts, "Continuity and Change in Bourgeois France," in Hoffmann, ed., *In Search of France*, p. 258; André Siegfried, *France, A Study in Nationality*, Yale University Press, 1930, pp. 12-13.

[7] Wylie, "Social Change," p. 224.

[8] *Ibid.*, p. 218. Two excellent sources are Gabriel Ardant, *Technique d'État*, Presses Universitaires de France, 1953; and Roger Grégoire, *The French Civil Service*, International Institute of Administrative Sciences, 1964.

to all change from already entrenched disciplines fearful of infringements on their *droits acquis*. The state has responded to this problem chiefly through the establishment of new institutions dedicated to the advancement of the new subjects. As a result there has been little if any gradual modification of older structures like that which has historically occurred in England. Instead, as each new structure becomes conservative in its turn, the advancement of knowledge and the consequent need for new scholarly specialization have been and are being accommodated through the establishment of still newer academic institutions. The consequence of this evolution has been institutional proliferation and intellectual fragmentation, features still characteristic of French science and education.

French society, then, is a well-balanced mechanism highly resistant to change. Though the centralized state has a monopoly of formal authority its power to act is severely limited and counterbalanced by the deep fragmentation of French life, by the force of intense individualism, and by the French concept of equalitarianism. These countervailing forces often produce an *immobilisme* which can be overcome only by major political and social upheaval. A new equilibrium, once established, resists further change until it can no longer hold back the pent-up forces of change.

It was the upheaval and reforms of the French Revolution and the reorganization of France by Napoleon that molded the institutions of French science into forms that have persisted to the present. The Revolution and Napoleon did not, however, create *de novo* the institutions of French scientific research and education; rather they gave expression to the dispositions inherent in the *ancien régime*[9] and gave them a

[9] This, of course, is the thesis of Alexis de Tocqueville in *The Old Régime and the French Revolution*, trans. Stuart Gilbert, Doubleday, 1955. For a discussion of alternative views of the impact of the Revolution on French sciences see Roger Hahn, *The Fall of the Paris Acad-*

permanence which only now, in the second half of the twentieth century, is being undone by the necessities of a world where the role of science in society is undergoing an immense transformation.

The immediate result of Revolutionary and Napoleonic reforms was to make more striking the scientific ascendancy of France that had begun around 1750.[10] During the first half of the nineteenth century Paris, in the words of the great German scientist, Alexander von Humboldt, was the "true metropolis of science to which scientists flocked from all over Europe to associate with such scientific greats as Cuvier, Lavoisier, and Laplace."[11] At this time the *Collège de France*, the *École Polytechnique*, and the *Muséum d'Histoire Naturelle* were the world's leading scientific institutions.

The reforms, however, did not result in maintenance of French scientific leadership. By 1840 this leadership had come to an end. Though France continued to produce such scientific giants as Claude Bernard, Louis Pasteur, and the Curies, French scientific leadership was passing rapidly to Germany. Even in physiology, whose foundations had been established by the French scientist, François Magendie, German discoveries, as measured by papers published, surpassed French for the first time during the decade 1840 to 1850.[12] In

---

emy of Sciences During the French Revolution, doc. diss., Cornell University, 1962, Chap. 1.

[10] This is a judgment shared by many historians of French science. See Henry Guerlac, "Science and French National Strength," in Edward M. Earle, ed., *Modern France*, Princeton University Press, 1951, p. 84; Maurice Caullery, *French Science and Its Principal Discoveries Since the Seventeenth Century*, Lectures delivered at the French Institute, New York, Mar. 1933. For a detailed history of French science, see Gabriel Hanotaux, *Histoire de la Nation Française*, Vols. 14 and 15, Plon, 1915, "La Science Française."

[11] Quoted in Rondo Cameron, *France and the Economic Development of Europe, 1800-1914*, Princeton University Press, 1961, p. 43.

[12] Joseph Ben-David, "Scientific Productivity and Academic Organiza-

chemistry, as well, the same pattern emerges. Though it was Lavoisier who founded the modern theory of chemistry, the development of the subject took place outside France, especially in Germany.

Though the timing is different, a similar pattern of ascendancy and decline is evident in French technological ingenuity. The French pioneered technical education and the application of science to industry.[13] The founding of the *École Polytechnique* in 1794 was inspired by the desire of the French to place industry on a sound scientific basis. Throughout most of the nineteenth century French engineers were among the best in the world and played an important part in the industrialization of Europe.[14] Especially during the Second Empire the graduates of the *École Polytechnique*—imbued with the Saint Simonian spirit of industrial progress—changed the face of the globe.[15] The Suez Canal, perhaps the foremost technological feat of the century, stands as a monument to this French engineering genius.

Then in the latter part of the century this French technological dynamism came to an end. After 1870 there is a perceptible decline in the vitality of French engineering relative to its own past and in contrast with German technological achievement. Though the French, along with the British, made many of the important inventions and discoveries which provided the basis for the new organic chemical and electrical power technologies, the development of these industries took

---

tion in Nineteenth Century Medicine," *American Sociological Review*, xxv, No. 6, Dec. 1960, 831.

[13] Frederick Artz, *The Development of Technical Education in France, 1500-1850*, MIT Press, 1967.

[14] Cameron, *France and Economic Development*, p. 54; Charles Kindleberger, *Economic Growth in France and Britain, 1851-1950*, Harvard University Press, 1964, p. 158.

[15] Fredrik Hayek, *The Counter-Revolution of Science*, Free Press, 1952, p. 11. See S. Charléty, *Histoire du Saint-Simonisme*, Hartmann, 1931.

place principally in Germany. France continued to fall behind technologically, which coincided with the recession of her military, economic, and political power relative to Germany's.

The reasons for this relative and absolute decline in French scientific and technological creativity cannot be traced to any single group of factors. They include all those elements Stanley Hoffmann includes in his brilliant analysis of "the stalemate society"—which France became late in the nineteenth century: (1) a preference for stability and protection over growth and competition; (2) a Malthusian fear of overproduction of material goods and of educated people; (3) the burden of social, religious, and political conflict; (4) the fragmented structure and conservatism of French industry; and (5) the domination of agrarian and colonial interests over domestic industrial interests.

While these and other social and political factors may be the root causes of France's loss of scientific and technological leadership in the late nineteenth century, the more immediate cause was that the scientific and technological institutions, shaped by the Revolutionary reformers and the First Empire and by this time firmly established, became increasingly incompatible with the changing requirements for scientific and technological advance. Outside France, and especially in Germany, the nature of the scientific enterprise was undergoing a rapid transformation. French institutions, on the other hand, were resistant to further evolution just at the moment that scientific research entered its greatest period of advancement and just when scientific theory had truly become for the first time the basis of technological innovation. Through subsequent military defeat and political change the essentials of the so-called Napoleonic system formed by the Revolution and First Empire remained unchanged. Consequently, the

[16] Hoffmann, "Paradoxes of the French Political Community," pp. 1-117.

over-all level of French scientific and technological performance suffered an eclipse which reached its nadir at the beginning of World War II.

To appreciate the decline of French science and technology
after the mid-nineteenth century and the problems faced by
the mid-twentieth-century reformers of French science one
must understand the Napoleonic system as it has affected the
three essentials of science as a social institution—the organization of scientific research, the professionalization of research,
and the governance of the scientific enterprise.

The Organization of Scientific Research

The impact of the French Revolution on the organization of
French science took place in two stages.[17] At first the Revolution in its fury swept away the institutions that had made
French science so outstanding under the *ancien régime*.[18] The
Academy of Sciences (*Académie Royale des Sciences*) founded
by Colbert in 1666 was abolished outright; the *Jardin Royal
des Plantes Médicinales* (founded 1635) was reconstituted as
the *Muséum d'Histoire Naturelle*; and the universities, except the *Collège Royal* (1530), which became the *Collège
de France*, were suppressed. Then, after this initial period of
destruction, and under the pressure of war, the Convention

[17] The only book-length treatment of science and the French Revolu-
tion is Joseph Fayet, *La Révolution Française et la Science, 1789-1795*,
Marcel Rivière, 1960. See also Stephen d'Irsay, *Histoire des Universités
Françaises et Étrangères des Origines à Nos Jours*, Picard, 1933-35, II,
215ff.; Hahn, *Fall of Paris Academy*; John Merz, *A History of European
Thought in the Nineteenth Century*, Dover, 1965, I, Chap. I. The
reader is also directed to the writings of R. Taton, Charles Gillispie,
Henry Guerlac, and L. Pearce Williams.

[18] On science under the *ancien régime* see Martha Ornstein, *The
Role of Scientific Societies in the Seventeenth Century*, Archon Books,
1963; Harcourt Brown, *Scientific Organization in Seventeenth Century France (1620-1680)*, Williams and Wilkins, 1934; L.-F. Alfred
Maury, *L'Ancienne Académie des Sciences*, Didier, 1864; D'Irsay, *Histoire des Universités Françaises*, I.

and Napoleon brought back many of the older institutions in new forms and founded new educational institutions such as the *École Polytechnique*, the *École Normale Supérieure*, and the *Conservatoire des Arts et Métiers*.

By the end of the First Empire the pattern of French scientific, technical, and educational organization, which would last until the end of the Second World War, had been firmly established. While there would be subsequent reforms and new institutions would be founded within that period of time, none of these measures fundamentally altered the basic features of the Napoleonic system.

The first feature of the Napoleonic system was the concentration of nearly all French scientific talent in Paris. The *levée en masse* in defense of the Revolution and the Empire had included scientists who went to Paris from all parts of the nation and found places in the newly created scientific institutions such as the *École Polytechnique*. "For the first time," Charles Gillispie has written, "a scientific community mobilized to serve the nation in arms."[19] Paris housed a scientific population unprecedented in history, and the "critical mass" of this talent resulted in one of the most creative periods in French science. The price France paid for this ephemeral brilliance, however, was high. "It may be," Gillispie writes, "that extreme centralization, basing higher learning upon a city rather than a nation, is what ultimately cost her the scientific leadership which was indisputably hers through the first third of the century. For the French way was to train an *élite* rather than a people, quality rather than quantity."[20]

The second feature of the Napoleonic system which has persisted is the functional fragmentation of French scientific and

[19] "Science and Technology," *The New Cambridge Modern History*, Cambridge University Press, 1965, IX, 122. Cf. Merz, *History of European Thought*, pp. 145-53.

[20] Gillispie, "Science and Technology," p. 123.

intellectual life into three separate sets of institutions.[21] Scientific research, the teaching of science, and professional education in engineering and medicine were made the responsibilities of separate organizations. Even though the same individuals frequently hold positions in all three domains, this administrative cleavage among functions which should be performed in concert had a detrimental effect on French science and technology especially after the middle of the nineteenth century.

The most distinguished of the scientific institutions founded, or in some cases refounded, by the Revolution were the *"grands établissements scientifiques"* such as the *Collège de France* and the *Muséum d'Histoire Naturelle.* The early nineteenth century was the great era for both of these purely research establishments.[22] The scientists associated with them, such as Cuvier, Ampère, and Berthelot, were among the greatest in the history of science. But they were academicians rather than teachers, and as such failed to educate a large number of students to carry on their lines of inquiry.

The teaching of science under the Napoleonic system was made the responsibility of two other sets of institutions for higher education which have not until recently been important centers for scientific research: the university *facultés* and the *grandes écoles.* The former are essentially professional schools for the training of medical doctors or teachers for the *lycées.* The *grandes écoles,* of which there are today (1968) approximately 20, train rather narrow technical specialists for the technical ministries.[23] The two great exceptions to this latter gen-

[21] Joseph Ben-David and Awraham Zloczower, "Universities and Academic Systems in Modern Societies," *European Journal of Sociology,* III, No. 1, 1962, 77.

[22] D'Irsay, *Histoire des Universités Françaises,* II, 145-78; D. McKie, "Science and Technology," *The New Cambridge Modern History,* Cambridge University Press, 1965, VIII, 115.

[23] For a critique of the *grandes écoles* see *Les Conditions de Développement, de Recrutement, de Fonctionnement, et de Localisation des*

eralization are the *École Polytechnique* and the *École Normale Supérieure.*

The founding of both the *École Polytechnique* and the *École Normale Supérieure* represented the creation of an essentially new type of scientific and educational institution.[24] Though it was not the first time in history that scientists became professors and students were taught science, science was taught as valuable in itself and not merely as auxiliary to some other profession.[25] It was at the *École Polytechnique* and the *École Normale Supérieure* that the most eminent of French scholars, scientists, and mathematicians assembled in the early part of the nineteenth century. Their students and those of their successors were to constitute the intellectual, political, and administrative elite of France throughout the century, even to the present.

The *École Polytechnique* was not only the first school to give systematic technical training to engineers,[26] but it introduced the research laboratory into the domain of higher education.[27] For the first time, an institution of higher education was also a center of research; its laboratories were the best equipped in the world. From all over France the greatest scientists of the land were assembled to teach and to do research. Their number included such men as Monge, Fourier, Laplace, Berthollet, and Chaptal.[28] As a consequence, though it was

---

Grandes Écoles en France, Rapport du Groupe d'Études au Premier Ministre, Sept. 26, 1963, La Documentation Française, 1964.

[24] Joseph Ben-David, "Scientific Growth: A Sociological View," *Minerva,* ii, No. 4, Summer 1964, 467.

[25] The writer is indebted to Roger Hahn for this distinction. See also Gillispie, "Science and Technology," p. 123; Ben-David, "Scientific Growth," pp. 466-67.

[26] Charles Gillispie, *The Edge of Objectivity,* Princeton University Press, 1960, p. 176.

[27] Ben-David, "Scientific Productivity," p. 834.

[28] Everett Mendelsohn, "The Emergence of Science as a Profession in

ostensibly a professional school of engineering, the *École Polytechnique* during the early part of the nineteenth century became a leading center of scientific research and the first to do systematic basic research.[29] Unfortunately, for reasons not to be discussed here, though the *École Polytechnique* continued to be an important technological institution, it declined as a center of scientific research during the course of the century.[30]

Unlike the *École Polytechnique*, which became a military engineering school separate from other institutions of higher education, the *École Normale Supérieure*[31] (organized in its present form by Napoleon in 1808) trained the teachers required by the newly established system of secondary education. The *École Normale* passed through a precarious existence during much of the first half of the century and finally emerged in the latter part of the century as the great training ground of French scholars and scientists. There the most eminent of French scientists and mathematicians have been educated and have taught. But, for reasons treated below, the *École Normale* proved too narrow a base on which to build a sound scientific edifice.

Yet another cleavage in French higher education produced by the Napoleonic system has been that between theory and practice. The fragmentation of universities into separate *facultés* (see below), the division between the university system and the *grandes écoles*, and the separation of the individ-

---

the Nineteenth Century," in Karl Hill, ed., *The Management of Scientists*, Beacon Press, 1964, p. 11.

[29] A. C. Crombie, ed., *Scientific Change*, Basic Books, 1963, p. 741.

[30] Some of the reasons for its decline are discussed in L. Pearce Williams, "Science, Education, and Napoleon I," *Isis*, XLVII, No. 150, Part 4, Dec. 1956, 369-82; R. Taton, "The French Revolution and the Progress of Science," *Centaurus*, III, Nos. 1-2, 1953, 84; Artz, *Development of Technical Education*, pp. 230ff.

[31] Fayet, *La Révolution Française et la Science*, Chap. 10. It should be noted that the *École Normale* has both a scientific and a literary section.

ual *grandes écoles* from one another, have left gaps between the institutions responsible for advancing scientific knowledge and those responsible for training the professions which would apply knowledge toward useful ends.

The French, of course, with the founding of the *École Polytechnique* had taken the initiative in founding the modern engineering school with its emphasis on scientific education. Nevertheless, in contrast to the German polytechnic schools (*Technische Hochschulen*) French engineering schools generally lacked the spirit of modern scientific research.[32] The student at the *grandes écoles* learned the content of science but not the methods of science. They became either abstract mathematicians or engineers of production who applied present knowledge, rather than research engineers who could make substantial advances in the state of the art.[33]

The French engineering schools also suffered from parochialism. Though one had to have an extensive and broad mathematical education to be selected for one of the engineering *grandes écoles*, the training and curriculum at each school were designed to train civil servants for a particular ministry. (The *École Polytechnique*, for example, has been primarily a school for civil and military engineers.) Consequently, it was impossible in the nineteenth century to receive there a broad education in chemistry—the science most basic to nineteenth-century industry. In fact there was no place in France where one could major in chemical engineering—though France did produce some important men in the field.[34]

In the latter part of the nineteenth century, especially after

[32] See John Beer, "The Emergence of the German Dye Industry," *Illinois Studies in the Social Sciences*, XLIV, 1959, p. 57; Merz, *History of European Thought*, p. 166.

[33] This of course was much less true of the *École Polytechnique* than the other *grandes écoles*.

[34] Beer, "Emergence of German Dye Industry," p. 37.

1880, the French government made a number of attempts to improve the scientific foundations of French engineering. Several *facultés* of science, such as those at Nancy and Grenoble, established laboratories for industrial research, as did the *Conservatoire National des Arts et Métiers*.[35] More importantly, the number of engineering schools and institutes was greatly expanded, especially in chemistry, electricity, and other science-based technologies then coming into importance. Whereas in 1880 there were only nine *grandes écoles* and 11 lesser engineering and technical schools, between 1880 and 1900 approximately 15 new schools were founded.[36] Between 1900 and 1919, 26 engineering schools were added and immediately after World War I six important new schools were created. Because of this evolution France after 1880 developed a great number and variety of engineering and technical schools. However, even though a number of these new schools were founded within the university system, their establishment did little to bridge the gap created by Napoleon between the institutions for basic science and those for engineering education.

Turning to biology and medicine one sees again this separation between theory and practice endemic to the Napoleonic system. The situation then and today was described in a report published in 1957 on the status of French science:

> A medical doctor specializing in physiology cannot teach it in a *Faculté des Sciences*, if he is not a doctor of science, whatever his scientific titles and the value of his work. A biochemist possessing all the qualifications provided by a *Faculté des Sciences* cannot become a professor of biochemistry in a *Faculté de Médecine*. . . . In most of the scientific

[35] La Documentation Française, *La France Devant les Problèmes de la Science*, Part 1, June 20, 1959, pp. 43-47.
[36] *Ibid.*, Part 2, p. 4.

grandes écoles, a large proportion of the teaching personnel are recruited among the former students of the school, who are not necessarily equipped for teaching or research.[37]

This administrative and intellectual cleavage has had a detrimental effect both on science and on the practical professions such as medicine and engineering. Without the free flow of scientists and professionals among institutions there cannot take place that circulation of ideas which fructify one another. Instead a sclerosis affects the institutions and outmoded concepts and practices are perpetuated from generation to generation. At its worst, this fosters a feudalistic relationship of teacher and student that enforces orthodoxy and stifles new ideas.

The third feature of the Napoleonic system was the overcentralization of the university system. Initially the Revolution eliminated the several universities as embodiments of that corporate privilege against which so much of the Revolution's force had been directed.[38] Napoleon then revived the university system in a new form and with an entirely new purpose.

The Napoleonic law of 1808, which created what is today the *Université de France,* embodied that fundamental tension in French society between vertical administrative centralization and horizontal institutional fragmentation. Universities throughout France, which had been autonomous, self-governing bodies, were brought under one central administration. Each university was fragmented into several *facultés* such as those of science, medicine, or law—which had little to do with one another and which would thereafter be administered di-

[37] "Colloque de Caen," *Les Cahiers de la République,* No. 5, Jan.-Feb. 1957, p. 86.

[38] According to the famous *loi le Chapelier* of 1791, which embodied the theory of the revolution, there were to be no intermediate bodies (class, locality, religion) between citizen and nation. F. Ridley and J. Blondel, *Public Administration in France,* Routledge and Kegan Paul, 1964, p. xiii.

rectly from Paris. Thus at the same time the *Université de France* came into existence, the individual universities ceased to exist in fact as well as in name. In the reorganization they were replaced by a scattering of professional schools (*facultés*) administered by what is today the Ministry of National Education.

In the latter part of the nineteenth century the Third Republic sought to reverse the Napoleonic reorganization of the university and to create true universities in France. The reform law of 1896 regrouped the separate *facultés* in a city or region into unified institutions. The hope, as expressed by Raymond Poincaré, was to introduce into France the autonomous university as it then existed in Germany, which would be a center for uniting teaching and research and for enabling science to contribute to French life.[39] These reforms, however, did not alter the essence of the university structure.[40] As one Frenchman has observed, "one of the French paradoxes is that it is certainly easier to change the government, or even the constitution, than to touch the university."[41]

In summary, it is perhaps not too much to say that the French scientific system has centered around the *grands établissements* of Paris with emphasis on a small scientific elite and the nurturing of quality. And while lip service has been paid to science as the basis of the useful arts, the system has actually inhibited the enrichment of the latter by the former. In Germany, on the other hand, scientific research was assimilated into the more broadly based university system, resulting in sufficient scientific manpower for the advancement of research across a broad front, the capturing of world

[39] La Documentation Française, *La France Devant les Problèmes de la Science*, Part 2, Oct. 20, 1959, p. 46.

[40] J.-B. Piobetta, *Les Institutions Universitaires*, Presses Universitaires de France, 1961, p. 10.

[41] "Faire l'Université," *Esprit*, Nos. 5-6, May-June 1964, p. 934.

scientific leadership, and the placement of German professions on a scientific basis.

Professionalization of Research

Between 1800 and 1850 science as a social endeavor became increasingly complex and technical.[42] More formal training, more specialization, and more professionalization were required. The modern research laboratory was founded and began to assume the central place it holds today. This was the period—at least outside France—when institutions of higher education (especially the university) replaced the academy as the seat of science. Although one can trace the beginnings of many of these features of modern science to French roots, their development and integration into the modern scientific enterprise was primarily a German accomplishment. In Germany, the political, social, and educational environment encouraged the development of a scientific enterprise adapted to the changing nature of science and its social role. As a result, the German scientific system, and not the French, became the model for other societies—including, to some degree, the French themselves. The contrast between the scientific enterprise in France and in Germany presented below, provides a valuable insight into the reasons for the decline of France and the great success of Germany after the mid-nineteenth century.[43]

[42] Richard Shryrock, "American Indifference to Basic Science During the Nineteenth Century," *Archives Internationales d'Histoire des Sciences*, No. 28, 1948-49, p. 14.

[43] At the time, the British scientific system was in contrast to both the French and the German systems. Highly individualistic British scientists produced many of the most brilliant and original ideas of the nineteenth century which were given greater exactitude by the French or were fully developed by the Germans. (Cf. Merz, *History of European Thought*, p. 300.) Furthermore, it should be pointed out that the German system has proven not appropriate for the mid-twentieth century. Cf. Organisation for Economic Co-operation and Development, *Reviews of National Science Policy—United Kingdom, Germany*, 1967.

The contrast between German success and French failure is perhaps most evident with respect to the supply of scientific manpower. In quantity and in most respects, quality as well, German scientists greatly surpassed French scientists following 1840.[44] An exploration of the reasons for this situation is the concern of the next several pages.

RESEARCH AS A CAREER

In her establishment of the Academy of Sciences France became the first nation to make scientific research a career and to recognize that the possession of highly skilled manpower was a basic factor in national power. In contrast to the fellows of the Royal Society of England, who were amateurs and private citizens, the members of the French Academy were appointed and supported by the King. The academicians pursued science as a profession and devoted the better part of their time to scientific and technical research. In this way, the French concept of the scientist as a state *fonctionnaire* was established.

Unfortunately, a science system based on a relatively small number of Parisian academicians was not appropriate for a period of rapid scientific advance and industrial expansion. No matter how advantageous it had been at first, the Napoleonic system of academic science and its emphasis on a restricted intellectual elite (see below) eventually had the effect of limiting the number of bright young men going into science, harming the quality of their training, and lowering the productivity of those few who did undertake a scientific or engineering career.

In nineteenth-century Germany, on the other hand, the professionalization of science advanced to the stage it occupied until the early decades of the twentieth century. The German

[44] Maurice Fauque, *L'Évolution Économique de la Grande Industrie, Chimique en France*, Éditions Universitaires, Strasbourg, 1932, p. 163.

university professor replaced the academician as the scientific professional *par excellence*; for the first time there was formal training for a scientific career; the virtuoso began to give way to the specialist. In short, the advance of knowledge was becoming less dependent on essentially self-taught men whose discoveries would span a broad front of the unknown, and more dependent on numerous, formally trained individuals, each pursuing his rather restricted specialization. Scientific advance and especially the application of new concepts became less a matter of individual genius and more one of sheer numbers, though the concepts themselves continued to be the product of the truly creative individual. In all the features of the modern scientific enterprise the Germans were the pioneers, and the French only now in the middle of the twentieth century are beginning to catch up.

In founding the University of Berlin, which set the pattern of German university organization, Wilhelm von Humboldt redefined the responsibility of the university to be the advancement of scientific knowledge while the function of teacher and pupil was to cooperate in the promotion of that knowledge. "The former is not for the latter, both are for science. . . ."[45] The professor's task was to make original discoveries and to reproduce in his students his own kind.

In marked contrast to the German conception, Frenchmen did not consider scientific research to be the true vocation of the professor. The professor on the French side of the Rhine was a state official whose task was to transmit a cultural tradition and to prepare students for the state examinations. The attitude toward research which has characterized French higher education is epitomized in the famous remark of a minister of national education made as late as 1933 that "re-

[45] See Frederick Paulsen, *The German Universities*, trans. Frank Thilly and William Elwang, Scribner's, 1906, p. 53.

search is an irregularity toward which we turn a blind eye."[46]
At the most, research traditionally has been regarded as a privilege extended to professors who have conscientiously performed their primary responsibilities of teaching and
examining.

This subordination of research to teaching and of higher
education to the needs of secondary education has been encouraged by a career pattern that routes the would-be university
professor through years of teaching in the *lycée* prior to his
securing a university position. With few exceptions French
scholars have spent many years teaching at the secondary level,
and some of France's most outstanding scholars, especially in
the humanities, by preference have remained in the *lycées*
throughout their lives. The philosopher, Alain, for example,
quite rightly regarded the better *lycées* as more distinguished
than the *facultés*. While this relationship of higher and secondary education has the advantage of having provided
France with an excellent system of secondary education, it has
meant that many promising scientists have been lost to science.

The institutional impediments to the transformation of the
French professor into a professional scientist on the German
model were traditionally reinforced by his self-image. The
French idealized the professor as a man of broad culture and
encyclopedic knowledge rather than as a narrow specialist
whose purpose was to make some original contribution to
knowledge. He was a *savant*,[47] steeped in an ancient and classic culture that was to be passed on via his students to the next
generation.[48]

---

[46] Quoted in Juergen Schmandt, "Le Scientific Statesman," *Les
Études Philosophiques*, No. 2, Apr.-June 1966, p. 176.

[47] Merz, *History of European Thought*, pp. 104-105.

[48] See the contrast between the scientist and the *savant* in Pierre
Lelong, "L'Évolution de la Science et la Planification de la Recherche,"
Revue Économique, No. 1, Jan. 1964, p. 8.

As the number of scientists increased, scientific knowledge expanded, and scientific research became more technical, specialization became increasingly necessary for the aspiring scientist. In the past, a Galileo or Newton had been able to make important contributions in several fields; and a man like Bacon could claim encyclopedic knowledge. By the middle—and most certainly by the end—of the nineteenth century the possibility of exercising such virtuosity was in rapid decline. One *had* to be a specialist and to devote full time to his more narrowly defined researches. To make a contribution to science it was necessary to specialize in a narrow field where one could be at the frontier of knowledge. In Germany there were far greater rewards to be gained by making some original discovery, than for being a man of great erudition with no discoveries to his credit.[49]

In France, on the other hand, the university has provided university professors with few incentives to specialize and undertake research. Regardless of a person's merit professors tend to have analogous careers and remuneration[50]—largely because professors are civil servants, under the over-all authority of the French civil service. This concept of "equal pay for equal work" has made it difficult to create incentives for professors to do research or to raise salaries in underdeveloped fields in order to attract young men. Even in recent decades the notion of equality has undermined attempts of the French government to stimulate greater research in the university. For example, the French government created a *prime de recherche* equivalent to 15-20 percent of base salary to encourage research—a "prize" now given automatically to all professors and assistants regardless of merit.

Instead of encouraging specialization and original research,

[49] Paulsen, *German Universities*, p. 52.
[50] Raymond Aron, "La Crise de l'Université," *Preuves*, May 1964, p. 22.

the structure of incentives influencing the professor's career has encouraged the cultivation of broad conventional interests. Because the relatively few *faculté* chairs were distributed among general fields such as zoology or physics, and one never knew which chairs would become available, it was prudent to maintain as broad a competence as possible and thereby increase one's options.[51] Nor could one risk entering a new field in anticipation that it would eventually receive recognition and that chairs would become available. In a period of static population and a Malthusian fear of overexpansion such as that which characterized France until 1945, very few new chairs were created, and the conservatism of the *facultés* severely limited the number of existing chairs that were converted from older, effete fields to newer, productive ones. Furthermore, the system by which professors were co-opted for the *faculté* chairs encouraged them to cultivate their erudition and not push too boldly against existing orthodoxies.

To summarize, in a time when only a professional specialist could hope to make original discoveries French science tended to remain the domain of the generalist. Though there were important exceptions, such as Pasteur and Bernard, who made brilliant discoveries in several specialties, the French ideal of the cultured aristocrat opposed specialization.[52]

TRAINING IN RESEARCH

The French, in founding the *École Polytechnique* and the *École Normale Supérieure*, became the first people to teach science in institutions of higher education. In the nineteenth century, however, the Germans took this French beginning an important step further. The purpose of the German universities was to teach research and not merely the content of science. The German ideal contrasted with the French which was

[51] Ben-David, "Scientific Productivity," p. 836.
[52] Pitts, "Continuity and Change," p. 247.

to train the student to become an independent scholar.[53] The crucial difference was that in Germany it was not enough to *know* science; one had to be able to *do* science.

The essential German contribution to higher education, then, was to tie teaching and research together. In France and Great Britain a scientific education tended to mean knowledge about science rather than knowing the art and practice of scientific research.[54] In each of these countries a person went to a prestigious institution appropriate for a gentleman or ambitious young man. The ideal student in Germany, on the other hand, studied under particular professors to learn his subject and prepare himself for a career in scholarship or science. Frequently this meant pursuing his studies at several universities during the course of his education.

The most important feature of the German system was the shift from the lecture to the laboratory. The purpose of the lecture method of teaching is to teach a subject to students; the purpose of laboratory teaching is to teach a method of inquiry through "patient practice, and not by listening to a description of it."[55] While the first teaching laboratory was probably that at the *École Polytechnique*, Justus Liebig, himself trained at the *Polytechnique*, innovated modern laboratory training at the University of Giessen in Germany. He had sensed a need for "an institution in which students could be instructed in the art of chemistry, by which I mean familiarity with chemical analytical operations, and skill in the use of apparatus."[56] Liebig's success was copied by his students who carried his ideas and methods throughout Germany and into other lands.

The entire national examination system in France was op-

[53] Paulsen, *German Universities*, p. 63. Cf. Beer, *Emergence of German Dye Industry*, p. 58.

[54] Crombie, *Scientific Change*, p. 664.

[55] Merz, *History of European Thought*, p. 30.

[56] Mendelsohn, "Emergence of Science," p. 19.

posed to the introduction of the German innovation of specialized training in scientific research. The examinations, founded on the Napoleonic law of 1808, gave the state a monopoly in the awarding of academic degrees, and thereby the ability to control access to the professions.[57] These examinations, such as the *baccalauréat* taken at the end of the *lycée*, were a logical part of the Napoleonic educational system, a system whose purpose was to train a relatively small and highly qualified elite to govern and manage France. The system functioned to keep standards high and insure a uniform product from a national education system.

Unfortunately this national emphasis on preparing students for a standard set of examinations has had a number of deleterious consequences for scientific education in France. Secondary and higher education became a prisoner of the examination system. In Paulsen's words "strict study regulations and prescribed curriculums and examinations controlled the entire system, and the professors were nothing more than official state instructors whose task was to prepare the matriculated students for the examinations. . . ."[58]

At the level of higher education the effect of the emphasis on national examinations has been to limit severely the freedom with which the *facultés* could create chairs in new specializations and give graduate education to specialists. The curriculum has had to be organized in terms of the national examinations and the needs of secondary education. Consequently, despite the expansion of knowledge and rise of new specializations abroad, the distribution of chairs among the original six Napoleonic disciplines (mathematics, zoology, botany, geology, chemistry, and physics), changed little during the nineteenth century and even well into this century.[59]

[57] Piobetta, *Les Institutions Universitaires*, pp. 8-9.
[58] *German Universities*, p. 52.
[59] Colloque de Caen," *Les Cahiers de la République*, p. 61.

Furthermore—and inevitably—the examination system diverted the energies of students from preparation for performing research to preparation for passing the examinations. This is particularly applicable to the so-called *concours* (any competitive examination for admission to a limited number of places). The *concours* control admission to the *grandes écoles* and frequently determine university careers (the *agrégation*). In fact, there is hardly any aspect of professional or academic life in France that has not been governed by the *concours*. Even in the latter 1960s they remain extremely important although their grip on French life is weakening somewhat.

For the young Frenchman interested in attending one of the *grandes écoles*, for example, the admissions examination has meant spending two or three years in the study of mathematics after his graduation from the *lycée* at age 16 or 17. His chances of success are slight, but successful or not he will have spent several of his most creative years learning abstract mathematics, which is of little use for either an engineering or research career.[60] Parenthetically, the heavy emphasis placed upon mathematical competence in the *concours* for entry to the *grandes écoles* has been a major factor in the traditional strength of the French in pure mathematics. On the other hand, the prestige of pure mathematics has no doubt diverted talented men from other fields such as applied mathematics and mathematical physics.[61]

Of all the *concours* perhaps the most damaging to the cause of French science has been the *agrégation*. Originally an ex-

[60] OECD, *Reviews of National Science Policy—France*, Paris, 1966, p. 114.

[61] Caullery, *French Science*, p. 116, also observed that the emphasis on mathematics in French education has drawn talented Frenchmen away from physics and chemistry. For a discussion of the dominant role of mathematics in French education see Jean Mayer's contribution to Julian Park, ed., *French Culture in Our Time*, Cornell University Press, 1954.

amination to select teachers for the *lycées*, it became in the late nineteenth century by an unwritten law, along with the *doctorat d'État*, the prerequisite to the better positions in the *lycées* and to all university teaching positions. Therefore, postgraduate education (*post-licence*) became too devoted to preparation for the *agrégation* to permit much time for training in research in contrast to the situation in Germany. Whereas the German professor was selected because he had demonstrated a capacity for original scientific work, the French professor was selected by an examination of his grasp of already existing knowledge. The French system produced an elite of great erudition for the universities and *lycées*; the German directed capable persons into research, resulting in creative research scientists.[62] One writer reviewing the decline of French chemistry in the nineteenth century wrote, "The universities taught chemistry with a view toward preparing the examinations and not from the point of view of its applications."[63]

The *concours* system rests on several features of French psychology. It is a mechanism to reduce the possibility of favoritism and to counter the fear of arbitrary action, both of which haunt every Frenchman. Also, the *concours* reflects a longstanding French commitment to equalitarianism and Malthusianism that has afflicted French society for so long.[64] In a society whose citizens believe there is a limited and nonexpandable number of choice positions the *concours* gives each person a theoretically equal opportunity for the best career in France and assures that the "best" will be selected for positions of public responsibility.

[62] See "Faire l'Université," *Esprit*, Nos. 5-6, May-June 1964, p. 802. See also the criticism of the *agrégation* by Raymond Aron, in *Le Figaro*, Sept. 19, 1960.

[63] M. A. Wahl, "Le Problème de la Fabrication des Matières Colorantes Organiques en France," *Revue Scientifique*, LIV, 1916, 10.

[64] See Alfred Sauvy, *La Montée des Jeunes*, Calmann-Levy, 1959, for an excellent discussion of the consequences of the Malthusian fear of overproduction on French education.

The concept of equality which the French have built into their examination and education system is that of Condorcet and not Rousseau. Whereas Americans, along with Rousseau, tend to believe all men are by nature equal, the French accept more readily the fact of human differences but hold fiercely to the conviction that each person must have an equal *opportunity* to prove his competence. From the earliest grades, where students are ranked by class standing, right through the national examinations, individuals know where they stand in the French intellectual hierarchy. The French educational system seeks throughout to select and promote those few persons of promise rather than to maximize the possibility of everyone achieving his full potential.

While the *concours* has fostered men of great genius it is unfair to the vast majority of youths and limits severely the development of scientific and technical manpower. In theory both the university *facultés* and the *grandes écoles* are highly equalitarian—every *lycée* graduate can attend the university and take the competitive examinations (*concours*) for the *grandes écoles*. But in practice opportunity has been very unequal. For example, though free, the *lycées* have been relatively few in number and have not been distributed evenly throughout France. Also, few French families of working-class and peasant background have been able to afford to support children attending the *lycées*, the *facultés*, or the preparatory classes for the *grandes écoles*. As a consequence, France, even more than many other societies, has drawn her scientists and engineers from a restricted social base composed of the wealthier classes.

In the contemporary world the *concours* is a holdover from a society where the educational system was far in advance of the economic system. The French system of secondary and higher education in the nineteenth and early twentieth centuries was able to produce a greater number of highly qualified persons than the economy was able to absorb. At a time when a small elite was sufficient to govern a largely agrarian society, the *concours* made some sense. But today, when the population and the economy are in rapid expansion, the series of *concours* which each Frenchman must overcome in the pursuit of a career has seriously limited the output of scientists required by an expanding economy.[65]

THE SUPPLY AND UTILIZATION OF SCIENTISTS

Francis Bacon foresaw the day when many ordinary men, properly trained and organized, would displace genius as the mainstay of scientific progress. In nineteenth-century Germany the advancement of science became increasingly a matter of numbers and organization. Throughout the German university system, hundreds of "ordinary" men were trained in the new analytical techniques of chemistry and physiology. Numerous laboratories were established and the rapid spread of the research institute after 1830 brought the organization of research to a higher level of efficiency. Under the leadership of Liebig and other understanding researchers the institutes provided scientists with excellent equipment and a stimulating atmosphere. This institutional achievement was the beginning, as one authority has put it, of systematic "experimental science" and was responsible in large measure for Germany's rise to scientific preeminence.[66]

In an age when leadership in science became increasingly dependent on organization, French scientists remained highly individualistic and few in number. Following the lead of Descartes and not Bacon, the French emphasized individual creative genius rather than the training of large numbers of

[65] Vladimir Kourganoff, *La Recherche Scientifique*, Presses Universitaires de France, 1961, p. 13.
[66] Crombie, *Scientific Change*, p. 664.

men in scientific method.[67] Though the French Academy had pioneered cooperative research,[68] French science in the nineteenth century was highly individualistic; scientists were not brought together in well-equipped and competently staffed institutes.

The heroic period of French science, from 1800 to 1830, was the product of two important factors: Revolutionary and Napoleonic reforms had established institutions and an environment where French genius could flourish; and knowledge in many fields had advanced to the point where it lent itself to mastery by the peculiar strengths of the French mind. Around 1800, in chemistry, natural history, physiology, and other areas, someone was needed to bring order to the disarray of conflicting opinions and positions. Such a task required the patience, brilliance, and individuality of men like Lavoisier who founded the use of precise measurements in chemistry and systematized the subject.[69] French genius fashioned the paradigms,[70] or revolutionary new theories, that guided scientific research for much of the nineteenth century. As John Merz has pointed out, "in France during the early part of the century the foundations of nearly all the modern sciences were laid. Many of them were brought under the rule of strict mathematical treatment."[71]

Throughout the nineteenth century and into the twentieth, French science continued to be distinguished for the number and value of its great discoveries rather than for its general mass of scientific production.[72] But the development of scientific concepts and especially their technological exploitation,

[67] Caullery, *French Science*, p. 211.
[68] Merz, *History of European Thought*, p. 298.
[69] Crombie, *Scientific Change*, p. 429.
[70] This is the expression used by Thomas Kuhn, *The Structure of Scientific Revolution*, University of Chicago Press, 1962.
[71] *History of European Thought*, p. 75.
[72] Caullery, *French Science*, p. 210.

is dependent not just on great discoveries but on "the patient and methodical work which uses [great discoveries] and prepares the discoveries to follow."[73] It is an effort that requires large numbers of scientists and efficient organization. Therefore, though it took a genius such as Lavoisier to systematize modern chemistry, the methodical development and commercial exploitations of his theories took place elsewhere, especially in Germany.

The difference between the French and German intellectual approach has been reflected in differences in scientific organization.[74] In France the typical scientific institution throughout the nineteenth century and even today is the small personal laboratory which comes with the professor's chair (*laboratoire de chaire*). There the professor can pursue his personal inclinations with a few assistants, though the research might not be at the frontiers of scientific advance and the laboratory might be too small, ill-equipped, and isolated to be efficient. In contrast, the German ideal has been the research institute with its systematic exploitation of a subject, where each researcher is integral to the over-all, concerted effort.[75]

In the latter part of the nineteenth century the rapid advance of science in Germany stimulated scientist-patriots such as Pasteur to plead for greater support of science by the government and the establishment of research institutions. In founding the *École Pratique des Hautes Études* in 1868 and other research institutions and laboratories in specialized areas of research,[76] the French did begin to give recognition to the important role research institutes and well-endowed laboratories

[73] *Ibid.*

[74] The contrast between French genius and German method is developed by Charles Newman, *The Evolution of Medical Education in the Nineteenth Century*, Oxford University Press, 1957, pp. 265-67.

[75] Merz, *History of European Thought*, p. 213.

[76] La Documentation Française, *La France Devant les Problèmes de la Science*, Pt. 2, Oct. 20, 1959, No. 2,580, p. 46.

had played in enabling Germany "to reach the high development in the experimental sciences of which we take note with *troubled sympathy.*"[77] Despite this acknowledgement, however, the over-all character of French science has remained individualistic to this day and the French have continued to allocate their scarce scientific resources equally and very inefficiently among the many *laboratoires de chaire.*[78] This situation has been summarized by one French authority in words that deserve repeating in full:

> The Frenchman does not possess the gregarious instinct; the individual is jealous, perhaps even too much so, of his independence and personality. He does not willingly let himself be absorbed into the team. There have been schools around the great masters of science, but their number has certainly been more limited than in other countries. Many masters have not especially sought to surround themselves with disciples. We can say that in France we have not fully benefitted from average talents, because they are insufficiently organized under leaders and insufficiently disciplined. French science is above all individualistic.
>
> If this inclination tends to preserve individuality, it frequently has the drawback of scattering effort instead of concentrating it, and of breaking up resources to too great an extent. This criticism can certainly be made of the present condition [1933] of the French scientific world where there would be every advantage in lessening somewhat the number of laboratories and at the same time equipping them more efficiently.[79]

[77] Statement of Victor Duruy, Minister of Instruction under Napoleon III, quoted in Paulsen, *German Universities*, p. 220.
[78] This was a complaint of the second "Colloque de Caen" held in November 1966; *Le Monde*, Nov. 11, 1966.
[79] Caullery, *French Science*, pp. 210-11.

Many of the reasons for France's failure to produce a large number of scientists in the nineteenth century, and even today, are readily apparent: the elitist character of her educational system; the debilitating effect of her national examinations; and the fear of overproduction of intellectuals. But perhaps of even greater importance, the character of French society has operated to limit severely the number of educated Frenchmen entering a scientific career.

A key to scientific and technical leadership lies in the career patterns that channel the energies of society's most creative members. Talented and ambitious persons pursuing their chosen careers provide in a very real sense the motive power of any society. For this reason the factors such as prestige which influence the choice of careers, the rules which govern the pursuit of various careers, and the criteria of "social success" in any society are important determinants of the economic, scientific, and other outputs of the society.

In France the rules governing the careers of its creative minority have been defined to a degree seldom met elsewhere, except perhaps Confucian China, leaving little freedom for deviation, indecision, or reversal of one's career goals. The criteria of success are clearly identifiable, and there are few opportunities for overcoming a false start. What is important is one's early success in examinations and not his subsequent achievement. In few other societies can it be said of a man at the age of 22 that he has succeeded or failed.

The determinant of this situation, of course, is the French educational system and the crucial part it plays in a Frenchman's career.[80] While numerous reforms have been introduced in attempts to alleviate the problem caused by the highly integrated nature of the French educational system, that system has operated to limit the number of French scientists and engi-

[80] This point is developed by Pitts, "Continuity and Change," p. 293.

neers. For example, one has had to decide at an early age—around 15—whether he desired a scientific career. At an even earlier age the school system discriminates against lower class and peasant children and has routed most students into channels which virtually close to "late bloomers" the option of a scientific career.[81]

Yet another aspect of French education that has limited the number of scientists is the division between the university *facultés* and the *grandes écoles*. This fragmentation has had the unfortunate consequence of drawing the most scientifically gifted students away from scientific research. Whereas in Germany the students best suited for a scientific career tend to go to the universities, the students in France who have such an aptitude are more likely to be educated at the *grandes écoles*, and the students who couldn't make the *grandes écoles* have gone to the university.

The attraction of the *grandes écoles* over the *facultés* has been due to many things. First, upon entrance into one of the *grandes écoles* the student becomes a member of the civil service and is paid a salary. Equally important, the graduate of a *grande école* has a secure and promising career in government guaranteed to him; the top graduates of the various *grandes écoles* are practically assured brilliant careers in one of the elite *grands corps de l'État* such as the *Inspection des Finances* or *Conseil d'État*. In underindustrialized nineteenth-century France, where attractive positions were scarce, the *grandes écoles* became the entry for the ambitious bourgeois to the most prestigious careers in France. The situation today has changed very little.

The most brilliant career has traditionally begun at the *École Polytechnique*. After two years of general education there, including a heavy concentration on mathematics, the best stu-

---

[81] If one takes his *baccalauréat* in letters, for example, he usually has too little science for the *Faculté des Sciences*.

dents then have gone to the prestigious *écoles d'application* such as the *École des Mines* or the *École Nationale des Ponts et Chaussées*, where they specialized in a field of practical engineering. By tradition the top 20-25 percent of the graduating class (*botte*) of the *École Polytechnique* have entered one of the military corps such as naval engineering or one of the civil corps such as the *Corps des Mines* or *Corps des Ponts et Chaussées* (civil engineering).[82] Moreover, many quickly move into important administrative positions in private business (*pantouflage*). Consequently, although the students at the *École Polytechnique* have been among the most mathematically and scientifically adept in France, few of them have gone into scientific research. Research has not been a choice career; the way to the top is through administration, which should be entered as soon as possible. The Napoleonic ideal was the engineer-administrator, not the engineer-researcher.[83]

In the view of most French authorities the drain of scientifically talented graduates of the *École Polytechnique* and the other *grandes écoles* away from research into administration was a major cause of France's scientific and technical decline in the nineteenth century.[84] Even as late as 1964 François Bloch-Lainé could comment on the career pattern of France's most promising minds in the following words: "We have perhaps the most brilliant negotiators in the international negotiations, but we have no more Nobel prizes."[85]

Furthermore, even if the young *Polytechnicien* were interested in becoming a scientist he has been virtually blocked. There have been few research positions in government and the *grands corps d'État*; also a graduate of a *grande école*

---

[82] Ridley and Blondel, *Public Administration in France*, pp. 40-41.
[83] OECD, *Reviews of National Science Policy—France*, p. 53.
[84] Pitts, "Continuity and Change," p. 253; Caullery, *French Science*, p. 182.
[85] "Un Dialogue entre Louis Armand et François Bloch-Lainé 'Plaidoyer Pour la Technique,'" *Entreprise*, June 6, 1964, p. 55.

(except those schools attached to Ministry of National Education) could not easily opt to become a professor in order to pursue a research career. To become a professor one has to have a *doctorat d'État*, and, in practice, the *agrégation*; to acquire a *doctorat d'État* not only requires the preparation of two dissertations, but one has to possess, as a prerequisite, the *license*, a university degree not awarded by the *grandes écoles*. While this requirement can be waived for individuals with equivalent degrees, it has acted as a barrier to a scientific career.

In short, the Napoleonic reforms created a paradoxical system wherein the *grandes écoles* have nearly monopolized all the best science students and the *facultés* have nearly monopolized access to a scientific career. The great exception to this division has been the *École Normale Supérieure*, which is part of the University of Paris and whose students, in contrast to most of the other *grandes écoles*, can study under professors of the Paris *facultés*. The *École Normale* has been the only important point of contact between the most brilliant of France's students and the best of her scientists located at the *École* itself or at the *facultés*. This is another reason, then, that so many great French scientists and scholars have been *normaliens*. While the number of its graduates has been quite small (about 30 in science each year) without this training ground for the scientific and intellectual elite, French science might have died completely as a result of the Napoleonic system.

The Governance of Science

German science flourished and French science languished after 1840 because the former became a highly competitive, well supported, and, perhaps most important of all, self-governing enterprise. With the professionalization of research the establishment of publicly supported laboratories, and the rise of new, specialized disciplines, the problem of choice arose for the scientific community. Previously, for example, the "scientist" was self-selected and self-trained.[86] With professionalization the senior generation of scientists assumed the task of selecting and training their successors in carrying on the scientific tradition. Decisions had to be made on the appointment of scientists to academic posts, the establishment of research laboratories, and the distribution of research funds. As knowledge expanded and new fields of research opened up, scientists had to decide whether new specializations and chairs should be created and whether older ones should be cut back or eliminated altogether. As a consequence, there emerged what one might call policy-making for science.

In Germany these policy decisions devolved on the individual universities.[87] The university, in effect, became the seat of government for the developing scientific enterprise. Unlike the centralized French university system the nineteenth-century German universities were creatures of the individual states; they enjoyed a considerable degree of institutional autonomy and had a long tradition of intense rivalry. None clearly predominated over the others, as Paris reigned over the provinces. Scientific competition was no longer merely personal. In Germany it became interinstitutional, as well, as each German university sought scientific superiority.

As Michael Polanyi has characterized it, science became a self-governing enterprise.[88] The important decisions affecting the welfare of science were made by competing elites at the numerous universities and institutes. Coordination of the over-

[86] Actually the term "scientist" was of nineteenth-century coinage and is credited to William Whewell in his *Philosophy of the Inductive Sciences*, 1840. See Sidney Ross, "Scientist: The Story of a Word," *Annals of Science*, XVIII, No. 2, June 1962, 65-86.

[87] Paulsen, *German Universities*, p. 78. In speaking of "Germany," it should be appreciated that until 1860 this term referred to a cultural area and not a unified state.

[88] This theme is developed by Polanyi in "The Republic of Science," *Minerva*, Autumn 1962, pp. 54-73.

all national effort was not made by a hierarchical organization but through a "spontaneous adjustment" of curriculum and research programs in order to avoid unnecessary duplication and open up promising new fields. It was, in effect, a laissez-faire system, like liberal capitalism, where the division of labor and coordination of individual efforts were guided by the "invisible hand" of competition for priority of discovery. In pursuit of this goal new specialized disciplines arose to replace old, less productive ones; new research facilities were created and scientific training was expanded.[89]

Meanwhile, in France, the Napoleonic law of 1808 abolished the individual university as a corporate and self-governing entity which might have been a leader in the expansion and advancement of science. In its place, authority over the affairs of science was divided between two greatly separated and frequently opposed levels—the Ministry of National Education and the individual professors. Whereas the centralized administration in Paris has authority to fix curriculum, control finances, and supervise examinations, the professors have full control over what is to them most dear: appointments to *faculté* chairs. The separate universities, *facultés*, or academic departments have little authority in their own right, but derive what little power they do possess either from above (the ministry) or below (the vote of the professors).

Raymond Aron, an incisive observer of his professional colleagues, assessed the situation as follows:

> . . . the statist administration of the universities has [resulted in] the weakening of the authority of each *faculté* over its members. State *fonctionnaire*, the professor holding a chair is his own master before God. Neither the head of his department nor the dean is in a position to give orders or simple directives to his colleagues. The French professors are

[89] Ben-David, "Scientific Productivity," p. 835.

not slaves to the state, they are free, in most respects, to follow their own pleasure, to work little or much, to repeat or renew their courses. . . . Administrative rigidity and anarchistic liberty inside the rules: this combination, typically French, is also typically universitarian.[90]

At the root of the conservatism which has plagued French science has been the fact that under the Napoleonic system of higher education neither level has had an incentive to initiate actions which would advance scientific research. At the level of the Ministry of National Education the primary concern has been the professional education of secondary school teachers who must in turn prepare students for the national examinations. As such, the Ministry has been little concerned with the status of scientific research. But even if it were, the many and interwoven series of rules governing the French bureaucracy have made adjustment to rapid change such as that characteristic of science very difficult to achieve. Whereas in Germany response to the needs of science could be initiated at many points in the system, in France there was only one point from which real change could emanate—the Ministry in Paris.[91]

Unfortunately the initiation of change at the top of the Ministry has been inhibited still further because of the strong emphasis on uniformity in French higher education. This tendency is, of course, a necessary consequence of the fact that they are preparing students throughout the nation for the same examinations.[92] If a *faculté* were to establish specialized chairs in advanced fields of science at the expense of adequately preparing their students for the *licence* or the *agrégation*, this would be unjust to the students. *All* innovations therefore must be extended to *all* universities even if it makes little sense.

[90] "La Crise de l'Université Française," p. 12.
[91] Wylie, "Social Change at the Grass Roots," pp. 221-22.
[92] Aron, "La Crise de l'Université Française," p. 11.

In Germany, on the other hand, a university could establish with relative ease a new specialization; a similar adaptation to scientific advance in France, on the other hand, frequently meant national reform of the curriculum.[93] The scientific preeminence of the *Collège de France* is partially explained by the fact it has been relatively free to establish new chairs according to changing conditions in science.

The result of the French tendency toward uniformity has been a dispersion of scientific resources. The French have scattered their effort among myriad small, ineffective laboratories.[94] Outside of Paris there have been too few places around which talent in specialized fields could cluster.

At the same time that piecemeal reform has been extremely difficult to achieve, broad-scale reform to preserve the uniformity of the system has been equally out of the question. Broad reform involves the commitment of huge resources, many of which—e.g., the supply of scientists—have been scarce in France. Also of great importance, such reform means the joining of battle with the many vested interests committed to the status quo. In short, for the Ministry, reform has posed an insoluble problem: the achievement of piecemeal reform at the price of uniformity, or broad reform involving a widespread dispersal of scarce resources and political battle. In the absence of a strong incentive to overcome these obstacles, few measures were undertaken prior to the end of World War II by the Ministry of National Education to improve scientific research and education. Even today this is the root problem of French educational reform.

At the level of the individual *faculté* and university there has been no authority to curb the self-interest and individualism of the professor, and little incentive to make decisions that

[93] "Faire l'Université," *Esprit*, p. 936.
[94] *Ibid.*

could move science ahead. The French university (unlike the German) has lacked both the independent financial means and the goad of interinstitutional competition. Also, the diffusion among the entire *faculté* of the power over *all* nominations to vacant chairs has had a deleterious effect on the advancement of French science. A system of recruitment geared to a small *faculté*, it has become anachronistic with the increasing size of the *facultés*.

In contrast to university systems where the power of nomination is vested in disciplinary departments or is delegated to impartial committees which consult scientific opinion on the best candidate for a chair, French professors are nominated by the entire *faculté* through elections which resemble political campaigns and in which the Left is frequently pitted against the Right. Professors must pass judgment on scholars in areas unfamiliar to them. As such, a situation exists where personal, political, and other subjective elements are accentuated. As one person has characterized it, the whole process is governed by the *"loi de la cooptation des médiocres"* (mediocre men tend to select mediocre men).[95]

There can be little doubt that the "democratic" system for electing professors has contributed immensely to the conservatism of French science. The newer specializations and theories have no vote, and there is all too seldom any inclination within the *faculté* to take up the cause of new specializations. Instead, the innovation of new disciplines and fields of learning in France, as far back as the founding of the *Collège de France* in 1530, has been achieved primarily through the creation of new institutions, and to a lesser extent, by the creation of chairs in the newer specialization.[96] Both alternatives, however, mean

[95] André Weil, "Science Française," *La Nouvelle Revue Française,* III, 1955, 105.

[96] By tradition the first holder of a chair is appointed by the Minister, but all subsequent nominations are decided by the *faculté.*

a long-term commitment of new resources which the state is reluctant to undertake.

In the absence of authority at the university or *faculté* level it has been nearly impossible within the French university system to put money into new fields or to establish laboratories which consolidate the widely dispersed research effort. Any attempt to give priority to new fields and phase out old ones runs counter to the existence of *droits acquis* and the French insistence on the equality of all academic disciplines. Consequently, French science has been immobilized by an egalitarianism which holds that every science is as good as every other and which has resisted any priority system.

This institutional structure reinforced the inherent conservatism of science. As Thomas Kuhn has shown, scientists are little different from other people in the degree to which they are convinced of the correctness of their own ideas.[97] The history of science reveals that the long and intensive training of a scientist in a field of knowledge, as well as his deep commitment to and personal identification with a particular theory or hypothesis, may make him reluctant to accept new ideas. At the least there is inherent in science a tension between the safeguarding of "established theories" and the claims of new ideas. While, on occasion, the former give way to the latter with only a minor struggle, the great discoveries in science necessitate a revolution in the outlook of scientists and not infrequently the replacement of one scientific elite by another.

Conservative science can best be overcome by a social system with a high degree of decentralization and interinstitutional competition, such as that which characterizes nineteenth-century Germany and the twentieth-century United States. Competition among the universities and scientific oligarchies was the key to the progress of German science. It enhanced the

[97] Kuhn, *Structure of Scientific Revolution.*

willingness of a researcher to challenge established orthodoxy by giving him mobility, a precious thing to the revolutionary with new ideas. But in France, as Raymond Aron testifies, just the opposite has been the case:

> In the university the men of age are inevitably in the positions of power. They exert on the career of the young an influence often decisive. If the young do not find in the competition of the old or of the laboratories or the universities a chance for liberation, they risk being subdued, not without injury, to the authority of patrons who do not always have the sense of the future.[98]

Whereas the leadership of German science was provided by a number of competing institutions and scientific elites, French science was dominated by one elite whose members have held the chairs at the *grands établissements scientifiques* and the *facultés* in Paris. They in effect controlled access to the important chairs, admission to the *agrégation*, and the conferring of awards. While this Parisian elite has served the useful function of offsetting the deleterious effects of the administrative and functional compartmentalization of French scientific life it has had a very conservative influence on French science. In the words of Caullery, "rare are the great careers in science which have been shaped outside Paris. Paris has absorbed all that appeared outside its walls. This has had an undeniable disadvantage in that it made difficult the development of any ideas which contradicted those of the eminent men who enjoyed unlimited authority at the moment."[99]

In contrast to politically decentralized Germany, which has lacked a strong science academy,[100] the *Académie des Sciences* has exercised a significant influence over French science, due

[98] "La Crise de l'Université Française," p. 22.
[99] *French Science,* p. 214.
[100] Ornstein, *Role of Scientific Societies,* p. 188.

in part to its role in appointments to the important scientific chairs such as those at the *Collège de France*. Regrettably the Academy has been a conservative force mainly because of its septuagenarian membership (73 years being the average age in 1965) and limited size. The desire not to offend its members has greatly inhibited the daring of French scientists.[101] In contrast to the American Academy, which has expanded to admit new specializations and which has a relatively youthful membership, the membership of the French Academy has remained at about 70, and the represented specializations have changed little since the Revolution. Many of France's most eminent and daring scientists have been excluded from it. Marie and Pierre Curie were never members. André Lwoff, who won the Nobel Prize in 1965, was at the time a member of the American and British academies, but not the French, which has no section for biochemistry or genetics. In fact, all Nobel Prizes awarded to Frenchmen have gone to individuals who were not members of the Academy at the time of the award.[102]

The rigidity of the French system of higher education, its conservative leadership, and the neglect of science by the state make all the more remarkable the success of a Claude Bernard or a Louis Pasteur in the nineteenth century.[103] Pierre Curie, for another, had no research funds, no personal laboratory, not even an office of his own; his important work on magnetism was carried out primarily in a corridor, and his work with his wife, Marie, on radium was conducted under extremely ad-

[101] Alphonse de Candolle, *Histoire des Sciences et des Savants*, Libraire Fischbacher, 1885, p. 434.

[102] "L'Académie des Sciences en Accusation," *Le Figaro Littéraire*, Nov. 18, 1965, p. 14.

[103] For a discussion of the opposition to Bernard's work in physiology by naturalists and anatomists, see Caullery, *French Science*, pp. 152-63. The first chair of microbiology at Paris was established in 1960, the first chair of genetics in 1945. Cf. Jacques Monod, "Pourquoi la France est Scientifiquement Sousdéveloppée," *Le Nouvel Observateur*, No. 49, Oct. 26, 1965.

verse conditions.[104] On being proposed for the *Légion d'Honneur*, Pierre Curie wrote to Paul Appell: "Please be so kind as to thank the Minister, and inform him that I do not feel the slightest need of being decorated, but that I am in the greatest need of a laboratory."[105] The famous Radium Institute was established only in 1910, four years after his death; under his wife's guidance, it became a great center of physical research.

The straitjacket placed on French science by the Napoleonic system was pictured vividly in a report on the status of French science written not in 1857 but 1957. The report, using biology as its example, begins by pointing out that the structure of French higher education reflects the Napoleonic imperative of preparing a small elite of professors, doctors, and engineers:

> In most of the *Facultés des Sciences*, [biology] remains at the Napoleonic stage. For the preparation of the *license* required by the secondary school program, there is in each university a department of zoology and a department of biology. But the disciplines which developed after the beginning of the nineteenth century are practically not represented: only one department of genetics for all of France, even though of all the biological disciplines, genetics is perhaps the most fundamental, and one of the most important in its applications; only four departments of biochemistry in the *Facultés des Sciences* . . . although in the publications of the entire world biochemistry occupies by itself a greater place than all the other biological disciplines united. What is to be said finally about physiology in France, the homeland of Claude Bernard; this fundamental discipline has not been able to develop, due to lack of teaching, financial

[104] Guerlac, "Science and French National Strength," p. 87.
[105] Quoted in Gerald Holton, "Scientific Research and Scholarship— Notes Toward the Design of Proper Scales," *Daedalus*, Spring 1962, pp. 364-65.

means, and university graduates; if it were not for some lonely talents, French physiology would be absent from the scientific world. In France in 1956 one could be a college graduate in the biological sciences, or even an *agrégé* without ever seriously studying genetics, without knowing physiology more than stating what is in the teaching manuals for secondary education, and without knowing any biochemistry.

It is the same in physics and chemistry. The chairs of general physics or general chemistry everywhere today maintain in general, the classic disciplines and teach a science which is still principally that of the nineteenth century. In all of France there are only two departments of physical chemistry, one of theoretical physics at Paris, recently well developed, and some timid attempts in the provinces conducted by some unhappy *maîtres de conférence* [assistant professors] who debate among themselves in isolation and without students; there is no *agrégation* in theoretical physics. In 1956, in France, one could be a *licencié* [college graduate] in physics or graduate from the *École Polytechnique*, without even having heard a serious discussion of special relativity or of the elements of quantum mechanics, nor even of certain classic elements of physical chemistry. Finally, in 1956, nuclear physics, this discipline born in France and which determines the future of nations and the race, has only three university departments in our country, poorly equipped, of such character that the better young physicists leave the field or go to the C.E.A. [French Atomic Energy Commission].[106]

The critical ingredients missing from French science after

[106] "Colloque de Caen," p. 85. It is very important to realize that the term "department" is not used in the English sense—a sub-unit of a university with important powers of decision; it is rather a collection of chairs in a field.

1840 were adequate financial support, the stimulus of competition, and a strong leadership. The tightly meshed Napoleonic system arrested the exercise of any initiative, and a spirit of conservatism pervaded science, as it did many other aspects of French life. If one searches through this period he finds individual genius such as that of Claude Bernard, but he finds few of the scientific entrepreneurs like Liebig in Germany, who founded strong lines of research, important laboratories, and institutions for scientific research and training. There developed within the French university system no equivalent of the Cavendish Laboratory in England. Nor can one point to any educational leaders similar to the university presidents who brought to the United States in the last century the German system of scientific training and research.

The major exception to this generalization was Louis Pasteur, who left behind an important French tradition in microbiology and the institute which bears his name. It was he perhaps more than any other French scientist who desired greater recognition for France as a scientific nation and who tried to awaken his countrymen to the importance of science for the future of France.[107] But his plea which opens this chapter went largely unheeded in his own lifetime and was not answered until after the Second World War. For Frenchmen of the post-1945 generation, however, science was not to be the symbol "of progress and universal harmony." The explosion of the American atomic bomb over Hiroshima symbolized a new world wherein science would become inexorably tied to the state and the power struggle among nations.

[107] René Dubos, *Pasteur and Modern Science*, Doubleday, 1960, pp. 144-45.

Chapter 5 · The American Model of a Scientific State

[France] would like to draw upon the lessons of America without being obligated, however, to copy it.

—MICHEL DRANCOURT, *Les Clés du Pouvoir, 1964*

For Frenchmen sensitive to the American scientific and technological challenge, the United States is not merely a society to be feared but one to be emulated as well. Just as Napoleonic France and its scientific reforms became the benchmark for German reforms in the early nineteenth century, and German scientific institutions provided a similar prototype in the latter part of the century for other nations, so the U.S. in the middle of this century provides France and other nations with a working model of a highly advanced scientific state. French leaders seek, in the American rise to scientific and technological preeminence, some guidance for their own endeavors to transform France into a science-technology-centered society.

It is important, therefore, to discuss the lessons the reformers of French scientific and technological institutions have drawn from American—and to a lesser extent British—experience. But in emphasizing the importance of America as a model for the French scientific reformers, one should not lose sight of the fact that the nature of modern scientific research and development itself imposes certain unavoidable prerequisites on any society that desires a strong science and technology. The reform of French scientific institutions proceeds primarily from the inherent logic of modern science and technology rather than from a mere copying of American experience. Furthermore, the unique character of French scientific institutions and their important points of contrast with their American counterparts should be appreciated, despite the emphasis on the U.S. as a model. And lastly, in significant areas the French in recent years have been in advance of, or at least parallel to the United States, in the adaptation of their institutions to the evolving nature of contemporary science and technology.

What the American experience and example reveal is that there are certain "imperatives," due to the nature of the modern scientific enterprise and the new role of science in technological advance, which a society must meet if it is to achieve rapid scientific advance and exploit the advance for social, economic, and military purposes. The structure by which a society chooses to carry out these functions is largely determined by its own peculiar traditions, values, and political system. With this understanding in mind let us turn to a brief consideration of the American scientific system.[1]

The American Scientific System

French scientists' appreciation of the nature and strengths of the American scientific system has been one of the fortuitous consequences of World War II. During the period immediately preceding the war French scientists—with a few notable exceptions such as Jean Perrin, Paul Langevin, Frédéric Joliot, André Lwoff, Louis Leprince-Ringuet, and Louis de Broglie —were not in the mainstream of scientific advance. They tended to be isolated from their foreign colleagues and were not encouraged to journey abroad other than to the French colonies. In fact the rules governing the scientist's career in France actually discouraged study and lengthy stays abroad; one risked losing his position at home if he stayed far away. Foreign scientists, for their part, seldom taught or did research in France. As French professors are state officials, foreigners have been forbidden by law to hold academic chairs.

---

[1] The discussion below focuses on the merits of the U.S. system of interest to the French and is not meant to be a balanced appraisal including its weaknesses.

Also few research fellowships have been available for foreigners or, for that matter, even Frenchmen themselves.[2] As a consequence and in contrast to British, American, and German scientists, French scientists were largely uninfluenced by the changes sweeping the structure and organization of science in the interwar period.[3]

The war, Vichy, and the German occupation ended the isolation by forcing a number of prominent French scientists to flee and take up residence in the United States, Great Britain, or Canada. There for the first time they were able to witness at first hand the immense scale and efficient organization of American and British science, especially as science in these countries was transformed by the war effort itself. Many of these French scientists—Lew Kowarski, Jules Guéron, Bertrand Goldschmidt—themselves participated in the Anglo-Canadian aspect of the atomic bomb project and made significant contributions to its success—a point the French frequently make with some bitterness in response to their exclusion from the American-British nuclear weapons partnership.[4]

These and other influential French scientists who spent the war years abroad came to appreciate in full measure both the relative backwardness of French scientific organization and the extent and significance of the role British and American scientists and scientific institutions played in the allied victory.

[2] The story is told that Albert Einstein after fleeing Nazi Germany was denied a chair at the *Collège de France* because he was not a French citizen. In 1954 the position of Associate Professor was created to accommodate foreign scholars; this is, however, a two-year appointment, renewable only in exceptionable cases. OECD, *Reviews of National Science Policy—France*, Paris, 1966, p. 108.

[3] The spirit of this period has been captured by Robert Jungk, *Brighter Than a Thousand Suns*, Harcourt, Brace, 1956.

[4] Cf. Lawrence Scheinman, *Atomic Energy Policy in France under the Fourth Republic*, Princeton University Press, 1965, p. 24. See also Bertrand Goldschmidt, *The Atomic Adventure*, trans. Peter Beer, Pergamon Press, 1964.

The development of radar, penicillin, and the atomic bomb, to note only the most dramatic examples, signified for them not only a new phase of the industrial revolution but a radical change in the relationship of science and state in the modern world.[5] Due to the systematic exploitation of basic science in the innovation of military technology, the world was seen to be entering a totally new age where science would be the basis of economic and military power. This was a new age for which France appeared to be poorly equipped either by tradition or temperament.

From the wartime awakening one can date the beginning of the French awareness of the magnitude of the American scientific effort and the importance of scientific research to American economic and military power. This awareness grew after 1945 as increasing numbers of French scientists went to the U.S. to study and as the dimensions of American scientific-technological power became more manifest. By the time of the founding of the Fifth Republic a substantial body of influential French scientists, civil servants, and politicians were convinced of France's need to emulate certain characteristics of the United States essential to her emergence as a scientific state.

THE INDUSTRIALIZATION OF RESEARCH

A basic precondition for a scientific society, observable in the United States, is the industrialization of scientific research. Such a change in the organization of research becomes necessary as the scale, style, and consequently financial requirements of the scientific enterprise are radically transformed. This change began during World War II when large teams of eminent scientists and technicians representing a number of disciplines were organized by such men as Robert Oppenheimer

[5] Lew Kowarski, "Psychology and the Structure of Large-Scale Physical Research," *Bulletin of the Atomic Scientists*, v, Nos. 6-7, June-July 1949, 186.

and Isidor Rabi at Los Alamos and the Radiation Laboratory at the Massachusetts Institute of Technology, in order to solve specific scientific and technical problems. The result of this experience was a new form of scientific collaboration, something subtly different from the older German concept of a research institute. The latter has often meant, as Kowarski has described it, little more than a few researchers dwelling under a common roof and bringing their manuscripts to the same typist.[6] The new method depended on the cooperation and participation of many disciplines, introduced the idea of a "critical mass" necessary to a research facility for effective research, and demonstrated a change in the scale of the technology required by scientists to carry out their research.[7]

In the postwar period the new form of scientific collaboration has been extended to areas of basic research where multidisciplinary participation, "critical mass," and immense instrumentation are required for effective scientific research. At first these conditions were restricted to the field of atomic energy, but in the two decades since 1945 they have become typical of the newer areas of space, electronics, and even biological research. Consequently, though the individual creative scientist remains supremely important, in a considerable number of important fields large formal organization has become the dominant mode of operation.

Institutional transformation has come about through important changes in the character of scientific research. First, the contemporary scientific enterprise is experiencing a technological revolution. In increasing numbers scientists require massive and expensive equipment, the most dramatic examples of which are multimillion-dollar particle accelera-

[6] *Ibid.*, p. 188.

[7] *Ibid.*, pp. 188-89. Modern cooperative research actually began at the Cavendish Laboratory at Cambridge, England, and the Berkeley Radiation Laboratory, but its full merit was not really understood until World War II. Gerald Holton, in *Daedalus*, Spring 1962, p. 377.

tors. There is a need for large numbers of assistants and technicians. Second, the rapid advance of knowledge has led to greater and greater specialization at the same time that there is an increasing need for cooperation among specializations once thought to be far apart. Third, although the traditional scientific discipline remains the basis of academic organization, research is becoming increasingly organized according to specific problems such as the genetic code, or the development of a new technology which necessitates cooperation among scientists and technologists in many disciplines.

In contrast to France, where an emphasis is placed on individual creative genius in scientific or technical advance, the strength of both American and Russian science and technology rests on numbers and organization. Individual genius may provide science with its most original discoveries, but the intellectual development and technological exploitation of theoretical breakthroughs necessitate that a society have strength in depth. In basic research as in technological development, there is indeed such a thing as a critical mass of technical workers, which a society must have to bring to bear on the vast array of unanswered questions created by scientific research. The U.S. has been able to master this requirement for an effective national scientific effort because it has applied to the organization of research and development the same managerial and entrepreneurial skills Americans have employed in organizing other sectors of national life.

The factors, then, of massive technologies, a considerable division of labor, and the need for multidisciplinary coordination under skilled management account for the organizational transformation of modern science. Well-managed research teams and large, formal organizations are a necessary feature in both applied and basic research as well as in technological development. The university itself, as the seat of basic scientific research, may remain a community of individual scholars but it increasingly possesses the characteristics of a "knowledge factory" whose primary social task is the production of useful knowledge required by a demanding society and defense establishment.[8]

THE NATIONALIZATION OF RESEARCH AND DEVELOPMENT

As Kowarski and other French scientists realized, the Second World War transformed the relationship of science and state in the United States and in the other major victorious powers. In mobilizing science for war the American Government, with the advice of scientific leaders, made several important and far-reaching decisions that established the pattern of science-state relations in the U.S. throughout the war and into the postwar period.[9] The first decision was that government would give contracts to industrial and university laboratories to do military research and development, rather than conscript individual scientists and engineers into government laboratories. The second was the establishment of a broad and extensive liaison for the first time between the basic research of the universities, the applied research and development of industry, and the weapons programs of the military services. The third decision, related to the first, was that scientists and engineers who were given responsibility for mobilizing science for war retained their university or industrial affiliations and served government as short-term advisors or administrators.

[8] Two recent books by prominent university presidents give the flavor of the changing character of the American university: Clark Kerr, *The Uses of the University*, Harvard University Press, 1963; and James A. Perkins, *The University in Transition*, Princeton University Press, 1966.

[9] The first, and best, exposition of the war's impact on science-state relations is Don K. Price's *Government and Science*, New York University Press, 1954. In his later book, *The Scientific Estate*, Harvard University Press, 1965, Price goes far beyond his earlier study to present a reinterpretation of the American political system in the light of the scientific revolution.

After the war one additional, but very important, feature was added. In the past the American government and military had been content in general to adapt civilian technologies to military purposes. As a result, radical innovation was not characteristic of military research. During World War II, and because of the work of such scientist-dominated agencies as the Office of Scientific Research and Development and the Manhattan Project, scientific research—including fundamental research—was exploited for the development of novel and important technologies. For the first time in history technologies were innovated *during* the course of a war which had a significant influence on its conduct and outcome. This experience made a strong impact on American military and political leadership, and as Vannevar Bush declared in *Science, the Endless Frontier*, which advocated a national science foundation, basic science was a national resource which should be supported by federal funds.[10]

Though Bush's proposal was not immediately accepted, the American-Soviet political competition, which has manifested itself largely in a qualitative arms race, led to a new attitude toward basic scientific research. For security, economic, and health reasons government could no longer be content to let science and technology advance at a "normal" rate and along lines that might have relatively little social utility. It was no longer sufficient, in other words, for government merely to exploit the scientific and technological advances made by universities and industry. Instead, government itself must force the pace of new knowledge and innovation, especially in those areas judged to be of high military or social use. Thus the traditional laissez-faire *laissez-rechercher* attitude of the state toward science has given way to extensive intervention by government. Through a variety of institutions and mechanisms the state must attempt to accelerate scientific and technical

[10] Bush, *Science, the Endless Frontier*, Report to the President, 1945.

progress and key this advance to military, economic, and social objectives.

What has happened in the United States, as French commentators frequently point out, is that science in the world's leading capitalistic society has been nationalized (*la socialisation de la science*). While it is not surprising to the French that science in the Soviet Union is supported entirely by the state, it has been startling to learn that 75 percent of the research and development effort of the U.S., including that of private corporations, is financed directly by the Federal Government.[11]

In effect, science in the United States, including much industrial research and development, has become a quasi-public enterprise. This aspect of the American science system has come about because government and science have had to move toward one another. Due to the changes in the nature and scale of physical and biological research discussed above, science has need of unprecedented funds if it is to continue; for their monies scientists and even industries must turn to the only available source—the state. And the government is willing to subsidize university and industrial research because of the benefits which might accrue.

THE INTERRELATED SYSTEM

Another facet of the U.S. as a scientific nation-state which has been carefully noted by French observers is the organization of the national scientific effort. The war proved that in an era of scientific technology when scientific knowledge is advanced and exploited on a massive scale for the development of novel and powerful technologies, "there must be an active cooperation among the state . . . industry . . . the universities . . . and the defense establishments."[12] Each member of this

[11] Richard Lesher and George Howick, *Assessing Technology Transfer*, National Aeronautics and Space Administration, 1966, p. 20.
[12] Kowarski, "Psychology and the Structure," p. 187.

alliance has its vital part to play and without such cooperation no society can hope to achieve a prominent position in the modern world. The essential features of the wartime alliance among the American Federal Government, industry, and universities in the area of scientific research and development, were not only preserved but extended afterwards. While a complete description and analysis of the American science system that has evolved would take us too far from the primary concern of this study, an understanding of the "interrelated system," as one report has called it, is necessary.[18]

The Emergence of a National Science Policy. The first feature of the interrelated system is that important aspects of decision-making for science have shifted from universities and private institutions and become highly centralized in several governmental agencies. This is due to the increasing need of scientists for substantial financial support by the government. Though the initiation of research projects rests largely with individual researchers and research institutions, the decisions concerning which projects are to be supported, and to what extent, are now made to a considerable extent by such agencies as the National Science Foundation, the National Institutes of Health, the Defense Department, and the Atomic Energy Commission. With respect to basic research, however, these decisions are made largely on the advice of scientific advisors to these agencies.

At the same time, the necessity to establish priorities for funds among competitive scientific disciplines, to encourage research in important but underdeveloped fields, and especially to evaluate the accelerating demands of "big science" (oceanography, space, high energy physics) has led to the creation of a new order of institutions and offices at the Presidential level: Special Assistant for Science and Technology; the Federal

---

[18] National Academy of Sciences, *Federal Support of Basic Research in Institutions of Higher Learning*, 1964.

Council for Science and Technology; the President's Science Advisory Committee; and the Office of Science and Technology. The task of the scientists and officials who man these institutions is to coordinate the immense federal scientific effort and assist the President in the formulation of a national science policy.[14]

Both at the level of the individual disciplines and at the over-all level of the total national scientific-technological effort, there has emerged in the United States a somewhat diffuse but nevertheless identifiable mechanism for the governance of science. Whereas, prior to the Second World War, one would have been at a loss to determine who or what made the essential decisions affecting the welfare of American science, the task is less complicated today. Then, national science policy was nothing more than the end result of the uncoordinated activities of many individuals and institutions. Today, a number of official government bodies, along with the National Academy of Sciences and influential men within the scientific community, make what in effect is the science policy of the United States.

The Contract Mechanism. The second, and at least for the French the most interesting, feature of the American interrelated system is the use by the national government of the research contract (or project grant in the case of basic research) as a primary instrument for financing the national research and development effort. Research teams, universities, and industries are not administratively subordinate to the agencies of government supporting research; this gives both government and researchers considerable freedom of action. University laboratories and industries can formulate their own research programs and "shop around" for a government agency to support them. Conversely, the government agencies and their scientific advisory panels can select those projects which appear

[14] Price, *Scientific Estate*, p. 243.

134

to be of highest merit and, in general, most relevant to the government's objectives.

Perhaps the nature of the contract system will be made clearer by contrasting it with several other methods of support for scientific research. It should be understood that there is no country which uses one method to the exclusion of the others; the differences are matters of emphasis. First, the government can simply tell the scientists what research to do. This, of course, is the usual case in any technical agency of government where the research is primarily applied. Second, individual scientists or laboratories can be supported regardless of the merits of their research—essentially the system in the French university, which is a public institution and where the professor enjoys full academic freedom. Third, the government may give support to an institution to develop a particular discipline or area of research such as high energy physics or problems of water pollution. The decisions regarding which specific projects or individuals are to be supported are left to the institution itself; the "centers of excellence" program of the American National Science Foundation is of this type. And fourth, the government may support an institution without specifying (except where huge outlays of capital are involved) which disciplines or projects should be supported; this is essentially the procedure of the British University Grants Committee.

In contrast to these alternative methods, the contract, or project grant, system maximizes the competition among the researchers seeking support and the freedom of action among the government agencies granting support. Through the award of research and development contracts and project grants to individual researchers, university laboratories, and private industries, those competing areas of science and technology judged by federal agencies and their scientific advisors to be of greatest scientific or social merit can be emphasized

135

and given high national priority. Areas judged to be of relatively lesser utility can be deemphasized or eliminated altogether for lack of adequate financial support. Consequently, through the instrumentality of the contract mechanism,[15] researchers and industries have an incentive to undertake projects of "high" merit, and a relatively few government agencies, in conjunction with their technical and scientific advisors, are able to determine in large measure the scale and direction of the American scientific and technological effort.

Though the contract mechanism for the support of research and development has its own drawbacks, for the French it has three very attractive aspects. By shifting to the contract system the state can increase the incentive of scientists and industries to undertake research of national interest. Second, the state in a free enterprise economy can subsidize the research and development effort in selected industries. Third (and this is a point to be emphasized), contracting out is a means by which to increase political support for research and development throughout society. Finally, the contract system enables the state to mobilize and organize university, industrial, and private resources as part of a united national effort to carry out a specific task and develop a particular technology.

The success of the contract system in the United States, as it applies to basic research, is due to the acceptance by government and scientists of a compromise between the desire of the state that scientific research serve its policy goals and the desire of scientists to pursue that research which will advance scientific understanding. For its part, the state must acknowledge that in the long run the most useful research is basic research having no visible, immediate practical use; for this reason, in the area of basic research, the advisory panels of prominent scientists are relatively free to select projects solely on the basis

[15] Throughout this study the terms "contract mechanism" and "research contracts" should be read to include "project grants."

of merit. However, the scientific community, for its part, must accept the fact that in the last analysis social utility is the *raison d'être* of state support.

Yet these goals can and do conflict. There is always the danger that the state in its desire for useful results will stifle science. And there is the opposite danger that scientists, impressed with the purity of their calling, will fail to make their knowledge available to those members of society who can exploit it for the benefit of society. The balancing of the interests of the state and the scientific community in order to avoid both these dangers is one of the major problems facing France as it seeks to expand and exploit scientific research.

The Decentralized National Research Effort. The third feature of the American interrelated system is that although policy-making has become more centralized, the research effort itself remains highly decentralized and dispersed among many universities. Just as the rapid growth of German science in the nineteenth century resulted from the huge German cultural area of central Europe (the German confederation, the Austro-Hungarian Empire, and the German-speaking parts of Switzerland), American science in the twentieth century enjoys a full continent in which to expand. Though the number of research centers in the American scientific system is not as great as many Americans would wish, it is much greater than in any other nation today and far greater than the number which provided the base for Germany's rise to scientific preeminence in the nineteenth century. Whereas, for example, in France over 70 percent of research and development personnel are concentrated in the vicinity of Paris, and in the Soviet Union over 70 percent of the scientists and engineers working for the Soviet Academy are around Moscow and Leningrad (1957), the highest American concentration is only 30 percent, in California.[16]

[16] C. Freeman and A. Young, *The Research and Development Effort*

137

The decentralization of American science is a rather remarkable feature of the U.S. scientific system because there is a tendency for research to cluster at a few centers and for good centers to become better at the expense of lesser centers. Scientists and engineers are a highly mobile resource; they seek those locations where research is most advanced and interesting. The phenomenon of the brain drain both within individual nations and among nations is the consequence of this tendency. Nevertheless, the United States has been less subject than other nations to the evil effects of overconcentrating its scientific resources at a few centers of importance.

The wide dispersion of the national research effort in the United States is a fortuitous legacy of the Morrill Act of 1862, which created the land-grant system of agricultural and mechanical colleges—one in each state.[17] These schools provided the nation with the university base which has been so vastly expanded since 1945 through the influx of federal funds. As a result, no Paris or high-prestige university has dominated American science. Instead there has been an intense interinstitutional competition for scientific prestige, talented professors and students, and research funds from the Federal Government which science requires to thrive and advance.

THE FUNCTION OF THE UNIVERSITY

Underlying the present role of the university in the nation's scientific, industrial, and military affairs is the American concept of the university. More than the German university, the American university, with its highly developed graduate school, has united research and teaching. In Germany institutes developed in the latter part of the nineteenth century to

---

in Western Europe, North America and the Soviet Union, OECD, 1965, pp. 61-62.
    [17] A. Hunter Dupree, *Science in the Federal Government,* Harvard University Press, 1957, p. 150.

138

accommodate new fields of research that could not gain entry into the university curriculum. In the U.S. the university incorporated new fields directly into the curriculum. As a consequence one can detect as early as the first decade of this century the beginnings of the science gap between the U.S. and western Europe in terms of numbers of researchers produced and the encouragement of newer fields then coming to the fore.[18]

The second important feature of the American and, to a lesser extent, British university which has benefitted scientific research is its organization by disciplinary departments rather than by chairs or institutes. The departmental type of organization composed of several professors of equal status and frequently with a rotating chairmanship decreases the power of individual professors over their juniors and encourages independence of thought. More important, the department as a corporate entity assumes the responsibility for the advance of the discipline through its power over appointments and curriculum.

Another striking aspect of the American university is its commitment to public service. This notion that one function of the university is to transform society and in general be socially useful is alien to European university systems. The European university was conceived to educate an elite, a social class; the American system has sought to train *en masse* the scientists, technicians, and professionals required by an expanding industrial society.

Whereas the European university systems have been set apart from society and its concerns, the American system has been responsive to society's need for applied research, technical advice, and even developmental work. The function of

[18] Joseph Ben-David and Awraham Zloczower, "Universities and Academic Systems in Modern Societies," *European Journal of Sociology*, III, No. 1, 1962, 45-84.

the American university system is not merely the preservation and advancement of knowledge but the transmission of new knowledge to agriculturalists, engineers, and industrialists.

The idea of the university as a responsive part of society profoundly affects the attitude of the American university professor toward industry and government. The American professor is generally free of the attitude of the European professor, who disdains sending his students to industry or refuses himself to work in individual laboratories or under contract on practical problems. Therefore there is that flow of personnel between university, industry, and government laboratories which is so important in translating basic knowledge into new technology.

THE ECONOMIC ROLE OF SCIENCE

The changes in the nature of American scientific research and the role of the Federal Government in research and development have been accompanied by a fourth and no less important change—the attitude of American industry toward the importance of scientific research. This change completes the triangle of government-university-industry, cooperating in research and development. It has brought about that united national effort which Kowarski saw as appropriate for an era of scientific technology. Though something of an oversimplification, it is perhaps not too much to say that this partnership is one where universities supply the basic scientific knowledge, industry develops it into new technology, and government underwrites the greater part of the cost of both the research and the development. As *Recherche Scientifique et Indépendance* has summarized it, this triangular partnership has resulted in a new industrial revolution in American industry.[19]

[19] Délégation Générale à la Recherche Scientifique et Technique, *Recherche Scientifique et Indépendance*, 1964, p. 13.

While the new industrial revolution would have taken place in any event, the U.S. Government—through its research and development contracts, especially for military and space technology—has accelerated it.[20] The assessment of the nature and extent of this "spinoff," "fall-out," or, as the economists would say, "externalities," is difficult. The most frequently mentioned, and actually least significant, type of spinoff is that of new products entering the civilian economy. The *Boeing 707* aircraft, for example, began as a military tanker aircraft, and many electronics products such as the computer were financed originally by the government. While one can argue that spinoff from military or space research is an inefficient way to stimulate the innovation of products for the civilian market, it is probably better than nothing at all. Second, and more important, the value of government contracts to industry lies in their payment of the overhead costs of private laboratories and provision of support for more wide-ranging research with direct civilian application: the invention and development of the transistor at Bell Telephone Laboratories. In this category one would put a type of spinoff of great concern to the Europeans: the development of new techniques. "The European companies," *The Economist* reports, "consider . . . that the American and Russian space effort[s] have had a profound effect on reliability and automation, and through these, the whole of the engineering industries."[21] Third—and most sig-

[20] The costs and benefits to the civilian economy of "spinoff" from military and space projects is a subject about which there is much opinion but few concrete findings. Though not an unbiased source, one attempt to get at the facts is Lesher and Howick, *Assessing Technology Transfer*. The present writer's opinion is somewhere between the enthusiasts of the spinoff theory and those who argue that the cost to the civilian economy of these space-military programs is damaging to the over-all welfare of the society.

[21] *The Economist*, Sept. 30, 1967, p. 1205. Richard Foster and Francis Hoeber, "The Technological Feedback from Defense R and D," Stanford Research Institute, 1967. See also Christopher Layton, *Trans-Atlantic Investments*, The Atlantic Institution, 1966, p. 96.

nificant of all—the rapid progress of electronics, nuclear, and aerospace industries, whose research and development efforts have been subsidized so heavily by government contracts, has had a great psychological impact on the rest of the economy. The research revolution which began in the national security and space industries has generated a new dynamism and set of attitudes throughout the rest of the economy. Industrialists, politicians, and economists have become appreciative of the new role of scientific research and development in economic growth and competitiveness.

Whereas advances in technology traditionally have been treated merely as a residual factor in the theories of economic growth, during the past decade or so technological progress has moved to a central position.[22] In part, the past failure to appreciate the importance of technology may be accounted for by the methodological bias of any science to deal with static situations before attempting to understand change, and to emphasize those variables which are quantifiable and therefore manageable. Technological change (a qualitative factor) was too difficult to fit into theories of economic growth. But perhaps of greater importance in explaining the failure to understand the relationship between technology and economic growth is that it emerged into undeniable significance only after the middle of this century.[23]

In economic competition technological innovation has become a primary determinant of the competitive position of a

[22] The classic study reversing the former tendency was Robert Solow, "Technical Change and the Aggregate Production Function," *Review of Economics and Statistics*, xxxix, August 1957. Cf. Richard Nelson, Merton Peck, and Edward Kalachek, *Technology, Economic Growth, and Public Policy*, The Brookings Institution, 1967.

[23] Paul Samuelson, *Economics*, McGraw-Hill, 1964, p. 734. A valuable summary of the literature on this subject is Richard Nelson's "Science, the Economy and Public Policy," unpub. paper, The RAND Corporation, Apr. 1964.

firm. As the French frequently point out, this is due partly to the fact that product innovation is in some indeterminate degree replacing price as the basis of economic competition. In addition, technological advance also affects the efficiency of industrial processes, thereby enabling a firm to lower prices and improve its market position. But whatever the appropriate role to assign technological innovation in economic competition, there can be little doubt that American businessmen by the 1960s had assigned it great importance.

Though the German chemical industry was the first to establish industrial research laboratories and methodically apply scientific theory to technological innovation, American industry pioneered the broad and systematic application of research to ever-increasing sectors of the economy.[24] As a result, the post-World War II period saw the same shift away from the individual to the team in industrial research as is occurring in basic research: "Invention is today less and less the fruit of chance and solitude; discovery is to the contrary more and more often the result of the methodical work of teams of which the efficiency is all the more elevated when it possesses a base of permanent organization and modern material of an often high cost."[25]

This research revolution, the French believe, could not have taken place without the financial support of the Federal Government, or without the large scale of American corporations. Both the external and internal sources of financial support enable American industry to do the type of "oriented fundamental research," applied research, and development work which pays off in revolutionary products entering the world market. Today U.S. corporations have less need for the stimulus of government contracts but are willing and able to in-

[24] National Academy of Sciences, *Basic Research and National Goals*, Mar. 1965, p. 74.
[25] "Recherche Scientifique et Indépendance," *Le Progrès Scientifique*, No. 67, p. 2.

vest their own funds. Equally important, the American financial community has come to appreciate the value of research and to accept the risks involved in technological undertakings.

Basic to what has happened is the two-way traffic between industry and the university. At the same time that there is a growing industrial and military dependence on the basic research of the universities the university research effort itself benefits from its new liaison with technology. There is little doubt that the growing demands of the economy, the military establishment, and the medical profession for new scientific knowledge have an accelerating effect on scientific advance. The search for new sources of energy or a cure for cancer, have revealed gaps in man's scientific understanding and thus have led to important scientific discoveries.

But the way science is transforming the American economy and society should not be viewed simply as the application of scientific theory to technological innovation. Of similar significance is the organizational and managerial revolution taking place because of the application of the scientific method and of new technologies to problems of decision-making and managerial control. Again originating to a large degree in the security and space areas and then diffusing throughout the whole society, operations research, systems engineering, and computer technology are revolutionizing the ways in which the United States organizes and manages its society.[26]

Since the end of the Second World War, a virtual revolution has taken place in the relationship of the social sciences and society. In both the private and public spheres, the concepts and findings of the social sciences are transforming the methods by which decisions are made and the technique for

[26] For example, one French writer, while contrasting the competitive advantages of American and European corporations, pointed out that American industry employs 30,000 computers as against 5,000 in the rest of the world. *Le Monde*, Sept. 23, 1966.

executing them. In short, the applied social sciences of decision and control are profoundly altering the management of social, economic, and political affairs.

What underlies this phenomenon is a threefold development. First, there has taken place in the United States a data revolution. Since the middle 1930s, the quantity and quality of social and economic data available to decision-makers have increased greatly. Census data, surveys, economic indicators, and social indicators are now readily accessible or are rapidly being developed. Second, a number of conceptual and theoretical developments have occurred which are having a profound impact on decision-making and management. In the application of linear programming, systems analysis, and macro-economic theory, one again sees demonstrated Henry Adams' paradoxical observation that as science becomes more abstract, its power and utility increase in geometrical progression. Lastly, the invention of the computer provides an instrument which can be used to manipulate the relatively large number of variables and the quantity of data increasingly required in decision-making and management.

These managerial changes have been made possible by the *élan* of the modern American corporation. In contrast to its usual European competitor (and one would have to exempt Philips, Shell, and Volkswagen, among others), the American corporation acquires its dynamic quality from essentially three elements of American economic life. The first element was the decision taken in the early part of this century in the framing of antitrust legislation and in judicial decisions on interstate commerce to organize the emerging national economy in terms of competition and a national market rather than cartelization and local markets. The second and related factor was the concentration of entrepreneurial energies on the creation of a mass home market with corresponding economies of scale rather than the dispersion of effort on colonial empires and export markets. And, third, with growth in corporate size has emerged a separation of management from ownership which has enabled ambitious and competent professionals to advance to the leadership of America's major corporations.

Underlying, then, the research revolution in American industry is a transformation of American corporate management. In effect a skilled, technical elite has taken over the management of America's large corporations.[27] Physicists, economists, and graduates of high-level business schools have joined bankers, lawyers, and traditional businessmen in the power structure of American corporations. But of even greater importance is the spirit of the change taking place. From product innovation through marketing these men understand better than their predecessors or European competitors the economic significance of the contemporary scientific revolution and have learned how to manage the advanced technologies to which it is giving rise.

The French Strategy of Modernization

As the French see it, the United States since the end of the Second World War has been fashioned into a new type of society. Under the impetus of the arms race with the Soviet Union, and as a result of the competition between domestic industrial giants, the U.S. has gone far toward the achievement of the national organization of science foreseen by Francis Bacon. As Bacon predicted, science has become organized on a massive scale not inherently unlike any other productive enterprise, where ordinary men trained in appropriate methods are able to advance new knowledge and to utilize it toward the end of increasing man's power over nature—and not infrequently over his fellow man.[28]

To respond to the contemporary scientific-technological rev-

[27] Jay Gould, *The Technical Elite*, Augustus Kelley, 1966.
[28] Francis Bacon, *New Atlantis*, Macmillan, 1911.

olution there are essentially three strategies which France or any other country can emphasize. The first is that of following in the footsteps of the larger scientific states and seeking to overcome their considerable lead across a broad front of basic research and technological development. A second strategy is to select specific areas in the advanced fields of science and technology which could be seen to be important for the future development of national and industrial strength, and to concentrate R and D resources in these areas. A third strategy is to concentrate on a relatively narrow range of technology but to do very little basic research, as is the case with the second strategy; instead, emphasis is placed on the purchase of selected American licenses and the concentration of indigenous technological expertise in such areas in order to develop products for subsequent export.

The first strategy is essentially that which has been selected by the Fifth Republic. Basically, of course, prestige and military rather than economic considerations weigh heavily in this approach. The second strategy of conducting basic research and technological development in a few industrial areas has been followed by the Dutch, the Swiss, the Swedes, and increasingly the British. The third strategy of investing heavily in American licenses has been followed by the Japanese in achieving their amazing record of growth and success in world trade; they excel, of course, in science as well.

In the view of President de Gaulle and his advisors the key to America's rise to scientific and technological preeminence is its space and military programs. Contrary to the widespread view of American intellectuals and public officials who argue that these programs divert scarce human and material resources away from more worthy programs and weaken America's over-all scientific-technical position, the view of the Fifth Republic is that these programs are essential for modernization. This is held to be true not merely because the possession of independent nuclear weapons and space capabilities is the *sine qua non* of a Great Power in the contemporary world; of equal importance is what happens to a society in the process of acquiring a nuclear and space capability. Under the guise of national security, and principally through the research and development contract, these programs because of their immense scale are believed to provide a democratic society with the necessary leverage for reforming scientific, educational, and economic institutions.

For the leadership of the Fifth Republic, the choice is not between costly military and space programs and less ambitious but economically more practical programs, but instead between modernization and stagnation. In the age of the scientific state they are believed to provide the motive power behind economic growth and military capability. The advanced industries—computers, electronics, and atomic energy, to name a few—could never have been developed with such rapidity without strong government subsidies and an attack on all fronts at the same time. Without the U.S. space effort (financed by the Federal Government), for example, microminiaturized electronics and therefore the computer would not have been developed nearly so rapidly.[29] "The objective of industrial development," the French believe, "plays an enormous role in the American space program."[30]

From this perspective, the nuclear and space programs of the United States and the Soviet Union are not infantile and wasteful competition for international prestige, but "a motor" which motivates a society for higher achievements and transforms its traditional economy.[31] In the short run, the space

[29] United Kingdom Council of the European Movement, "European Co-operation in Advanced Technology," Report of a Conference, London, July 1965, p. 41.

[30] Pierre Piganiol and Louis Villecourt, *Pour Une Politique Scientifique*, Flammarion, 1963, p. 59.

[31] *Ibid.*

effort is creating new materials, fuels, and electronics that are necessary for an advanced economy. In the long run, nuclear and space research will bring about a mutation in the entire social and economic order. If it forsakes space research, a society risks falling behind in all areas, because modern technology and modernization are so tightly integrated. Atomic energy, electronics, and space are part of one complex technological and economic whole. "Modernization," de Gaulle's former science minister told the Franco-American Society in 1963, "cannot be broken down. We cannot have an industry belonging to the end of the twentieth century and have it coexist with a defense that is not appreciably different from that of the nineteenth."[32]

The second principal feature of the French effort to relate scientific research to the military, economic, and social ends of the state is their four-year plan for social and economic modernization. Begun in the era of postwar reconstruction, the plan has become under the Fifth Republic one focus of French political and economic life. The plan must become, de Gaulle has told his fellow Frenchmen, the "grande affaire" of France.

The essential purpose of the French plan is to achieve that type of cooperation among all sectors of society which is necessary for productive efficiency in the modern world. The planning commission and its committees composed of representatives from all sectors of French society provide a mechanism where Frenchmen, long divided into groups with conflicting social and economic interests, can seek to establish a consensus on national goals and the means to achieve them. Thus while the plan is French in style and conception, it is a device by which to duplicate that climate of social collaboration "which is the secret of American industrial efficiency" and to under-

[32] Ambassade de France, Press Release, June 7, 1963.

take on a national basis the long-term planning that is built into American corporate management.[33]

The essence of the challenge facing France in carrying out this strategy and in emulating the American system is found in the obstacles to this development caused by traditional French attitudes, socio-political institutions, and resources. Can traditional French attitudes adjust to the nature of the contemporary scientific enterprise? Can modern scientific and technical institutions be grafted onto ancient French social and political institutions? Can France succeed in transforming itself into a twentieth-century scientific state? To these questions we now turn our attention.

[33] Maurice Laure, *Révolution, Dernière Chance de la France*, Presses Universitaires de France, 1954, p. 160.

Chapter 6 · Reform Under the Fourth Republic

I will state quite simply that if this country does not make the necessary effort to give science the importance it merits and to give those who serve it the prestige necessary for their influence to be felt, it will sooner or later become a colony.

—FRÉDÉRIC JOLIOT-CURIE, *1945*

France of the 1920s rebuilt in the image of her prewar self.[1] The year 1945 was the beginning of a period of reform which continues to the present day. The humiliating defeat of 1940, the experience of Vichy and the Occupation, and the spirit of the Resistance loosened the tight synthesis and balance of forces that had resisted change for so long. Attitudes and institutions which had held French science and technology in check for over a century began to give way, though slowly, to the forces being released by the renewed commitment to economic growth and industrial modernization.[2]

The spirit of reform sweeping French science was the product of two very different sets of forces. First, the push for reform emanated from the French scientific community itself. French scientists, stimulated in part by their wartime experiences abroad, but also by the frustrations of inactivity imposed by war and the Occupation, wished to recommence the rebuilding of their science which had hardly begun in the 1930s before it was quickly arrested by the collapse of France. After the Liberation the younger generation of French scientists, led mainly by Frédéric Joliot-Curie, a hero of the Resistance, was anxious to make up for lost time and was convinced of the

[1] Cf. Ernst Curtius, *The Civilization of France*, Vintage Books, 1962, p. 224.

[2] Stanley Hoffmann, ed., *In Search of France*, Harvard University Press, 1963.

151

absolute necessity for a searching reform of the organization of French education and science.[3]

At the same time, the Provisional Government of General Charles de Gaulle, and later the Fourth Republic, were receptive to the entreaties of such scientists as Joliot-Curie and Pierre Auger that France make a major commitment to scientific research, especially in the newest area of atomic energy. Nuclear energy was seen to be vital to France not only because of its long-term military importance, but also because, in the immediate future, its exploitation promised an end to the acute shortage of energy which had plagued French industrialization for so long.[4]

Under the impetus of these two forces for reforms—scientists themselves and French political leadership—the overhaul of French science was begun. From 1945 to the founding of the Fifth Republic in 1958 French scientific research experienced its greatest expansion and reform of institutions since the Revolution and Napoleon. On this foundation, laid down by the Fourth Republic, the Fifth would be able to build and extend the change in the traditional relationship between science and state in France.

The achievements of the Fourth Republic in scientific research and technological advance, which this chapter will treat, are impressive. The founding of new institutions for scientific research, atomic energy, and related areas, the reform of education and outstanding technological innovations

[3] The part French scientists played during the Resistance, their plans for reform, and the early postwar period are discussed by J. G. Crowther, *Science in Liberated Europe*, Pilot Press, 1949. The role of Joliot-Curie in the postwar revival of French science is portrayed by Pierre Biquard, *Frédéric Joliot-Curie, The Man and His Theories*, trans. Geoffrey Strachan, Paul S. Eriksson, Inc., 1966, Chap. 5.

[4] Charles de Gaulle, *The War Memoirs of General Charles de Gaulle: Salvation 1944-1946*, trans. Richard Howard, Simon and Schuster, 1960, pp. 269-70.

are characteristic of the change in the pace of French scientific-technical life, and constitute the bulk of this chapter. In particular, the establishment of two scientific institutions ranks as the most important contribution of the Fourth Republic to the advancement and transformation of French science. One was the refounding in 1945 of the *Centre National de la Recherche Scientifique* (cnrs), the other the creation of the *Commissariat à l'Énergie Atomique* (cea).

A Nascent National Science Policy

To appreciate the nature, successes, and failings of the CNRS it is necessary to recall its origins in the Third Republic and the need it was meant to fulfill. Following the ignominious defeat of France in the Franco-Prussian War of 1870 and the founding of the Third Republic in 1875, Frenchmen turned for the first time in several generations to a reappraisal of their educational and scientific system. For Louis Pasteur and other French scientists the defeat signified the superiority of the German system for the support of science. Further, in the leadership of the Third Republic French scientists had sympathetic allies who revered science as a liberating force to be used against the oppressive forces of the Right and the Church.

But while a number of reforms were carried out by the Third Republic between 1875 and 1900 none altered fundamentally the plight of French science. The Third Republic, after all, was the *république des professeurs*. It found its ideal in Henri Poincaré, a great mathematician and philosopher, who "exposed around 1900 the doctrine of the individualistic *savant*, sensitive to the esthetic of the most abstract scientific creation,"[5] and its intellectual spokesman in Ernest Renan who might argue that the state should support science lavishly

[5] Pierre Lelong, "L'Évolution de la Science et la Planification de la Recherche," *Revue Économique*, No. 1, Jan. 1964, p. 8.

but whose views on such science policy matters as the quality of training in science, the recognition of new scientific disciplines, or the expansion of research facilities carried little weight.[6]

Despite pretensions to the contrary, a remark of Henry Guerlac is equally applicable to the Third Republic as to earlier French governments: "It is curious that no country in the past has written more in praise of science or has set a higher intellectual value upon scientific accomplishment than France, and yet none has been more unimaginative and parsimonious in providing scientists with the facilities and resources they require."[7]

In the latter part of the nineteenth century this laissez-faire attitude toward science began to change as the time between the discovery of scientific knowledge and its application narrowed. One did not have to wait two generations to solve a technical problem; the scientists of one's own generation were finding new knowledge in chemistry, electricity, and biology of immediate practical importance. From a recognition of this fact it was a short step to the idea that research which might lead to the solution of practical problems should be supported.

The creation in 1901 of the Scientific Research Fund (*Caisse des Recherches Scientifiques*), to support university research that might have useful application, represented the first step in France toward a national policy of scientific research.[8] Although the state previously had established laboratories to advance specific areas of applied research the Fund was the first systematic attempt by the state to encourage the development of fundamental research in a direction where it could

[6] This is not the optimistic Renan of *L'Avenir de la Science* (1848) but the Renan of *La Réforme Intellectuelle et Morale* (1872).

[7] Henry Guerlac, "Science and French National Strength," in Edward Earle, ed., *Modern France*, Princeton University Press, 1951, p. 88.

[8] La Documentation Française, *La France Devant les Problèmes de la Science*, May 28, 1960, Part 3, p. 3.

make a greater contribution to technological innovation. Though its success was negligible the Fund foreshadowed an important change in the relationship of science and state in France.

During World War I another step toward closer liaison between state policy and scientific research was taken with the establishment of the Directorate of Inventions (Direction des Inventions) within the Ministry of National Education. This agency appears to have been the first in over a century in which a central organization operated to conduct research and development in the national interest. In it some of France's most eminent scientists, like Jean Perrin and Paul Langevin, did research on military technology.[9] The greatest consequence of the war for French science, however, was the terrible loss of life among young men with scientific potential.[10] There can be no doubt that this carnage set French science back by at least a generation.

At the end of the war, as after the Franco-Prussian War, many thoughtful Frenchmen recognized that the power of Germany rested ultimately on its scientific and educational system. France had to make sweeping changes if scientific research were to be expanded and especially if science were to make a significant contribution to French national strength. A symposium, *L'Avenir de la France*, held immediately after the war, gave national prominence to the view that science must play a great part in national life and should come out of its ivory tower to do so.[11]

The outcome of the postwar concern over science was the creation of a number of new laboratories and the establishment in 1922 of the *Office National des Recherches Scientifiques, Industrielles et des Inventions* which incorporated the

[9] Jean Mayer, in Julian Park, ed., *The Culture of France in Our Time*, Cornell University Press, 1954, pp. 287-88.

[10] *Ibid.*, pp. 286-87.

[11] Guerlac, "Science and French National Strength," p. 98.

Fund of 1901 and the Directorate of 1915. Its purpose was to "provoke, coordinate and encourage" all types of research and especially research of potential industrial importance. In addition, the *Office* was made responsible for the management of the laboratories at Bellevue that had been established during the war.[12] To improve fundamental research a new National Science Fund (*Caisse Nationale des Sciences*) was established in 1930. All of this, however, had only slight effect on the financial and even more troublesome organizational problems of basic and applied research in France.

An attack on the more fundamental difficulties of French scientific organization was begun by such scientists as Jean Perrin, Paul Langevin, Émil Borel, and Henri Laugier, who desired a genuine reorganization of French science. Perrin and Langevin, who introduced the modern physics of the atom and relativity into France, began to lobby for scientific reform. Both men had been inspired by Renan's views on the need for a national organization of science and on science's proper role in advancing human welfare. Both, too, were passionate socialists intimately associated with the leading members of the Socialist Party, including Léon Blum himself.

Perrin, Langevin, and their associates were among the most outstanding scientists in France, occupied important academic chairs, and directed some of France's most important research institutes. They were close personally as well as professionally, summering together in Normandy. Two of their number married in the case of Frédéric Joliot and Irène Curie, the daughter of Pierre and Marie Curie. Joliot was then a young and promising scientist who became Irène Curie's student at the recommendation of Paul Langevin. Irène held the chair of Nuclear Physics and Radio-Activity at the University of Paris (the chair went to Joliot after her death). Together

[12] La Documentation Française, *La France Devant*, p. 3.

they took the name Joliot-Curie and collaborated on scientific research, for which they won the Nobel Prize in 1935.[18]

In the 1930s few French scientists were Communists, but they did belong to the parties of the Left. Langevin only joined the Communist Party after the Liberation and Joliot-Curie joined it in 1942.[14] Like their scientific colleagues in the United States and Great Britain, they were appalled by the barbarism of Naziism and the terrible consequences of the Depression; at the same time, they were attracted by the social role science and scientists appeared to be playing in the new soviet state in Russia. "This theme," David Caute writes, "the comparison between Soviet and capitalist attitudes toward science and its social applications, was the one which most influenced the political orientation of French scientists who later became Communists."[15]

A number of these scientists, including Langevin and Henri Wallon, visited the Soviet Union in the late 1920s and the 1930s. There they had been impressed by the honor rendered to science by the new Russian leaders and especially by the task assigned scientific research in promoting social and economic betterment. In 1936 Langevin stated that "an important characteristic of Soviet construction, which places it in the great line of human progress, is the confidence it inspired in scientific effort and in its organization, in close harmony with technique."[16] In contrast to France, where scientific research was undervalued and was almost totally separated from technique, the Soviet experiment must have seemed heroic indeed.

Two aspects of the Soviet science system, in particular, were impressive. The organization of Russian research institutes around practical problems and the testimony of Russian scientists appeared to demonstrate overwhelmingly that the division

---

[18] David Caute, *Communism and the French Intellectuals, 1914-1960*, Macmillan, 1964, pp. 308-309.
[14] *Ibid.*, p. 309.   [15] *Ibid.*, p. 304.   [16] *Ibid.*

of scientific research into basic and applied research, and the isolation of the former from man's social concerns was wrong. To the contrary, as Henri Wallon testified in 1933, the Soviet experience proved the Marxist contention that the most rapid theoretical advances were made in a society where they are linked directly to the solution of practical social problems.[17] Theory and practice, he believed, had to be united in the organization of French science.

Next, if science was to fulfil its proper function as the servant of progress and be freed from its subservience to monopolistic capitalism, there was need for a powerful and centralized organization to coordinate and give direction to French science. The goal of these scientists, therefore, was "the general organization of scientific research into a great national service of the state."[18] Properly organized and coordinated, French science—like Soviet science—could be made to serve society. "Our end," said Jean Perrin, "is to facilitate and multiply those discoveries which constitute the sole means by which humanity can surpass its old dreams in power and liberty, in art and beauty, in fraternity."[19]

In 1933 Perrin persuaded the Minister of National Education to establish a *Superior Council of Scientific Research* to coordinate fundamental research. Other than administering the relatively few funds of the Science Fund which it had absorbed, however, the Council had little immediate influence, and many of its functions were taken over by yet another new Research Fund—*Caisse Nationale de la Recherche Scientifique* —established in 1935.[20]

[17] *Ibid.*

[18] Henri Laugier, *Service de France au Canada*, Éditions Valiquette, 1941, p. 13.

[19] Quoted by Léon Blum in the preface to a published collection of Perrin's writings, *La Science et L'Espérance*, Nouvelle Collection Scientifique, 1948, p. xli.

[20] La Documentation Française, *La France Devant*, p. 4.

But the *Front Populaire* made support of scientific research an important part of its program.[21] Upon its election (June 1936), Léon Blum, at the suggestion of Perrin, made Mme. Irène Joliot-Curie Under Secretary of State for Scientific Research[22] and created at the same time a new agency within the Ministry of National Education for the support of research. With the approach of war the *Conseil Supérieur* proposed a new organization to mobilize science for the war effort. The result was the creation in September 1938 of the *Centre National de la Recherche Scientifique Appliquée* (CNRSA).

Finally in October 1939 the *Centre National de la Recherche Scientifique* was founded by Henri Laugier under the Ministry of National Education. The CNRS, a merger of the CNRSA and the several separate agencies then existing for the support of fundamental research, was composed of two divisions, one for applied research, one for fundamental. During its brief operation prior to the French defeat the CNRS did much to mobilize science for the war. But with the collapse of France and the Occupation CNRS became relatively inactive; it came to life again at the conclusion of hostilities. Its founding, however, symbolized a profound change in the attitude of an influential body of Frenchmen toward science and was the culmination of the slow evolution away from the Napoleonic system that had begun with the Third Republic.

Centre National de la Recherche Scientifique (CNRS)

In general, French science under Vichy and the Occupation came to a standstill, but a few attempts were made to organize science for industrial research. The two divisions of CNRS were incorporated into one and the responsibility of

---

[21] Crowther, *Science in Liberated Europe*, p. 16.

[22] Mme. Curie held this office briefly, and was replaced by Perrin. OECD, *Reviews of National Science Policy—France*, 1966, p. 19. A second creation of Perrin at this time was the Palais de la Découverte for the popularization of science.

CNRS for the conduct of research was enlarged.[23] A few new research organizations such as the National Institute of Health (*Institut National d'Hygiène*) were founded, but it was only after the war that they became important in French science. French scientists, led by Frédéric Joliot-Curie, fought in the Resistance and prepared for the peace when they could rebuild French science and make it serve the political philosophy of the Left. Many foresaw a new world where Perrin's vision of the uniting of science and human welfare could come true.

After the Liberation Henri Wallon, the Commissioner for National Education, made Joliot the director of the CNRS; Joliot's concept was that it should play a central coordinating role like that of the Soviet Academy and take responsibility for applied as well as basic research.[24] Its basic ordinance of November 2, 1945 gave it the responsibility to develop, orient, and coordinate *all* French science. Though the achievement of this objective was to be frustrated, the accomplishments of the CNRS were to be substantial and to have a profound impact on the organization and development of scientific research, the availability of scientific and technical personnel, and the general support of science.

Through the establishment of numerous laboratories and research facilities the CNRS has provided France with an infrastructure of research institutes similar to that created in Germany after 1911 by the Kaiser Wilhelm Society (today the Max Planck Society).[25] In effect, the CNRS has been able to establish and administer laboratories in newer fields of research which could not be placed within the French university structure. Also, as in Germany, this support has been given to

[23] Lelong, "L'Évolution de la Science," p. 17.

[24] See Frédéric Joliot-Curie, "Note sur la Science Soviétique," *La Pensée*, Apr.-June 1946, pp. 29-32. Joliot's concept and reform of CNRS are discussed in Biquard, *Frédéric Joliot-Curie*, pp. 67-71.

[25] For a complete listing see *Répertoire des Laboratoires Scientifiques*, published by the National Bureau of French Universities and Schools.

social and historical studies as well as the natural sciences and mathematics.

The second important CNRS contribution has been in advancing the professionalization of research. The founders of the CNRS sought to make scientific research a career and to expand greatly the number of scientists employed in France. While some of the important reforms in this area did not take place until after the founding of the Fifth Republic, four principal lines of development were established in the early postwar years: (1) The laboratories established by the CNRS provided an expanded base for a research career outside the traditional university structure; as in the *grands établissements* like the *Collège de France*, a scientist in these laboratories can devote full time to research. (2) The CNRS "loans" researchers to university laboratories (this may be the most important way in which CNRS has advanced research in France). Though these scientists remain attached to CNRS with respect to questions of recruitment, promotion, salary, etc., they are fully integrated into the university laboratory and its research program. Of the 4,500 CNRS scientists in 1964 about 85 percent were located in university laboratories.[26] (3) CNRS acts as the national training ground for research workers; the supply of scientists in France is determined to a considerable extent by the number of research posts available in the CNRS. (4) CNRS has provided the numerous services, assistants, and pieces of equipment required by present-day scientists. It supports colloquia on scientific subjects and finances the attendance of French scientists at international conferences. It subvenes scientific publication and the purchase of instrumentation. It provides French scientists and technicians such services as documentation, specialized training, and assistance on patentable inventions. The CNRS also makes available to university and other non-CNRS scientific laboratories the great variety of tech-

[26] OECD, *Reviews of National Science Policy—France*, p. 41.

nicians and engineers who must handle the equipment of modern research; this is one of its most vital services. In 1964 these assistants numbered 6,300, 50 percent of whom were loaned by cnrs to other institutions.[27] In short, the cnrs in a relatively short time introduced into France many of those aspects of contemporary scientific organization which hardly existed prior to 1945. Its substantial achievements warrant the often repeated testimonial that without the cnrs French science would have died.[28]

In two important respects, however, cnrs has not lived up to the aspirations of the founders. It has not provided French science with strong leadership. Neither has it succeeded in closing the gap between scientific knowledge and technological innovation. While there are many reasons for not attaining these goals, two central ones have been the subordinate position of cnrs within the Ministry of National Education, and the internal structure of cnrs.

With the rapid increase in the number of ministries supporting scientific research after 1945, the task of coordinating all the activity became an increasingly complex assignment for cnrs. Moreover, with the narrowing of the distinction between basic and applied research the problem of coordination took on new dimensions. It was no longer sufficient merely to coordinate the various undertakings in fundamental research, but the different spheres responsible for research and for development had to be coordinated with one another. Research in the university or in cnrs, for example, had to be keyed, at least in considerable measure, to the economic, military, and other needs of society. What was really required was some coordinating mechanism *above* the ministries, rather

[27] *Ibid.*

[28] For a list of accomplishments see French Cultural Services, "Scientific Research in France," Documentation No. 14, n.d., pp. 5-6.

than one occupying a subordinate position in the Ministry of National Education.

The internal structure of CNRS also has hampered its ability to carry out its leadership and technological responsibilities. Responsibility for decision-making within CNRS is fragmented between the director and the 32 sectors of the National Committee (*Comité National de la Recherche Scientifique*) representing all the areas of research (different disciplines) supported by the CNRS. The director, assisted by an administrative council and a directorate, coordinates the activities of the disciplinary sections and has considerable authority with respect to the over-all allocation of funds among the sections. The disciplinary sections, on the other hand, have the power of decision in matters of promotion of CNRS researchers and distribution of research funds and positions among specific laboratories. As in the case of the university *facultés*, this decentralization of authority has made it impossible for CNRS to provide French science with the leadership it requires.

The disciplinary sections are in effect relatively autonomous legislative bodies a majority of whose 22 members are elected by a complex electorate of 12,000 members designated by the Minister of National Education.[29] This electorate includes the professors of the *facultés*, certain members of the *grands établissements*, and career researchers in CNRS. As a consequence of this supposedly "democratic" system for selecting membership, the sections tend to be dominated by older professors or by conservative, career scientists in the CNRS. The tendency of the sections has been to divide funds and posts evenly among the established fields and laboratories rather than give greater priority to new and promising areas of

[29] The membership of each section (in 1967) is: 12 members elected, five selected by the Minister of National Education, and five selected by the Prime Minister. These latter five were added by a reform of December 1955. See below.

research. It is ironic that the same academic conservatism the founders of CNRS sought to avoid now pervades it.

The organizational structure of the sections has been partially responsible for the failure of CNRS to advance French technology. At the time of its reestablishment the original distinction between applied and basic research was abolished. Instead each project was to be considered from the point of view of both fundamental science and possible application. Unfortunately for applied research, however, the sections were organized by traditional academic disciplines rather than by technical or social problems. Naturally the sections have been dominated by pure scientists, and although CNRS has made some important technological innovations, the tenor of the organization has been set largely by individuals who have not been interested in applied research and have not encouraged close collaboration between science and industry.

Commissariat à l'Énergie Atomique (CEA)

As Lawrence Scheinman reminds us in *Atomic Energy Policy in France Under the Fourth Republic,* atomic physics began in France in 1896 at the laboratories of Henri Becquerel and the Curies. In 1939 in France Frédéric Joliot-Curie, in collaboration with Hans Halban and Lew Kowarski, developed the concept of the chain reaction.[30] Subsequently, however, the war greatly stimulated British, American, and Russian nuclear science at the same time that it retarded research in France. Furthermore, nuclear research in recent years has undergone rapid transformation with the discovery of subatomic particles and the interest in harnessing atomic energy for economic and military purposes. To enter this kind of sci-

[30] Lawrence Scheinman, *Atomic Energy Policy in France Under the Fourth Republic,* Princeton University Press, 1965, p. 3. The following discussion rests heavily on Scheinman's study, and to a lesser extent, on Bertrand Goldschmidt's, *The Atomic Adventure,* trans. Peter Beer, Pergamon Press, 1964.

entific and technical research a nation requires not merely costly equipment but an organization of immense scale, large numbers of scientists, and a huge staff of supporting technicians. Both the scientific and industrial aspects of atomic energy have to be developed and linked to each other if nuclear science is to be exploited.

The problem has been an unprecedented one for France. As noted earlier, the scale of atomic research was beyond the capabilities of the French university to manage. Also, the military security aspects of atomic energy warranted an organization which gave the government more control than is desirable in academic affairs.

Nor did the traditional ministerial form of organization seem appropriate. The large scientific-technical content of atomic energy as well as the importance and *mystique* of the subject called for an organization where scientists themselves shared influence with the traditional French administrative class, the *grands corps de l'État*. For these reasons, therefore, a novel and unique administrative structure was erected to handle the development of atomic energy. Several features of this structure must be noted with regard to the significance of the CEA in transforming the traditional structure of French science.

Perhaps the foremost characteristic of the CEA derives from the fact that it was founded in October 1945 under an unusual ordinance, one which gave it considerable administrative and financial autonomy. The CEA was freed from the heavy red tape customarily imposed on the ministries by the Minister of Finance and other rule-making bodies. It was placed directly under the authority of the Prime Minister, who is president of the administrative body of the CEA. Thus administratively, financially, and politically the CEA enjoys an elevated position in the French government.[31]

[31] Scheinman, *Atomic Energy Policy*, p. 12.

The second unusual feature of the CEA is that natural scientists were given formal positions of authority in the organization. In the first place, scientists are represented on the Atomic Energy Committee, the highest policy-making body of the CEA.[32] More important, responsibility for the daily affairs of the CEA was divided between dyarchical authorities—the High Commissioner and the Administrator-General. The High Commissioner was designated as a natural scientist who would be responsible for the scientific and technical tasks of the agency; the Administrator-General—an administrative expert —was to be responsible for the administrative and financial aspects of the organization. In addition to assuming these policy-making and administrative positions, natural scientists, along with industrial and government participants, were heavily represented on the numerous advisory committees and in particular on the Scientific Council and Scientific Committee, which have an important influence on the functional aspects of the CEA. For the first time since the Revolution natural scientists *as natural scientists* were to hold significant offices in an agency which itself was in a strategic position.

The third feature of the CEA is the breadth of its mandate. By virtue of the importance of atomic energy, the strong desire of the French "to catch up with the Anglo-Saxons," and the closeness between the science and the technology of atomic energy, the Commission's responsibility and authority extend from basic research to industrial and military application. The CEA's mandate was to conduct scientific and technical research in the various domains of science, industry, and national defense.[33] It can enlist the cooperation of other ministries, let

[32] In 1960 the Committee had 11 members, four of whom were natural scientists—Francis Perrin, Jean Coulomb, Louis Leprince-Ringuet, and Yves Rocard. Cf. Commissariat à l'Énergie Atomique, *The French Atomic Energy Commission, 1945-1960*, Mar. 1960.

[33] "Les Problèmes Administratifs en France Relatifs à l'Utilisation

contracts to industry and universities, and engage itself in a great variety of activities. For the first time, therefore, the French created a powerful instrument for bridging the gap between basic science and technological innovation, and began the construction of that united national effort among government, universities, and industry that Kowarski argued was necessary in an age of scientific technology.

The subsequent history of the CEA has been too well discussed by Scheinman to merit extended presentation here. Perhaps it will suffice, however, to point out that this history may be divided into three rather distinct phases. The first, from 1945 to 1951, was the formative. During this period the infrastructure of facilities, scientific-technical personnel, and institutional relations was established; on this foundation the future industrial and military exploitation of atomic energy could be built. The second phase, from 1951 to 1955, is the industrial development phase; during these years the emphasis was on the development of high-power reactors, the production of plutonium, and the construction of an atomic energy industry.[34] And last, in 1955, and even more emphatically after 1960, there begins the military phase of the French atomic energy program. It is, however, only the first phase of this history which concerns us at the moment; the second and third will be discussed in later sections.

What is perhaps most noteworthy about this first period is the role played by natural scientists in reforming the spirit and structure of French science. In large measure this role was possible because of the unique character of the CEA and the prominent place it gave to scientists. Equal credit must be given, however, to the energy and leadership of one man, Frédéric Joliot-Curie, who activated the CNRS after 1944 and

Pacifique de l'Énergie Atomique," La Documentation Française, *Notes et Études Documentaires*, No. 2,856, Feb. 1, 1962, p. 6.

[34] Scheinman, *Atomic Energy Policy*, p. 85.

then, 18 months later, went to the CEA. For not only was he a great scientist, he was an institution builder and entrepreneur of a rare order. Until his "downfall" in April 1950, he provided French science both within the atomic energy area itself and across the board, with its first strong leadership in over a century and a half.

Indeed, a basic weakness of French science, as was pointed out in the preceding chapter, has been the absence of strong leadership. With the appointment of Joliot as High Commissioner of the CEA an energetic reformer was given the power to make a number of the necessary and important tough decisions facing French science. In this effort Joliot benefited from two things: his high standing within the French scientific community (at that time he was the last French scientist, along with his wife Irène, to have been awarded the Nobel Prize); and, the CEA, which he dominated, enjoyed relative freedom of action and support (financially modest though it might be) from French political leadership and especially from de Gaulle, whose confidence Joliot enjoyed. Further, he had the strong support of several other outstanding French scientists, including the leaders in the wartime Anglo-Canadian team who had returned to France in 1945—Pierre Auger, Jules Guéron, Lew Kowarski, and Bertrand Goldschmidt. In the Canadian project Auger had directed the physical research; Guéron and Goldschmidt had led the chemical sections. Kowarski was responsible for the construction of the first Canadian heavy water reactor.[35]

The accomplishments of Joliot and his scientific lieutenants were threefold in the years 1945 to 1951. First, they began what was most basic in the development of a French nuclear science and technology program—the training and recruitment of scientists and technicians. Starting with little more

[35] Goldschmidt, *Atomic Adventure*, p. 32. For an appreciation of the task in launching the CEA see Biquard, *Frédéric Joliot-Curie*, pp. 72-85.

than the few who had worked in the Anglo-Canadian project, by 1950 the CEA had some 250 engineers and scientists in addition to several hundred other personnel.[36]

The second accomplishment of this initial period was the establishment of facilities and the provision of necessary resources. Much of the effort went into the securing of an adequate supply of uranium, heavy water, and reactor-grade graphite—not an easy task because of the technical problems and Anglo-American monopoly of the world's supply of uranium.[37] On December 15, 1948 the first western European atomic reactor outside Great Britain went into operation at Châtillon; code-named *ZOE* (for zero-power uranium oxide heavy water), it was an extension of the work begun in Canada during the war.[38] Most significant, work was begun in 1949 on France's first big atomic research center at Saclay, 15 miles from Paris. Here would be constructed a more powerful experimental reactor, particle accelerators for nuclear research, and a complex of new laboratories.[39] The importance of Saclay —in addition to the fact that it has become one of the most important centers of nuclear research in the world—is that it symbolizes the beginnings of a transformation of French scientific institutions. In place of the small and poorly equipped laboratories of individual professors that had traditionally characterized French science, at Saclay limited scientific resources were consolidated in a complex of modern laboratories. In place of individualistic professors there were now teams of researchers and supporting technicians. The industrialization of basic research was begun.

Perhaps the most important accomplishment of the CEA in these early years was psychological. The novelty, importance,

---

[36] Commissariat à l'Énergie Atomique, *French Atomic Energy Commission*, p. 29.

[37] Goldschmidt, *Atomic Adventure*, p. 37.   [38] *Ibid.*, p. 62.

[39] Commissariat à l'Énergie Atomique, *Developments and Programs*, June 1964, p. 9.

and scale of atomic research were such that it could not be absorbed by the traditional structure of French science.[40] Neither the universities nor the *grands établissements* could handle it nor resist its development for long. Atomic science is a young man's game and the CEA provided the younger generation of French scientists with the necessary leverage to begin the reformation of traditional institutions and practices. The CEA gave encouragement and research contracts to newer areas of research that could not get adequate support within the university or other traditional institutions. Through its fellowship program and the establishment of training facilities the CEA began the development in France of true graduate training in scientific research like that in the United States.

Of crucial importance in the evolution of the French nuclear program was that on their return to France in 1945 French atomic scientists were almost completely cut off from American and British nuclear technology. In December 1944 the French sought to establish an information exchange program with the British. This was blocked by President Roosevelt as a violation of the Quebec agreement of August 1943 between the American, Canadian, and British governments. Under the terms of the agreement the U.S. would share nuclear information with the British if the latter agreed not to assist a third country unless it had American permission.[41] The denial of

[40] This change was reflected in the rapid growth of the CEA budget. See CEA, *French Atomic Energy Commission*, p. 31.

[41] Goldschmidt, *Atomic Adventure*, pp. 37-39. The British-American agreement has been a very sore point with the French. In their eyes the British, in agreeing not to share atomic information with third parties without American concurrence, broke an earlier British-French agreement on nuclear cooperation. Since the French Government held the original patents on atomic energy, which they had shared with the British, and French scientists had assisted in the British nuclear program, this British "betrayal" has been especially bitter. Cf. "Le Développement Nucléaire Français Depuis 1945, *Notes et Études Documentaires*, No. 3,246, Dec. 18, 1965, La Documentation Française, pp. 4-6.

nuclear information to France was continued after the war and acted as a deterrent to other European nations from associating with France lest they jeopardize their own chances of obtaining nuclear assistance from the United States.[42] The American refusal to provide France with information given to another ally and possessed by the common enemy not only embittered French-American relations but profoundly influenced the direction of the French nuclear program and cut the French off from nuclear collaboration with other Europeans until the founding at Geneva of the European Center for Nuclear Research (CERN) in 1953.[43] It was only following the Geneva Atoms for Peace Conference in 1955 that the French and the rest of the world were given greater access to American and British information related to peaceful uses of nuclear power.

Despite this handicap, the accomplishments of the CEA during this initial period were remarkable. The CEA not only made important advances in nuclear science but substantially influenced the over-all status of French science. Most significant of all, it laid the scientific basis for the development of nuclear technology which began in earnest after 1955.

Other Scientific Reforms

Before leaving this discussion of scientific reform in the early postwar period, several other important developments in addition to the founding of the CNRS and the CEA must be mentioned briefly. While none of the other organizations rank with CNRS or CEA, they do represent significant departures in French scientific and technical organization.

The first was the National Institute of Agricultural Research (INRA), originally established in 1921 and reorganized by the law of May 18, 1946. Before this, agricultural research in

---

[42] Goldschmidt, *Atomic Adventure*, p. 82.
[43] *Ibid.*, p. 83.

France had been dispersed among several agencies within the Ministry of Agriculture and had been plagued by the Malthusian attitude which asked: Why produce more when there is no one to eat it?[44] The reform created two centralized agricultural research complexes at Jouy-en-Josas and Versailles, in addition to several regional centers—an important first step. Subsequently, under the Fifth Republic, which hopes to establish France as the breadbasket of western Europe, the research and extension service efforts of INRA and the Ministry of Agriculture have been greatly expanded.[45] Between 1960 and 1965 the number of research workers in the agency increased from 452 to 721 and research expenditures between 1958 and 1964 increased from 27 million francs to 117 million francs.[46]

Another important departure for French science was the reestablishment in 1945 of the National Institute of Health (INH) by the Ministry of Public Health and Population.[47] Its assigned mission was to play much the same role in medical research as CNRS in other areas of basic research. Specifically, INH's task was "the direction, organization, and coordination of scientific medical research." While it would contribute to a revival of French medical research, the tremendous task of reforming an almost medieval system of medical-biological research was beyond the intent of its longtime director, Louis Bugnand, and certainly beyond his power. In general, the INH supported clinical research in hospital laboratories but did relatively little to overcome the more basic problems of breaking down the barriers that separated fundamental biological

[44] Jean Meynaud, *La Révolte Paysanne*, Payot, 1963, p. 205.

[45] The problems of French agricultural research and education remain enormous. An appreciation of them and recent reforms can be gained from Colloque de Montpellier, Oct. 4-6, 1962, "Université-Agriculture"; *L'Expansion Scientifique*, Nos. 16-17, Jan.-May 1963.

[46] OECD, *Reviews of National Science Policy—France*, p. 41.

[47] The INH was actually founded in 1941, but its history as an effective organization begins in 1945.

research from medical practice or of encouraging doctors and medical schools to do more fundamental biological and medical research. The beginning of the necessary reforms in these areas would have to await the coming of the Fifth Republic.

In addition to these essential scientific research organizations a number of new organizations of a more technological nature were established; they will be discussed in the next section. Mention should be made here of one unusual scientific-technical agency, the Office of Overseas Scientific and Technical Research (ORSTOM). Established in 1944, its responsibility was to do research of interest to the French colonial empire, primarily of course, on problems of tropical agriculture. It has continued to be an important instrument of the French assistance program for the French-speaking states of Africa.[48]

In addition to the foundation or reestablishment of these scientific institutions, the state also sought to change the educational system to make it more democratic and increase its production of scientists and engineers. The leadership for this effort was provided by natural scientists (especially those of the Left) who held the top positions in the Ministry of National Education. Many of the main ideas underlying this attempted reform had been generated during the Resistance or were based on the experience of French scientists during the war with American, British, and Canadian education.[49]

Of the proposals for reform the most significant was the so-called Wallon-Langevin Report, named after Henri Wallon, Minister of National Education, and Paul Langevin, Chairman of the Commission for the Study of the Reform of Educa-

[48] Pierre Piganiol and Louis Villecourt, *Pour Une Politique Scientifique*, Flammarion, 1963, pp. 150-53.

[49] This discussion is based on Crowther, *Science in Liberated Europe*, Chap. I. Actually many of the ideas go back to the so-called *X-Crise* movement of the early 1930s. Composed largely of *Polytechniciens*, its proposals for a more rational socio-economic order also found favor for a while under Vichy.

tion. It proposed, among other things, expansion of educational opportunities for all classes of Frenchmen, emphasis in secondary and higher education on scientific-technical subjects rather than humanistic-literary studies, and elimination of the fragmentation among educational institutions, especially that between *facultés* and *grandes écoles*. On the other hand, the report was actually complacent with respect to the reform of the university—a reflection no doubt of that curious French phenomenon that politically Left professors tend to be very conservative toward university reform.

A second major proposal was that of Pierre Auger, who had been very much influenced by his experience abroad during the war. As the first Director of Higher Education after the war Auger proposed that French education beyond the secondary level be reorganized into three cycles. The first, or intermediate, cycle of two years would be common for all students, including those desiring to attend the *grandes écoles*, though students would "major" in different scientific, technical, or humanistic subjects. Students would be admitted to the second, or training, cycle of two to four years by special examination; its purpose would be to train students for their profession and would correspond to existing *faculté* and *grande école* training. The most important feature of Auger's proposal was to be the creation of a third cycle devoted to advanced training in scientific research or technical education. Special institutes would be established in the universities to combine training and research, and the teaching staff would be greatly expanded at all universities to include tutors and other personnel who could give greater attention to individual students. Additionally, universities would be reorganized, in order that some might develop specializations and more effective use might be made of limited resources.

The reforms suggested by Wallon-Langevin and Auger were much too radical and costly to be accepted in full, but a beginning was made—such as the creation in 1947 of a first cycle in the *facultés*. More important, the proposals became part of the program of action for scientists of all persuasions interested in educational reform. Ironically, many of the major educational reforms which would be implemented by the authoritarian Fifth Republic may be traced to the ideas of these early scientist-reformers of the Fourth Republic.

The record of the Fourth Republic in educational reform is not, however, merely one of frustrated ideals. Of primary importance, in this writer's opinion, were the steps taken to improve the graduate training of scientists and engineers. The expansion of graduate training was made possible by the fellowship and training programs of the CEA and the CNRS. Increasingly, the most highly qualified of France's potential researchers would have the opportunity to receive support from one of these institutions while preparing for the *doctorat d'État* at a university or at new research training institutions, such as the National Institute of Nuclear Sciences and Technologies established at Saclay in 1956.

The most important innovation in the area of training was the January 1955 creation by the Minister of National Education of a new fellowship and degree program—the *doctorat de troisième cycle*.[50] In contrast to the much more prestigious *doctorat d'État*, which can only be awarded by a university *faculté*, this degree may be awarded under certain conditions by institutes such as the *École Pratique des Hautes Études*. In addition, it requires much less time in preparation, as the candidate has to submit only one thesis, compared to two for the *doctorat d'État*. (A third doctorate, *doctorat d'université*, is regarded by Frenchmen as of little value and is taken primarily by foreigners.) Though the *doctorat d'État* continues to be the requisite for university teaching, the program sup-

[50] J.-B. Piobetta, *Les Institutions Universitaires*, Presses Universitaires de France, 1961, p. 76.

porting the *doctorat de troisième cycle* has become an important new source of funds for graduate training; it is also a device for testing the research aptitude of students.[51]

Regarding the more fundamental problems of the content of graduate studies and university reform in general, the achievements of the immediate post-Liberation period were a disappointment. On the subject of graduate training a 1956 report on French higher education concluded: "actually the third cycle [graduate studies] does not in fact exist in the French university."[52] Mostly, as in the nineteenth century, the prospective researcher still had to train himself; inadequate training facilities existed and too few programs were geared to teaching the student how to be a research scientist.

The Advancement of Technology

In technological innovation, as in scientific research itself, there was a significant change after the end of the Second World War. The psychological revolution which blew winds of change through science also stirred the inventive vigor of the French that had lain dormant since the end of the Second Empire. This development has been effectively summarized by Charles Kindleberger:

> What seems to have happened is that, with the change in attitude toward economic progress . . . there occurred simultaneously a change in the importance attributed by society to technological progress and to engineers—and a change in the attitude of the engineers themselves. Technical people already lodged in government achieved prominence somewhat more readily there than in private industry, at least at

[51] The value of the *doctorat de troisième cycle* is an issue of considerable debate. See "Faire l'Université," *Esprit*, Nos. 5-6, May-June 1964, pp. 810-11, for an evaluation.

[52] "Colloque de Caen," *Les Cahiers de la République*, No. 5, Jan.-Feb. 1957, p. 97.

the start. But the change was pervasive and spread to private industry.[53]

This revival of the Saint Simonian spirit, with its emphasis on technical advance and state planning (*étatisme*), has already been noted in the establishment of the CNRS, CEA, and lesser scientific institutions. In the case of CNRS the initial hopes of its founders that it would advance technology met disappointment. But the CEA became after 1955 an important technological institution, providing France with the only important atomic power industry in western Europe, and eventually with the technology to construct her own nuclear weapons.

THE ATOMIC ENERGY COMMISSION

Between 1945 and 1951 the emphasis of the CEA program was on the first part of its mandate to "conduct scientific and technical research with a view to the utilization of atomic energy in the various fields of science, industry, and national defense."[54] By 1951 this task was well underway; by then France had sufficient scientists, technicians, and facilities to begin the commercial development of atomic energy. The pressure to do so was great. France, traditionally poor in energy resources, appeared to be facing the prospects of arrested economic growth unless she could increase her supply of energy. For France's economic planners and thoughtful politicians nuclear technology seemed to offer an escape from the difficult situation. Eventually a long-term plan of atomic energy development was prepared and in 1952 the French atomic energy program entered its industrial phase.[55]

The history of the transition period of the CEA, from a

[53] *Economic Growth in France and Britain, 1851-1950*, Harvard University Press, 1964, pp. 159-60.
[54] Quoted in Scheinman, *Atomic Energy Policy*, pp. 58-59.
[55] *Ibid.*, p. 60; Goldschmidt, *Atomic Adventure*, p. 79.

purely scientific to a scientific-technical organization, does not concern us here, yet mention should be made of some of the more important events. The first was the removal of Joliot-Curie as High Commissioner because of his membership in the Communist Party and his statements in support of the Soviet Union. He was replaced by Francis Perrin, the son of Jean Perrin, a respected but not as charismatic and forthright a leader as Joliot. Secondly, important organizational and personnel changes in the CEA decreased the influence of scientists, especially those of the Left. Leadership in the CEA shifted from the office of the High Commissioner to that of the Administrator General, and from Leftist to more conservative scientists such as Louis Leprince-Ringuet and to *anciens Polytechniciens* such as Pierre Guillaumat, a member of France's traditional administrative class. Guillaumat was Administrator General from 1951 to 1958, when he became the minister responsible for atomic energy matters.[56] And last, policy decisions were taken in the preparation of the first five-year plan for atomic energy, which placed France on the road to an industrial and military nuclear capability.

The most important policy issue decided at this time was, in the words of Lawrence Scheinman, "whether France ought to construct research reactors and attempt to put atomic energy to immediate industrial use, or to undertake the production of fissionable materials."[57] The first course of action would have meant that France would have had to import the necessary fissionable material (enriched uranium 235 or plutonium) from the United States or Great Britain. It was believed doubtful at the time that they would assist France. The alternative—producing her own fissionable material—would make France independent of the established nuclear powers.

[56] *Ibid.*, p. 81. This period is discussed by Pierre Biquard, *Frédéric Joliot-Curie*, pp. 85-92.

[57] Scheinman, *Atomic Energy Policy*, p. 65.

Since France was weak in technical capability, financial resources, and uranium, this alternative meant the construction of plutonium-producing reactors.[58] Thus began what one French writer has called the "plutonium way" of the policy of *indépendance énergétique* (see Chapter 8).

In selecting the alternative and deciding to construct two high-power, plutonium-producing reactors, Prime Minister Félix Gaillard anticipated the views of Charles de Gaulle on the relationship of technological independence and the future of France. "Nations," he warned, "which did not follow a clear path of atomic development would be, twenty-five years hence, as backward relative to the nuclear nations of that time as the primitive peoples of Africa were to the industrialized nations of today."[59]

Gaillard's decision to build an independent national atomic energy industry was embodied in the First Five-Year Plan for atomic energy, which was approved in 1952. It provided for the construction of two large reactors at Marcoule in the Rhône valley, which would be capable of producing fairly large quantities of plutonium.[60] This was a momentous decision for France. It created a French nuclear power industry based on natural uranium type reactors, in contrast to the American and Russian emphasis on refined and enriched uranium. In addition, it moved France toward a nuclear weapons capability. The steps toward an openly avowed military program were subsequently taken one at a time until 1958, when, according to the judgment of Scheinman, all the necessary preparations, including the assent of public opinion, had been completed. All that remained for the Fifth Republic to do was to bring these preliminary efforts to frui-

[58] Goldschmidt, *Atomic Adventure*, p. 123.
[59] Scheinman, *Atomic Energy Policy*, p. 69. Cf. Leonard Beaton and John Maddox, *The Spread of Nuclear Weapons*, Praeger, 1962, p. 82.
[60] Goldschmidt, *Atomic Adventure*, p. 81.

tion. This is a subject which will be discussed further in Chapter 9.

TECHNICAL MINISTRIES AND NATIONALIZED INDUSTRIES

Some of the most spectacular achievements of French technology since the end of the Second World War have been performed by the research and development organizations of certain technical ministries and by the nationalized industries. In these institutions the Saint Simonian spirit of the *anciens élèves* of the *École Polytechnique* could make itself manifest. One must consider, therefore, the role of these two types of institutions in the revival of French technological *élan* after the Liberation, beginning with the research and development organizations established by the technical ministries. Because there are so many, only a few of the more important will be discussed.[61]

One of the most important technical research and development institutes established after 1945 was the National Center for the Study of Telecommunications (CNET). Under the Ministry of Post Office and Communications it is France's foremost center for communications and electronics research, playing a role in France similar to the Bell Telephone Laboratories of the United States. Its most noteworthy commercial success has been the development of the French system of color television which is competing for acceptance as the basis of an all-European color television network. In addition, the CNET has become an important part of the French space program.

Among the numerous technical agencies established under the Ministry of Defense the most important was the National Office of Aeronautical Studies and Research (ONERA). Though

[61] See "La Recherche Appliquée en France," *La Documentation Française*, 1955, and Robert Catherine, *L'Industrie*, Presses Universitaires de France, 1965, pp. 220-41.

devoted primarily to military research and development, it has made important contributions to civilian technology, including the *Caravelle* jet airliner. With the advent of the space age in 1957, the "A" in ONERA came to mean "aerospace" rather than "aeronautics" and ONERA became an integral part of France's space program.

Undoubtedly the most remarkable aspect of France's technological revival after the Liberation was the part played by the newly nationalized industries such as the Électricité de France (EDF) and Société Nationale des Chemins de Fer (SNCF). As in the case of scientific organizations, such as the CEA under Joliot-Curie, these industries were motivated by audacious and enterprising men. Almost to a man, technological and industrial entrepreneurs, such as Louis Armand of SNCF and Pierre Massé of EDF, were *anciens Polytechniciens*. Their accomplishments and organizations renewed a war-devastated France and placed her in the lead in numerous technological areas. In summarizing the technological progress of postwar France, Kindleberger attests to the role of the nationalized industries in the following words:

> Much of the stimulus for technological change came from nationalized industry—from Renault, the aviation companies, the Charbonnages de France, Électricité de France, and the Société Nationale des Chemins de Fer. The machine-tool industry of Renault; the Caravelle and the Mystère, the middle-distance jet transport plane and the jet fighter; the direct feeding of current into electric locomotives at 20,000 volts, or the voltage of transmission, thus eliminating the need for stationary transformers; and the generation of power at higher and higher voltages—these are among the innovations of nationalized industries.[62]

[62] *Economic Growth*, p. 159. The nationalized industries are prevalent in the basic areas of energy, transportation, and communications.

PRIVATE INDUSTRY

Though much less spectacular than in the public sector, the research and development activities of private industry also expanded after the Liberation. Within private industry, research is pursued in varying ways. First, there are the industrial research cooperative associations which serve an industrial sector such as steel or wine production. There are the research and development facilities of individual companies. And— much less important—are organizations such as the *Études et Recherches Scientifiques et Industrielles* (ERSI), which do research under contract for small and medium-sized firms.[63]

In the category of industrial research cooperative associations there are approximately 90 technical research centers. Varying greatly in name, legal structure, methods of operations, and financing, these centers, under the leadership of the National Association of Technical Research (ANRT), carry out cooperative research for a specified, competitive industrial sector. In this fashion these centers, such as the Iron and Steel Research Institute (IRSID), improve the state-of-the-arts of the different areas of French industry but contribute little to the innovation of important new products. Cooperative research of this type does not lead to important technological innovations because the research association cannot help an individual firm to develop a particular idea, nor can it finance development.[64] Most of all, the effectiveness of the associations is undermined by the intense suspiciousness and secretiveness of French businesses.

[63] D. Mazellier, "Les Centres de Recherches Industrielles Sous Contrat à Lyon," *Service Direction*, Nov. 1961, pp. 1,011-16. For a full account see Ministère de l'Industrie, *La Recherche Industrielle en France*, 1963.

[64] "La Recherche Scientifique et Technique Dans le 4ᵉ Plan," *Patronat Français*, May 1962. See Conseil Économique et Social, "Promotion de la Technique Par les Centres Professionnels," *Journal Officiel*, No. 20, Oct. 18, 1960.

In the last analysis, the responsibility for industrial research and product innovation must rest with the individual firm. Here, too, one saw in postwar France a new spirit of enterprise and innovation among such companies as Saint-Gobain and Rhône-Poulenc. Again, as Kindleberger has commented, "private industrial circles were not without their independent innovations."

In automobiles, Citroën's *DS-19* and the *2-CV* exceeded Renault's *Dauphine* in the extent of the departure from conventional standards. A brand-new firm, Bull, rose to international prominence in computers. Pechiney in aluminum, and a number of companies which combined to solve the problem of desulphurization of Lacq natural gas, demonstrated that French invention flourished in chemicals as well as in the mechanical industries.[65]

WEAKNESSES IN TECHNOLOGICAL DEVELOPMENT

Despite impressive innovations France's long-term technological position remained threatened by several significant weaknesses. French industry as a whole was giving too little attention to scientific research and development.[66] The foundation for continued technological vitality was being undermined by the failure of French scientific institutions to develop newer fields of scientific research, such as solid state physics, which were expanding rapidly abroad, fields on which future technology would depend. Even where French scientists had taken up new and technologically important scientific fields very little was being done to convert the new knowledge into technological innovation.

Among the reasons for the failure of the French to combine scientific theory and technological innovation has been the

[65] *Economic Growth*, p. 159.
[66] For a discussion of the problems of French industrial research cf. Jean Chardonnet, *L'Économie Française*, Dalloz, 1958, I, 83-111.

almost complete absence of contact between the French university system, which is the home of fundamental research, and the French industrial system, which should turn theory into practice. One aspect of this *cloisonnement* has already been mentioned—the separation of higher education into the *grandes écoles* for training engineers, and the *facultés* for training scientists. Too few of the engineers who go into industry or even government service, for that matter, have an adequate training in scientific research. On the other hand, relatively few university graduates have gone into industry. Consequently, France has produced few of the research engineers or scientists who, trained in basic science, have largely replaced the traditional production-oriented engineer as the principal contributor to technological advance.[67] Nearly 40 percent of the American engineering force is in research and development, compared to only a small percentage in France.[68]

A second point of university-industrial contact, which is highly developed in the U.S. but much less developed in France, is that of contract research and consultantships.[69] Traditionally very few French industries have given research contracts to universities or hired professors as consultants; very few universities or professors, in turn, have been receptive to contracts or consultantships. In part, this situation has been due to regulations established in the late nineteenth century which severely restrict such an arrangement. Partly, also, it is due to the desire of industry to achieve quick returns on its research investment rather than look for long-term benefits

[67] Don Price, *The Scientific Estate*, Harvard University Press, 1965, pp. 31-32.

[68] OECD, *Reviews of National Science Policy—France*, p. 105.

[69] The director of one of the most important university physics laboratories in France told this writer in 1964 that neither he nor his laboratory had any contact with industry even though his research is of immense practical importance.

from investing in fundamental research.[70] Finally, French industry desires to retain full control over research by doing it in its own laboratories.

An exception to the generalization on the inadequacy of university-industry liaison has been the area of Grenoble. In this region, the second after Paris in number of research workers, industry and university have established close and harmonious relations. University graduates work in industry, the training and research programs of the university are keyed to the industrial needs of the region, and professors frequently work for industry. A nonprofit corporation, the *Association Pour le Développement de la Recherche à Grenoble*, has been established to administer research contracts between local industry and university laboratories and thereby avoids cumbersome government regulations. Grenoble, however, has long been an outstanding exception to the more characteristic cleavage between industry and universities in France.

The closing of the gap between the universities and industry has been resisted by political and other considerations. University professors tend to be on the Left politically and are wary of close association with industry. Many professors distrust industrialists, believing a number of them supported fascism. Most of all, they fear that the conditions imposed on the university in any university-industrial collaboration would lead ultimately to the suppression of the liberties of the university and undermine the true vocation of the university—to seek knowledge for its own sake.[71] Industry, for its part, distrusts the Leftist and "undisciplined" university world and much prefers the person who graduates from one of the *grandes écoles*. As a consequence, from both university and industry there is strong resistance to the notion that the uni-

[70] "Faire l'Université," *Esprit*, p. 798.

[71] A debate between traditional and modern views is contained in *ibid.*

versity play a larger part in meeting society's demands for technology and technologists.

The relative absence of oriented basic research in French industry has also been an important factor retarding technological innovation in France.[72] French industry has never had a strong tradition in research and innovation; it has preferred protectionism and a secure, limited market to a larger and more risky one. Thus French industry generally has not learned to accept the type of risk normal to a concern that engages in innovative competition. Nor have many French industries created the whole research and development structure that includes basic research, applied research, developmental research, prototype testing, and quality control. In place of truly innovative research, which can give rise to wholly new products or industries, French firms tend to do research directed at making marginal improvements on existing products or processes. Not infrequently almost all the firms in an industrial sector will be working on the same problems rather than seeking to open up new product lines.[73]

The period of national renewal that began immediately after the Liberation was one of impressive gains for French science and technology. A number of new important institutions, such as the CEA and the CNRS, began to foster significant scientific and technological advance. The conservative hold over French science, which traditional institutions such as the science *facultés* had long enjoyed was weakened by the newer

[72] There are exceptions. Approximately one-fifth of the total research program at Pechiney-Saint Gobain is in fundamental research. G. R. Pedraglio, "La Compagnie de Saint Gobain Face à la Recherche," *Revue Économique*, No. 1, Jan. 1964, p. 86.

[73] For an excellent discussion of the problems of French industrial research see Centre de Préparation à l'Administration des Entreprises, Faculté de Droit et des Sciences Économiques de Caen, *L'Investissement Intellectuel Dans l'Entreprise*, 1962, p. 116.

institutions, and in particular by CEA, whose important and expanding activities could not be contained in a traditional setting. At Saclay and elsewhere the organization of scientific and technical research was consolidated and rationalized in the form of teamwork and immense research technologies. The era of the isolated and individualistic researcher was beginning to give way to the united national effort about which Kowarski had written.

In the area of scientific education and training, the first steps were taken to establish a third cycle of graduate studies and to increase the output of scientists and engineers. This development was made possible by the training programs of CEA and CNRS. Of potential importance was the creation of the *doctorat de troisième cycle*.

In applied research and development there were some impressive French "firsts"—but France was doing far too little to develop those sciences of greatest relevance for the modern economy and to integrate new knowledge into the innovation of technologies. The frontal attack on these fundamental problems had to await the establishment by the Fifth Republic of a national policy toward science and technology.

Chapter 7 · Science Policy Under the Fifth Republic

A scientific research policy is indispensable nowadays to a country's independence. I mean independence in the widest sense, i.e., the possibility for a country to raise the standard of living of its own children while helping to raise that of children everywhere and to have a say in the affairs of a world in which technology is becoming increasingly important; in short, not to cease to express its own genius.

—GASTON PALEWSKI,
French Minister for Science, 1964

In France in the middle 1950s the awareness grew of the magnitude of the challenge posed by the scientific-technological revolution and of the backwardness of French science and technology relative to that of the United States, Great Britain, and the Soviet Union. The archaic organization of French research and development, the inadequate support given to scientific research, and the wide gap separating scientific research and technological development pointed to the need for a much more active and positive state role in the affairs of science. What seemed more and more necessary to many Frenchmen was the creation of institutions to articulate a truly national policy for scientific research and development.

The Movement for a National Science Policy

An early expression of the concern over the status of French science appeared in 1952 when the Commission on Education of the Planning Commissariat discovered that the demand of the French economy for scientists and engineers would soon exceed the supply.[1] Little resulted from this modest cry of

[1] Robert Clarke, "La Recherche Scientifique en France," *Tendances,* Sept. 1960, p. 352.

188

alarm, but in the framework of preparing for the next five-year plan there was included a Commission on Scientific and Technical Research. This commission was appointed in 1953 under the leadership of Henri Laugier, the former head of CNRS, and was assigned the task of drafting a plan for scientific development. The commission made a thorough study of the weaknesses of French science and generated an opinion among leading scientists and other influential Frenchmen that important reforms were required in the graduate education of scientists, the statutes of the CNRS, and the national coordination of research. Though it praised the principle of free fundamental research the commission emphasized the need to orient French science toward newer fields of research and to establish research priorities based on national needs. France required, the commission found, some authority to coordinate and direct the national scientific effort. The CNRS, it argued, was unable to carry out leadership responsibility because of its subordinate position in the Ministry of National Education and its weak internal structure.[2]

In order to improve the leadership and coordination of French science the commission proposed three new high-level agencies:

1. The creation at the cabinet level of a minister or other official attached to the prime minister and assisted by a Supreme Council for Scientific Research. This official would have the task of animating and coordinating, in conjunction with the interested ministers, the whole program of national research.
2. The creation, under the prime minister, of a permanent Commission on Scientific and Technical Research, charged with the responsibility of studying, proposing,

[2] Commissariat au Plan, Commission de la Recherche Scientifique et Technique, *Rapport Général*, Nov. 1954.

and supervising the establishment of a national science policy.

3. The creation, under the Commissariat of the Plan, of a permanent committee to study the problems of research, leaving to the interested ministries the full exercise of their responsibilities.

In response to this report, Prime Minister Pierre Mendès-France appointed Henri Longchambon in 1954 to be the Under Secretary of State for Scientific Research. And in late 1954 Mendès-France established a Supreme Council of Scientific Research and Technical Progress, directly responsible to the cabinet and under the chairmanship of Longchambon. In contrast to the CNRS, with its organization by academic disciplines, the council set up a number of committees concerned with interdisciplinary and general problems of French science and technology. The council and its committees were given the responsibility of drafting the report on science for the third plan of social and economic modernization (1957-61). Beyond the preparation of this report (see below), however, the council did not prove effective. It never had sufficient funds and Mendès-France's tenure of office was too short for his government to define a policy toward science. In particular, Mendès-France had sought to get France to expedite research on atomic energy and the development of a nuclear powered submarine, but he left office before these projects came to fruition.[3] Although succeeding governments preserved in their essence the institutional innovations originated by Mendès-France, they fell into disuse. The Supreme Council, remaining under the chairmanship of Longchambon, had little influence on government policy, but it did provide scientists, industrialists, and politicians with an excellent forum in which

[3] Bertrand Goldschmidt, *The Atomic Adventure*, trans. Peter Beer, Pergamon Press, 1964, p. 98.

to continue their discussion of the problems of French science and publicize the need for concerted national action.

In 1956 the Supreme Council decided to publish an alarming report—the Landucci Report—on France's decline in scientific and technical manpower. The report, *Pour Assurer l'Avenir, Investir en Hommes,* showed that the annual growth of the number of engineers in France was one-sixth that of the U.S. (1.1% compared to 6.7%); one-third that of Great Britain (3.6%); and one-fourth that of Holland (4.2%). Thus France was not only falling behind the giants but was losing ground to its European neighbors. The report concluded with a warning: "The peril that menaces the scientific future of our land is such that a truly *'mobilisation générale'* of all scientists must be decreed in order to save it, by education and the teaching of men. This is what has actually taken place in the United States, Great Britain, and the Soviet Union, on the appeal of the highest political authorities of the land."[4]

In the meantime, Mendès-France, who continued his interest in the status of French science, had initiated a parliamentary committee for the expansion of scientific research. In 1956 this committee, in collaboration with a number of scientists, called for a national conference to discuss the problems of French science and prepare a plan of action. The *Colloque de Caen* (November 1-3, 1956) brought together 150 persons—France's most eminent scientists, politicians of nearly every party, and important industrialists concerned over the rapidly deteriorating condition of French science. The conference drafted a 12-point national plan for the renovation of French science and technology. Almost all subsequent reforms and actions by the Fifth Republic can be traced to the ideas developed at Caen. Some of its more important points are:

[4] Conseil Supérieur de la Recherche, *Rapport Landucci—Investir en Hommes,* mimeo., 1957, p. 11.

1. A 10-year plan of scientific expansion in order to double the number of science students, triple the number of engineering students, and increase tenfold scientific and higher education personnel.
2. The organization of a true third cycle of graduate training in scientific research [see Chap. 6].
3. The reform of higher education, which would give greater autonomy to the universities and *facultés*, close the gap between the universities and the *grandes écoles*, and permit foreign scientists to be appointed to chairs in institutions of higher education.
4. The passage of a statute to confer permanent tenure on CNRS scientists and encourage university research.
5. The reform of medical education.
6. The stimulation and coordination of applied research through the establishment of national research funds administered by the Supreme Council and of mixed public-private societies to develop inventions.
7. The expansion of agricultural research.
8. The appointment of a government official specifically responsible for scientific research, its expansion, and coordination.[5]

The meeting at Caen precipitated a large debate in the National Assembly, at the conclusion of which all parties except the Communists and the Poujadists agreed on the need to give priority to scientific expansion in the Third Plan (1957-61) and to encourage more students to enter scientific and technical fields.[6] Equally significant, the colloquy led to the founding of the first scientific lobby in France, the Permanent Committee for the Expansion of Scientific Research (currently the Study Association for the Expansion of Scientific Research)

---

[5] The recommendations of the *colloque* and the papers presented to it are contained in *Les Cahiers de la République*, No. 5, Jan.-Feb. 1957.
[6] Clarke, "La Recherche," p. 352.

and of the first journal in France concerned specifically with the problems of science as a social institution, *L'Expansion Scientifique*. The list of this lobby for scientific reform includes some of France's most eminent scientists, including Nobel Laureat J. Monod and the distinguished mathematician, A. Lichnerowicz.

The recommendations of the *Colloque de Caen*, and the earlier Landucci Report, served as the basis for the scientific report of the Third Plan, prepared by the Supreme Council and published in June 1957.[7] The report pointed out that France had an annual deficit of approximately 5,000 engineers, 1,000 researchers, and 1,500 science professors. So that France could be informed the Council's report recommended the issuance of an annual report on the state of French science. Beyond this the report subscribed fully to the plan of action proposed at Caen and advocated the creation of a mechanism at the highest level of government to formulate a national science policy and to intervene in science in order to expand research into areas of national importance.

In October 1957 the Permanent Committee for the Expansion of Scientific Research held a second colloquy at Grenoble, concerned specifically with the "general problems of contacts between the universities and industry with respect to research."[8] Again there was broad representation from all parts of French society, but this colloquy did not enjoy the success of its predecessor because of the vastly differing perspectives of the university and industrial representatives. Nevertheless, the meeting was a landmark in the attempt to narrow the long-standing cleavage between these two groups, and several of its recommendations were important:

[7] Conseil Supérieur de la Recherche Scientifique, *La Recherche Scientifique et le Progrès Technique*, Projet de Rapport au Commissariat au Plan, 1957.

[8] La Documentation Française, *La France Devant les Problèmes de la Science*, Part 3, May 28, 1960, p. 25.

1. The decentralization of the university system and the creation of strong provincial centers for scientific research and training, keyed to regional economic and social expansion.
2. The training of engineers in the universities.
3. The creation of private institutions which would enable professors and industrial researchers to work together on scientific and technical problems.
4. The development of an atmosphere of confidence between industrial and university personnel through conferences and common activities.

Just before the fall of the Fourth Republic a third colloquy was called for April 1958 by an organization of university professors, entitled the National Movement for Scientific Development.[9] Though this movement was largely organized to protest certain prior government actions and to counter the argument that the universities were not contributing to the national interest, several of the colloquy's proposals with respect to the organization of the science *facultés* were very important. The first proposal was for the creation of new teaching-research ranks in the *facultés*. The second was for the strengthening of the administrative structure and autonomy of the *facultés*. In addition, the National Movement proposed a rapprochement between the *facultés* and the *grandes écoles* and endorsed the appointment of a high official (provided he was a scientist) to be responsible for the formulation of a national science policy.

As a result of the various colloquies and studies, by the time de Gaulle returned to power in the late spring of 1958, a number of specific proposals for scientific reform had been formulated. The political instability of France and its preoccupation with such problems as the Algerian War had prevented pre-

[9] *Ibid.*, p. 26.

ceding governments from taking the necessary initiatives. But influential opinion had been alerted to the desirability of action. The immediate impetus to act, however, was provided for France, as it was for the United States and other nations, by the startling encircling of the globe by the Soviet *Sputnik*. In response, one of the first acts of Charles de Gaulle on returning to office was the establishment of institutions for a national policy on science.

The Mechanism for Making Science Policy

In the late spring of 1958, soon after the formation of the de Gaulle Government, Minister of Culture André Malraux began to gather the views of a number of prominent scientists on the action needed to implement the many proposals for scientific reform. Minister of State Jacquinot was then given the responsibility of pursuing for the Prime Minister all questions relevant to scientific research and of making specific recommendations to the government on the establishment of machinery for the coordination of the national science effort.[10] The result of his deliberations was the decree of November 28, 1958, eliminating the Supreme Council created in 1954 and replacing it with the essentials of the present structure for the formulation of policy regarding civil, or nonmilitary, science.[11]

In order to place decision-making for nonmilitary research at a high political level the government instituted an Interministerial Committee for Scientific and Technical Research (*Comité Interministériel de la Recherche Scientifique et Technique,* or CIMRST) under the chairmanship of the Prime Minister. The committee has two types of members: one com-

[10] Pierre Piganiol and Louis Villecourt, *Pour Une Politique Scientifique*, Flammarion, 1963, p. 140. Actually the foundations for the instituted reform were laid by Pierre Guillaumat, Delegate Minister for science, 1960-61.

[11] La Documentation Française, *La France Devant les Problèmes de la Science*, Part 4, Nov. 30, 1960, p. 4.

posed of the ministers of the numerous ministries interested in scientific research—National Education, Defense, Finance, Industry, Agriculture, Public Health, Public Works, and Communications; and the 12 scientists who constitute the Advisory Committee for Scientific and Technical Research are also members of the Interministerial Committee. The CIMRST was given the responsibility for "recommending all measures tending to develop scientific research," and is responsible "in the light of the Plan (for economic and social development), to submit draft programmes for equipment and reallocation of resources, particularly the credits to be appropriated to the various Ministries under the national budget."[12]

To assist the Interministerial Committee in its deliberations there was also created an Advisory Committee for Scientific and Technical Research (*Comité Consultatif de la Recherche Scientifique et Technique*, or CCRST). This "Comité des Sages," as it is popularly called, was composed of 12 eminent scientists, engineers, and economists appointed for two-year terms and chosen on the basis of their individual competence rather than as representatives of any particular group. This basis for selection of an advisory group followed the tradition established in the CEA. It went one step further, however. For the first time scientists became directly involved in policy decisions for the whole of science at a high ministerial level. Meeting twice a month, the committee is responsible for "preparing the discussion" of the Interministerial Committee with respect to the science plan, the research budget, and other matters affecting the welfare of French science, exclusive of scientific problems relating to defense. From these natural and social scientists came most of the proposals for the reform of French scientific institutions that were implemented in the last months of the Fourth Republic and the early years of the Fifth.[13]

[12] OECD, *Reviews of National Science Policy—France*, 1966, p. 21.
[13] Pierre Lelong, "Le Rôle du Comité Consultatif de la Recherche

The third institution created was the General Delegation for Scientific and Technical Research (*Délégation Générale à la Recherche Scientifique et Technique,* or DGRST), which is the joint secretariat for the Interministerial Committee and the Advisory Committee. The DGRST was made responsible to the Prime Minister and the Minister for Science for the staff work associated with national science policy. Initially "its main tasks are to make a permanent inventory of research facilities in the public and private sectors, to prepare the work of the Advisory Committee and the Committee of Ministers in matters relating to the budget and planning, to administer the Scientific Research Development Fund, and to direct the work of French scientific attachés abroad."[14]

In addition, two posts were established to direct these new bodies. On the political side, a high official was made responsible for nonmilitary, atomic, and space research. As the title (and occupants) of this office have changed several times over the past several years, throughout this study I will use the short title, "Minister for Science."[15] On the scientific side, a General Delegate for Scientific and Technical Matters was appointed to supervise the work of the DGRST and to assist the Planning Commissariat in the preparation of the national science plan (see next chapter).[16]

Scientifique et Technique Auprès du Gouvernement," *Le Progrès Scientifique,* No. 41, Dec. 15, 1962, pp. 1-6. Five or seven members retire by rotation every two years and the chairman changes every two years in practice. OECD, *Reviews of National Science Policy—France,* p. 23.

[14] Pierre Frédet, "Organisation de la Recherche en France," *Nouvelle Frontière,* No. 8, 1964, p. 42.

[15] The title as of January 8, 1966 is "Minister for Scientific Research and Questions of Nuclear and Space Research."

[16] Several contrasts with the American organization for science policy might be noted. The U.S. President's science advisor has in effect the responsibilities of the French Minister of State for Scientific Research, the chairman of the Interministerial Committee, the chairman

While the importance of the institutional reforms should not be exaggerated, they were and continue to be significant, because at a crucial and rather fluid time, they put into positions of influence a number of highly competent and relatively young (under 45 years old) engineers, industrialists, and scientists, including social scientists. Significantly, at the time of their appointment none were members of the Academy of Science, yet in general they represented important new fields of research and technology. They contrast markedly with the Leftwing scientists who had dominated French science in the early postwar period. Whereas the latter admired the Soviet Union at the same time they opposed radical changes in traditional French scientific institutions, the former tend to take the United States as their model.

Reformers like Pierre Piganiol, the first head of the General Delegation, favored a vast regeneration of French science and expansion of its role in French society as an essential step toward a rejuvenated France. In the pursuit of this goal they were supported by the Gaullist Government and especially by de Gaulle's first Prime Minister under the constitution of the Fifth Republic, Michel Debré.

The Establishment of Research Priorities

With the creation of the Interministerial Committee, the Advisory Committee, and the General Delegation, France had for the first time established a high political mechanism that

---

of the Advisory Committee, *and* the General Delegate. Other than this the institutions are comparable:

American	French
President's Science Advisory Committee	Advisory Committee for Scientific and Technical Research
Federal Council for Science and Technology	Interministerial Committee on Scientific Research
Office of Science and Technology	General Delegation for Scientific and Technical Research

could take a broad look at the scientific situation and formulate policy objectives. Prior to this institutional arrangement France had had no permanent mechanisms for assembling information on the status of French science, maintaining a watch over its progress, and preparing remedial action.

Under the leadership of Pierre Piganiol the General Delegation rapidly developed a permanent, competent staff that could make the necessary studies of French science. For the first time statistics and inventories—those all-important data for policy-making in the modern world—were collected on a systematic basis to determine the scope, distribution, and deficiencies of the scientific effort in France. Implicit in this effort was an idea, revolutionary for France, that science was essentially a productive force, to be treated like any other economic factor; it reveals how far France had progressed in its attitude toward science. In 1963 the first comprehensive survey of industrial research in France appeared,[17] and, in separate publications, the first inventories of the agricultural and industrial research laboratories in France.[18] Also, the first inventory of French scientific personnel was begun; volume one was concerned with pure mathematicians and was published in 1962.[19] Other lengthy studies on such topics as university research facilities, oceanographic research, and water research were begun.

Of more immediate significance, the General Delegation, working with the Interministerial Committee under the chair-

[17] Délégation Générale à la Recherche Scientifique et Technique, "Recherche et Développement Dans l'Industrie Française en 1962." This first attempt to gather statistics on industrial research expenditures met with resistance from industrialists who feared the data might assist competitors and affect their taxes. The second survey, for 1963, was much more successful.

[18] Délégation Générale à la Recherche Scientifique et Technique, "La Recherche Agronomique," 1962 and "La Recherche Industrielle," 1962.

[19] Délégation Générale à la Recherche Scientifique et Technique, "Mathematiques Pures," 1962.

manship of Prime Minister Debré, and the Scientific Advisory Committee, led by such persons as Pierre Lelong, Pierre Aigrain, and Maurice Ponte, began to develop a plan for scientific development and to create the instruments with which to put such a plan into action. The principal resulting proposals during the first years of the Fifth Republic were as follows:

1. The formulation of a unified science budget or research package (*enveloppe recherche*).
2. The designation of certain research priorities (*les actions concertées*) and the creation of a research fund to support priority subjects.
3. The preparation by the CNRS of an annual report on the scientific situation in France (*la conjoncture scientifique*).
4. The creation of a large number of semiautonomous institutes for scientific and technical research.
5. The integration of science planning with economic planning.
6. The establishment within the Ministry of Defense of a Directorate of Research and Testing (*Direction des Recherches et Moyens d'Essais*, or DRME) whose responsibility would be the linking of fundamental research and weapons innovation.
7. The structural reform of important research institutions such as the CNRS, the Agricultural Research Institute (INRA), and the Overseas Research Institute (ORSTOM).

With one extremely important exception these reforms achieved considerable success in the first years of the Fifth Republic. The exception was the ambitious plan (no. 4 above) to establish national research institutes for "certain fundamental and applied research projects of exceptional national importance, and in particular research requiring considerable and therefore very costly equipment."[20] This overhaul of

[20] Quoted in OECD, *Reviews of National Science Policy—France*, p. 37.

French research was considered premature by the Interministerial Committee. Without doubt the concept of relatively autonomous institutes was resisted by the CNRS as a threat to its position, and by the Finance Ministry which disliked the financial freedom envisaged in the proposal.[21] As will be shown, the concept was revived in 1966 and steps were taken to create a series of semiautonomous research institutes.

The first three reforms proposed by the Scientific Advisory Committee are the subject of the rest of this chapter. The last three—the integration of science planning into national planning, the reform of defense research, and the institutional reforms are discussed in subsequent chapters.

THE UNIFIED RESEARCH BUDGET

With the post-1945 increase in the number of ministries supporting scientific research and the growing demands made by numerous research fields and projects on the limited, available financial resources, a need developed for some central mechanism to take an over-all look at the expenditures for scientific research. The final responsibility for preparing the budget in France rests with one agency—the Budget Directorate of the Finance Ministry, but this agency lacks the technical competence to evaluate the research and development programs of the various ministries. And more importantly, from the viewpoint of the new government, the tendency of budget examiners is always to cut back expenditures on all fronts and not to expand them even where necessary. What seemed required, therefore, was something to coordinate the budget requests of various ministries, to make recommendations to the Government on the allocation of resources for scientific research and to insure that ministries did not divert research funds to other activities.

[21] "La Recherche Scientifique au Sein du Ministère de l'Éducation Nationale à la Lumière des Récentes Réformes du CNRS," *Le Progrès Scientifique*, No. 95, Apr. 1966, pp. 11-12.

To meet this need, there was the decree of November 28, 1958, giving the Interministerial Committee the responsibility for recommending to the government "the apportionment of means and resources, and in particular the apportionment to be included in the budgets of the different ministerial departments concerned."[22] Commencing with the budget for 1961 each minister responsible for scientific programs (with certain important exceptions to be discussed below), when preparing his annual budget, separates out those items for research expenditure and submits them to the DGRST.[23] The items submitted are then grouped by the DGRST into a research package, or budget envelope, which is first examined by the Scientific Advisory Committee. The research budget goes to the Interministerial Committee along with the recommendations of the Scientific Advisory Committee. On the basis of the ensuing discussion within the Interministerial Committee, the latter "submits to the approval of the government . . . draft programmes for equipment and allocation of means, particularly by the appropriations to be made to the various Ministries in the national budget."[24] Furthermore, ministries included in the research budget cannot make capital investments unless it is provided for in the national plan, over which the science planners have some influence.

While this budgetary procedure has been beneficial as a means of exchanging information and focusing attention on neglected areas of research, the success of the research package as an instrument for research planning and coordination has been rather limited. In the first place, each minister retains full responsibility over the administration of his own research appropriations; the authority of the Interministerial Committee

[22] Piganiol and Villecourt, *Pour une Politique Scientifique*, p. 140.

[23] What constitutes a "research item," as distinct from an educational or developmental one, has been a difficult problem.

[24] OECD, *Reviews of National Science Policy—France*, p. 28.

and the Minister for Science over the way in which each ministry spends its allocated research funds is slight. Some advantage has been gained, however, and the Prime Minister's influence over research policy has been strengthened by the provision in the decree of November 28, 1958 that each ministry submit to him an annual report on its utilization of research appropriations.

A second weakness stems from the fact that it covers only a small percentage of the total French expenditure for research and development. While it includes one-half of the expenditure for fundamental research (CNRS, the universities, the *grands établissements*, agricultural and medical research, and the funds of the Minister for Science), it does not include military or atomic energy research, which accounted for over 60 percent of the state's total expenditure for research in 1963.[25] Nor does it include appropriations for CNET (telecommunications), for international science programs, or operational funds for university laboratories. Funds for space research and direct state assistance to technical development abroad are submitted to the Interministerial Committee for examination, but are not included in the research envelope. In fact, only about 15 percent of the total French expenditure for science and technology comes under the Committee's jurisdiction.[26] In general, the excluded items relate to appropriations where research is a secondary concern, or to areas touching directly on national security and delicate questions of national policy, such as the creation of the *force de frappe* and foreign relations, for example, technical assistance to the French-speaking states of Africa.

The third reason for the limited success of the Interministerial Committee in coordinating the national budget for research is due to the nature of the French budget system. In contrast to the U.S., where the total budget of an agency is reviewed each year, in France the review of the operating (in

[25] *Ibid.*, p. 30.   [26] *Ibid.*, p. 99.

contrast to the equipment) budget is restricted to requests for increments over the previous year's appropriation.[27] As a consequence, one agency's operating budget cannot be cut back in order to redistribute the funds thus made available to other agencies supporting research of greater priority. Newer fields of research can therefore gain support only through a general increase in the budget for science—which the Ministry of Finance is reluctant to approve. On the other hand, the system has merit, and is so defended, in that it assures the freedom and continuity of research against arbitrary state action.

TABLE II.

Research Envelope: Trend of Budgetary Appropriations and Employment[a]

	1959	1960	1961	1962	1963	1964	1965
Appropriations:							
Millions francs	249	403	463	579	719	975	1,073
Percent annual increase	——	62	15	25	24	36	9
Percent of state budget (operations of a final character)	0.35	0.55	0.57	0.65	0.78	0.94	0.97
Employment:[b]							
Research workers	——	——	——	4,745	5,259	5,809	6,157
Technicians	——	——	——	6,060	7,259	8,297	8,744
Total[c]	8,151[d]	9,420[d]	10,979[d]	12,448	14,347	16,176	17,081
Percent annual increase	——	15.6	16.5	13.4	15.2	12.7	5.6

[a] Adapted from OECD, *Reviews of National Science Policy—France*, p. 29.

[b] The staffs financed out of research envelope appropriations do not include research workers (teachers) in the universities, faculties and important scientific establishments, nor the staff of certain other institutions (such as the ORSTOM), for whom only appropriations specially allocated to research appear in the research envelope.

[c] Including office staff and manual workers.

[d] Estimates.

[27] *Ibid.*, p. 109.

Despite these serious limitations the Interministerial Committee and the research package procedure have been, on the whole, beneficial. They have provided a forum where scientists and administrators can discuss the state of French science, and where scientific research can be defended by the Minister for Science against the tendency to sacrifice it to immediate needs. Their success may be measured by the fact that the research envelope more than quadrupled and the staff supported more than doubled between its creation in 1959 and 1965 (see TABLE 11).[28] As these are expenditures in fundamental research and not the more costly item of development, this is an important and substantial increase. Moreover, on the basis of discussions with knowledgeable Frenchmen, it is apparent that the Interministerial Committee has had some influence on the research programs of the CNRS. The Committee and the Scientific Advisory Committee have been especially important in government decisions involving "big" science and technology where technical expertise must be brought to bear on questions involving a heavy investment of funds—e.g., the selection of computers.

PROGRAMS OF CONCERTED ACTION AND THE RESEARCH FUND

Without a doubt the most important innovation of the Scientific Advisory Committee and the General Delegation has been the creation of the programs of concerted action (or "combined activities") and the related Fund for Scientific and Technical Research (FRST). As an instrument of national policy it is certainly unprecedented for France, and to this writer's knowledge has no parallel in other nations. But, then, the problems it is designed to meet are in some ways uniquely French, at least in their magnitude. Developed largely under the leadership of Piganiol, the programs of concerted action

[28] *Ibid.*, p. 28. It should be noted that approximately one-third of this increase was negated due to rises in prices and wages.

have been among the most important activities of the General Delegation and the Advisory Committee.

The primary purpose of the programs of concerted action has been to establish research priorities in new and vital fields that are either totally absent or underdeveloped in France. As such, this "was a venture unprecedented in the annals of French history. It is the first time that scientists have been asked to specify clearly the objective to be attained in certain particularly important fields, and to assess the means of implementing the action that they recommend."[29] In contrast to the long established practice of dividing available research funds equally among established fields, institutes, and professors, the concerted action program uses the contract or project grant approach borrowed from the United States to support higher priority areas of research. In this way, the French state and the leadership of French science for the first time possess an instrument for intervening directly in the affairs of science.

A second feature of the program is that it has sought to modify the organization of French science. In order to counter the tendencies toward individualistic, fragmented, and discipline-oriented research, the programs of concerted action have sought to direct French scientists toward contemporary issues and encourage them to cooperate in an attack on particular questions of high value. They have had the further effect of bringing together university, government, and industrial scientists for the same purpose.[30]

The Mendès-France decree of September 14, 1954, establishing the Superior Council, foreshadowed these efforts at interdisciplinary research.[31] It called for the creation within the

[29] *Le Monde,* Apr. 9, 1960.

[30] Actually, such interdisciplinary research was conducted by the CNRS prior to World War II. Henri Laugier, *Service de France au Canada,* Éditions Bernard Valiquette, 1941, pp. 57-96.

[31] La Documentation Française, *La France Devant,* Part 4, pp. 12-17.

Council of "committees whose responsibilities shall be limited to specific problems."[32] Due to a lack of funds and insufficient support the committees were of no consequence, but the idea of organizing research around specific problems was made part of the Superior Council report for the Third Plan.[33]

During the first six months of 1959 the Scientific Advisory Committee set out to determine the research areas to be given priority. Three considerations guided it. Priority should be given to: (1) those fields heavily subsidized by governments abroad and whose underdevelopment in France constituted a national danger; (2) problems of urgent concern which could not be dealt with rapidly by existing policy machinery; and (3) fields of applied research which require that "the entire resources of the country ... be mobilized. ..."[34]

Employing these criteria the Scientific Advisory Committee and the DGRST selected 10 areas and submitted them to the Interministerial Committee for decision. On December 9, 1959 two decrees were issued. One established a special financial body responsible to the Prime Minister—the Fund for Scientific and Technical Research—to "develop, coordinate, and animate urgent or concerted actions."[35] The second created a series of study committees to draw up research programs in the selected priority areas and submit to the Prime Minister:

A report on the advisability, possibility, and, where applicable, the financial conditions under which concerted action could be carried out for scientific research of national importance in the following fields: Demographic, economic, and social analysis; Application of genetics; Molecular biology; Cancer and leukemia; Conversion of energy; Documentation; Marine exploration; Neurophysiology and psychopharmacology; Animal and human nutrition; Economic science and development problems.[36]

[32] *Ibid.*, p. 12.   [33] *Ibid.*, p. 13.   [34] *Ibid.*
[35] *Ibid.*   [36] *Ibid.*, p. 14.

Earlier a special committee had been established under Pierre Auger to draft a policy toward space research to which the Government planned to give highest priority.

In contrast to the sections of the CNRS which are organized by specific disciplines, these study committees were oriented toward general interdisciplinary problems, and brought together specialists in the various disciplines relevant to the study of a problem. Early in 1960 the committees worked out a series of research programs in each of the 10 selected areas. These committee proposals, with the exception of that regarding documentation, were incorporated into a five year "program-law" by the DGRST and the Scientific Advisory Committee. After this was approved in late May by the Interministerial Committee a sum of 100 million francs was appropriated for the 1961 budget and a total of 320 million francs was allotted for the period 1961-65. Of this initial program 130 million francs were for spatial research and the other 190 million were for the other selected areas.[37] Subsequent appropriations brought the total to 480 million francs.

Several features of the first programs of concerted action should be noted.[38] The first is that five of the 10 fields chosen were in the biological sciences. Subjects such as molecular biology or neurophysiology possess great potential importance for the practice of medicine and agriculture. Other areas were keyed to immediate, practical programs—energy, nutrition, and space. The selection of energy, for example, reflected France's long concern over its deficiency in energy resources.

The third feature of the programs selected is that they are areas which were in rapid development abroad, especially in the United States and the Soviet Union. In general, the moti-

[37] Louis Villecourt, "Les Actions Concertées de Recherche et la Politique Scientifique Française," *Revue Économique Franco-Suisse*, No. 3, Oct.-Nov. 1963, p. 58.
[38] In March 1962 a tenth program of concerted action in electronics was added.

vation behind their selection was not to meet immediate problems for France, but to develop a national capability in scientific and technological areas of potentially great consequence and of high prestige.

The Fund and the programs of concerted action are administered for the Prime Minister by the General Delegation, with the advice of the Scientific Advisory Committee. Under their direction the committee, or Round Table, established for each combined activity works out the details of the research program, allocates funds among various laboratories, and then supervises the execution of the research work. Individuals or research teams apply to the Round Table for support for specific projects. By the end of 1963 over 600 research contracts had been placed.[39] The project grant usually covers 50 percent of the cost of the research; the laboratory's own budget covers the other half. Also, training grants are given to increase the number of specialists in such fields as genetics, oceanography, and electronics. In addition each Round Table sponsors frequent discussions to foster close collaboration among the laboratories concerned. In this way an attempt is being made to break down the Napoleonic barriers between the laboratories of the different ministries, the *facultés*, and the industries that are working on essentially the same scientific or technical problems.

The underlying assumption has been that the programs of concerted action would be temporary, but that once they were initiated other agencies would be encouraged to assume permanent responsibility for them. The first five-year program (1961-65) had its greatest success in this respect with the creation on March 1, 1962 of the National Center for Space Studies (CNES).[40] In addition other new research institutions, such as the Institute of Molecular Biology at the University of Paris and

[39] OECD, *Reviews of National Science Policy—France*, p. 36.
[40] La Documentation Française Illustrée, *La France et la Recherche Spatiale*, No. 195, Mar. 1964.

a CNRS institute for genetics research, have been founded.[41] The proposal of the French Government for an International Cancer Institute evolved out of a concerted action program.

In one area, concerted action programs have not been as successful, largely because of the strong opposition of conservative elements in the CNRS. The example of resistance was the opposition of CNRS to a concerted action in the area of scientific documentation. CNRS apparently feared the science planners' proposal to automate the French system of information storage and retrieval would undercut its established position in the documentation field.

Perhaps the most important single aspect of the programs of concerted action has been the idea of using the research contract or project grant as a mechanism for reorienting the whole trend of French science. Piganiol, the originator of the program, had been impressed by the ways in which the United States used the research contract to coordinate public and private research, open up new fields of research, and relate scientific findings and technological innovation. He hoped the concerted action programs would provide a means by which the state could achieve particular goals.[42] Hopefully, other research supporting agencies, witnessing the success of the programs, would follow suit.

The achievement of this fundamental purpose of the program of concerted actions has been frustrated, with one major exception—the Ministry of Defense (see Chapter 9). Otherwise the extension of the contract mechanism to other agencies

[41] The underlying spirit of the programs is discussed in "La Recherche Scientifique en France et dans les Grands Pays Étrangers," *Problèmes Économiques*, No. 809, July 2, 1963, p. 11.

[42] Pierre Piganiol, "La Recherche Scientifique Française et ses Perspectives," *L'Économie*, No. 705, Nov. 19, 1959, pp. 5-7. For a discussion of the significance of the introduction of the contract and project grant into France see Piganiol and Villecourt, *Pour Une Politique Scientifique*, pp. 61-62.

has been resisted. The technical ministries prefer to do their research in their own laboratories rather than involve university or industrial researchers. The Ministry of Finance has been reluctant to modify the regulations governing contracts to take account of the peculiar nature of scientific research: the fact that in the search for the unknown one cannot specify clearly and in detail what is being purchased nor what ultimate costs will be.

From the perspective of the science planners the research contract lessens the rigidity of the status quo and increases the freedom of action for the government in its attempt to advance French science. It permits the Round Table to exercise judgment with respect to the merits of various research projects competing for funds. But the view of its critics is that the abandonment of traditional practice introduces the possibility of unwarranted and arbitrary action on the part of certain scientists or the government. They fear an aggrandizement of power by the state or special cliques of scientists.

In spite of these problems, and even though the funds devoted to the concerted action programs are relatively small—amounting to only 10 percent of the research package appropriations,[43] and about four percent of the total public expenditures for research and development—the programs' impact on French science has been significant. The initial success of the first series of concerted actions led in 1962 to an increase in the funds devoted to them (480 million francs), and a second series of nine was incorporated in the Fourth Plan (1961-65). In contrast to the first series the second, launched in 1963, was more technical. These new programs, whose total cost was approximately 290 million francs, were in the following areas: electronics, computers, automation, macromolecular chemistry (plastics), water resources, civil engineering, applied econom-

[43] Again it should be remembered that the research package itself represents only 15 percent of the total spent by the French government for scientific research.

ics, earth sciences, and agriculture. A third series was incorporated in the Fifth Plan (see next chapter). The total allocation of funds for the first two series can be seen in TABLE 12.

The success of the Fund and the programs of concerted action should not be measured, however, primarily in monetary terms. More important are the administrative and psychological aspects. Administratively the Fund provides the Prime Minister and his science advisors with a flexible and rapid form of finance which can be employed with a minimum of bureaucratic encumbrances. But the foremost accomplishment of the programs has been psychological. First, the organization of research around specific problems has brought together researchers from various disciplines and sectors (industrial, university, etc.) of French science and given them the responsibility for developing a field of research. The hard and fast divisions among fields and institutes are beginning to break down. Second, the programs of concerted action have given encouragement to French scientists interested in newer and "unorthodox" fields of research.[44] In all, its objective, in the words of the third report on the program, has been "much less to achieve immediately usable results than to put the French scientific research mechanism in a position to attain them, to eliminate bottlenecks for this purpose and to maintain unity on the research front."[45]

THE ANNUAL REPORT OF THE CNRS

To overcome the failure of the CNRS to play a strong leadership role in fundamental research, one of the decrees of December 9, 1959 gave it the mission, "to develop, orient, and coordinate scientific research of all orders and to analyze on a permanent basis for the government the *conjoncture scien-*

[44] *Le Monde,* July 23-24, 1961.
[45] DGRST, *Les Actions Concertées, Rapport d'Activité,* 1963, p. 9. OECD, *Reviews of National Science Policy—France,* p. 35.

TABLE 12.

Appropriations for Concerted Action Programs, 1961-65[a]
(in millions of francs)

	1961 program	1962 program	1963 program	1964 program	Total	Est. 1965 program
Electronics	——	8.0	19.50	15.00	42.50	17.00
Computers	——	——	3.50	3.00	6.50	7.00
Energy conversion	10.60	8.40	11.00	9.40	39.40	3.60
High energy acceleration	——	——	1.50	3.00	4.50	3.00
Automation	——	——	1.00	5.00	6.00	5.00
Macromolecular chemistry	——	——	5.00	6.00	11.00	6.00
Mechanics	——	——	6.00	6.00	12.00	6.00
Housing and civil eng.	——	——	1.00	4.00	5.00	4.00
Earth sciences	——	——	4.00	5.00	9.00	5.00
Exploitation of seas	19.45	11.60	9.95	1.45	42.45	5.55
Water	——	——	0.50	4.00	4.50	4.00
Molecular biology	13.00	7.70	6.30	3.50	30.50	8.50
Cancer and Leukemia	6.00	6.00	7.00	2.70	21.70	3.30
Functions and diseases of brain	1.33	3.00	2.00	2.50	8.83	——
Applications of genetics	0.90	0.75	1.00	1.40	4.05	0.20
Agricultural technology	——	——	6.50	10.50	17.00	10.50
Animal and human nutrition	0.90	1.35	1.25	1.70	5.20	0.55
Economic and social pop. analysis	1.00	0.90	1.00	1.65	4.55	——
Economics and development problems	1.65	1.30	1.50	2.55	7.00	——
Planning problems	——	——	3.00	4.55	7.55	6.00
Measuring instruments	——	——	——	2.20	2.20	2.20
Atmospheric research	——	——	——	0.50	0.50	2.50
Total	54.83	49.00	92.50	95.60	291.93	99.90

[a] Adapted from OECD, *Reviews of National Science Policy—France*, p. 36.

213

tifique."[46] The key feature of this attempt to strengthen the CNRS was the provision that it present an annual report, or *conjoncture scientifique*; its objective was that of "defining the needs in each branch of science and considering the direction to be given to research in the years to come, whether the necessary means are to be supplied by the CNRS, higher education, or any other body."[47]

To facilitate this task "rapporteurs" were designated for each section and instructed to make a detailed investigation of all research institutions in France. On the basis of this study each section prepares an analysis of the state of research in its branch of French science in order to give the government advice on such matters as manpower problems, promising but neglected research areas, and institutional reform.[48]

By a related decree the Government, in order to make the CNRS more responsive to its policies, changed the composition of the scientific sections and the directorate. Whereas in the past all members of these two policy-making bodies had either been elected by the scientists or appointed by the Minister of National Education, this decree provided that the Prime Minister should appoint members from outside the Ministry of National Education. In part, the desire for broadened representation was motivated by the new responsibility of CNRS to survey *all* French science and make recommendations to the Government on science and technical policy. Perhaps of equal weight in the Government's decision was its desire to see a greater representation of individuals responsive to the Government's views.

It had been the expectation of the Interministerial Commit-

[46] Piganiol and Villecourt, *Pour Une Politique Scientifique*, p. 148. Actually 12 decrees relating to the CNRS were issued on December 9, 1959. A number of the others will be discussed below.

[47] La Documentation Française, *La France Devant les Problèmes de la Science*, Part 4, p. 5.

[48] *Ibid.*

tee that the preparation of the annual report and the increased representation of scientists from outside the universities would encourage each section to define priorities in the scientific discipline for which it was responsible, and would encourage the Directorate to establish priorities *among* the various scientific fields. If this could be achieved, then, the *conjoncture scientifique* would serve as the basic document for the preparation of the concerted action programs and for the five-year plans.

Unfortunately this hope has not been fulfilled. The annual *conjoncture scientifique* has contained valuable information, but it has not provided a basis for the establishment of scientific priorities. Prepared by a number of independent, disciplinary or interdisciplinary commissions, the report does not present an over-all view of the state of French science to decision-makers. Even though the sections are moving toward the designation of research priorities, they continue to be reluctant to acknowledge that one area of research within a discipline is more deserving of support than others. The Directorate, for its part, has been even more cautious in approaching the question of science planning and the establishment of research priorities. It has not tried to synthesize the reports of the individual sections or to guide the sections in the preparation of their studies. Nor has it taken the step of selecting priorities among the disciplines. Instead, in the preparation of the annual report it has tended merely to compile the section reports without providing the Government with an over-all judgment on the state and needs of French science.[49] To do more than this would require an administration sufficiently powerful to impose its will on the sections of the National Committee of CNRS which are intent on defending their own disciplines and programs.

This resistance of the sections to change was illustrated fur-

[49] Cf. Centre National de la Recherche Scientifique, *Rapport National de Conjoncture 1963/1964*, I, pp. 1-8. This is the fourth annual report and appears in three large volumes.

ther by a new program initiated by CNRS itself—the cooperative research program.[50] Begun largely to counter the threat of the Government's concerted actions, this program encouraged interdisciplinary research among the CNRS laboratories on specific problems. By this mechanism the CNRS sought to break down the barriers among the sections which make interdisciplinary research difficult and to insure that new fields not represented by the traditional organization of the sections would be covered. Unfortunately it continues to be a very small program and absorbs only a small percentage of the total CNRS budget. Again, in the absence of strong administrative authority over the sections, the success of such a program was doubtful from the start. It sought to overcome what is essentially a political problem—the excessive decentralization of decision-making authority within the organization—through the mechanism of horizontal cooperation.[51]

For Jean Perrin and the other founders of the CNRS the problem of reforming scientific research had been essentially one of finding a sufficient number of good men and giving them the support they required.[52] Though many of the reformers were Marxists, impressed with the Soviet system for the support, coordination, and exploitation of science, in the last analysis they believed that fundamental science flourished best under a laissez-faire system. Thus the state should assist the scientist, but the determination of research priorities and the direction of the scientific enterprise should rest with scientists themselves. The CNRS and even the CEA, although in lesser degree, were founded on the assumption that the governance of science should be solely in the hands of scientists.

[50] "La Recherche Scientifique au Sein du Ministère de l'Éducation Nationale à la Lumière des Récentes Réformes du CNRS," p. 11.
[51] Frédet, "Organization de la Recherche en France," pp. 41-43.
[52] Laugier, *Service de France au Canada*, pp. 57-96.

With the coming of the Fifth Republic the goal of scientific reform was not the advancement of science for its own sake but for the sake of serving the state. The budget envelope, the programs of concerted action, and the *conjoncture scientifique* of the CNRS were innovations intended to expand and channel the national scientific effort along more socially "productive" lines. Of greatest long-term significance, however, has been the attempt of the Fifth Republic to utilize scientific research in the pursuit of its two major but interrelated political goals: the social and economic modernization of France; and the development of capabilities in advanced military weaponry (especially nuclear weapons) and space technology.

The formulation of a national science policy to achieve these goals advanced rapidly in the initial years of the Fifth Republic. Two of the three major features of a national policy toward science were well underway. First, necessary though not sufficient steps were taken to insure an adequate number of scientists and engineers. Second, measures were promoted to bridge the gap between knowledge and production. The third and most vexing problem—which fields and projects to support—had to be faced for the first time. In the years subsequent to 1960 the integration of science planning with socio-economic planning became a major preoccupation of French scientific and economic planners.

Chapter 8 · The Fifth Plan, 1966-1970

It would be most grievous if national independence, which is assured on the military plane, should be insidiously destroyed in the scientific domain, which even though it appears more peaceful is of vital importance for the conquest of markets and the strength of our industries. Let us feel assured that the objective of the Plan is that the nation, with the support of all, will be able to guard its scientific and technical independence, the keystone to the development and independence of a modern nation.

—Pierre Cognard, *DGRST, 1964*

The immediate postwar period brought an important new departure in Western political history. Traditionally the economic function of the Western state had been that of refereeing the struggle among conflicting economic interests over the distribution of national wealth. Though the role of the state in economic development was certainly not negligible, it had assumed no general responsibility for the creation of wealth and the management of the economy. The emphasis of national economic policy had been on the distribution of the nation's income and not the promotion of economic growth.

In 1945 this limited economic role of the state and the assumption that wealth was a static factor came to an end. The social welfare preamble of the Constitution of the Fourth Republic, the report of the Beveridge Committee in Great Britain (*Full Employment in a Free Society*, 1944), and the Full Employment Act of 1946 in the United States symbolized a new, positive role for the state in the economy. Today almost every Western state assumes the task of stimulating economic growth. Though intergroup conflict over the distribution of wealth has not ceased, the emphasis is on fostering cooperation among economic groups in order that all might benefit from an increase in the gross national product.[1] This was the attitude underlying the remark of Pierre Mendès-France that "historians a hundred years hence [will judge us] on the total volume of goods we have been able to produce. . . ."[2]

This idea, insofar as it is a correct description of contemporary politics, manifests itself in contemporary France in the four-year plans for social and economic modernization.[3] The first plan, by Jean Monnet in 1946, was merely a device to channel investment funds into the six primary sectors of the economy, like electricity, farm machinery, and transportation, on which the reconstruction of the devastated French economy depended. Under Monnet's successor, Etienne Hirsch, however, the scope of the plan was broadened to include investment in secondary economic sectors. It showed concern with such socio-economic matters as industrial productivity, housing, and the marketing system. Finally, due largely to the influence of Pierre Massé, who headed the Planning Commissariat from 1959 until 1965, the plan in present-day France has become one of the central features of French political life. Though its actual efficacy may be a matter of dispute, its scope now includes nearly the whole nonmilitary sphere of social and economic activities for which the modern state has assumed a responsibility—for example, public health, education,

---

[1] An excellent analysis of this "revolution" in Western economic thinking is Andrew Shonfield, *Modern Capitalism—The Changing Balance of Public and Private Power*, Oxford University Press, 1965.

[2] Pierre Mendès-France, *A Modern French Republic*, trans. Anne Carter, Hill and Wang, 1962, p. 88.

[3] The Fifth Plan (1966-70) is actually for five years. There are a number of good books on French planning. Two of the more valuable studies in English are: John and Anne-Marie Hackett, *Economic Planning in France*, Harvard University Press, 1963; Pierre Bauchet, *Economic Planning—The French Experience*, trans. Daphne Woodward, Praeger, 1964. An excellent short statement of the plan's value is Raymond Aron, Preface to Jean Lecerf, *La Percée de l'Économie Française*, Arthaud, 1963. And one of the best and most concise statements is Pierre Massé, "La Philosophie des Plans," *La Revue des Deux Mondes*, May 15, 1962, pp. 161-75.

and economic growth. The plan has become, in fact, one of the principal ways in which French society evaluates the state of its over-all well-being and establishes the goals to be accomplished in each succeeding five-year period.

Before proceeding further I should state briefly what the plan is and is not in terms of its economic, political, and psychological functions. In contrast to the Soviet five-year plan, the French is "indicative" and not "imperative."[4] The purpose of the French plan is to indicate the goals of French development and the steps to be taken in achieving them during the lifetime of the plan. The Planning Commission has no powers in its own right, and the French Government itself cannot force the private sector to adhere to the plan, though it can exert an indirect influence on business decisions through its control over the credit system and other economic levers.

More specifically, the economic function of the plan has been essentially one of pressuring both the state and business to take a forward-looking view. In a society where economic information has always been relatively unavailable, the plan gives French ministries and industries the information necessary for wise investment decisions. By providing private industry with information on the anticipated state of the economy and an indication of the state's own future expenditures, the plan seeks to overcome the traditional fear of overproduction that has so long hindered the growth of the French economy. While the plan is far from an outright state control of the economy, it does enable the planners, through personal persuasion and the urgency of their studies, to exert a significant though indefinite influence over the economy and to promote cooperation among all economic sectors. The goal, as one expert has called it, is an *économie concertée*.[5]

[4] *Ibid.*, pp. 161-75.
[5] For the history of this term see *Esprit*, Nos. 7-8 July-Aug. 1962, p. 65.

In addition to its economic goal the plan has an important political function. The French administrative structure, with its strong vertical lines of centralized power, was excellent for the management of a relatively static society. On the other hand, the consequent compartmentalization of the bureaucracy and the absence of many horizontal connections among ministries has made interagency planning and coordination very difficult. Even the phenomenon of the interdepartmental committee, of which there is such a plethora in the United States, is much less apparent in France, though Michel Debré did create many in the early years of the Fifth Republic. The administrative structure is one built to withstand change and even violent revolution, not one to accommodate itself to an era of rapid social and technological evolution.

The preparation of the plan seeks to overcome the usual obstacles by forcing both the government and the French people to become conscious of the necessary choices before them and to consider possible ways to adjust themselves.[6] In the rigid and highly integrated French society, where social experimentation is difficult, the plan's purpose is to build steady and gradual adjustment to change into the fabric of the political system.[7] It seeks to substitute coordinated and rational adjustment to change for the French propensity to resist change until the crisis is upon them.

The plan is also social and psychological. Historically the various social groups and classes of French society have been cut off from one another—ruling class and masses, university and industry, capital and labor. Communication has been scant; the consensus connecting them has been a fragile one at best. Instead, they have successfully checked one another

[6] Aron, Preface to *La Percée de l'Économie Française.*
[7] Jacques Fauvet, *The Cockpit of France,* trans. Nancy Pearson, Harvill Press, 1960, p. 38.

throughout French history, producing what Hoffmann has called the stalemate society.[8]

The plan's social function, therefore, is to facilitate communication among these fragmented and disparate groups. Through bringing them into its discussions the Government hopes to ready society for its programs and to provide an acceptable set of objectives for the whole country. In short, the Plan is a means of fostering a national consensus and overcoming the social, institutional, and intellectual cleavages that have plagued French society for so long. The making of the plan should be, in the conception of Charles de Gaulle, the central concern of the French people—an undertaking that unites them and replaces social conflict with national unity. Only in this fashion, it is argued, can a small nation like France husband its limited resources to obtain maximum return. However, the plan's success is another matter.[9]

A Brief History of Science and the Plan

Until the Fourth Plan the French plans were formulated with little reference to the scientific-technological revolution. Though Joliot-Curie was a member of the original Monnet Committee, scientific research was not one of the areas selected for investment. The most pressing need at the beginning was to revive and rebuild a traditional industrial economy; scientific research was a secondary concern. Furthermore, although Frenchmen did sense the importance of science in the postwar world and indicated it by the establishment of the CEA, the CNRS, and the CNET, they had little appreciation of the need to relate scientific research to economic and social goals.[10]

[8] Stanley Hoffmann, ed., *In Search of France*, Harvard University Press, 1963, Chapter 1.

[9] Cf. Aron, Preface to *La Percée de l'Économie Française*, for a critical evaluation of the plan.

[10] J. G. Crowther, *Science in Liberated Europe*, Pilot Press, 1949, p.

In the preparation of the Second (1954-57) and the Third (1958-61) Plans, commissions on civil, or nonmilitary scientific and technical, research were established for the first time. As noted in Chapter Seven, they had a relatively minor role in the development of a national plan; no attempt was made to relate science policy to economic policy. But these initial efforts did pave the way for the next stage in the relationship of science planning and economic planning—which began with the preparation of the Fourth Plan (1962-65). The planners, and particularly Pierre Massé, realized by then that scientific research and development had become a major factor in production, with considerable importance for the achievement of France's long-range objectives.[11] In the words of the introduction to the Fourth Plan, science had to be "integrated" into the formulation of the plan because of "the ardor of scientific and technological competition, the intensity of innovation, and the rapidity of change."[12] This innovation within the Fourth Plan was the beginning of the continuing, systematic attempt to relate scientific and socio-economic planning. The goal of science planning was no longer to be merely the advancement of knowledge for its own sake, but the establishment of scientific priorities based on the economic, social, and military needs of France.

Advancement of scientific research, however, is not merely an objective of the plan. The work of scientists and engineers impinges on deliberations in all sectors of the plan and all areas of national policy-making. In order to establish long-term goals and make present-day policies, decision-makers must know how science will change the technical realities of the

---

24. In April 1946 an Interministerial Commission on the organization of scientific research was set up but had no influence.

[11] "La Préparation du Vème Plan de la Recherche," *Le Progrès Scientifique*, No. 67, Feb. 1, 1964, pp. 2-3.

[12] Commissariat Général au Plan, *Quatrième Plan de Développement Économique et Social (1962-1965)*, 1962, p. 1.

world. How will the new technologies which science is making possible affect the control of a disease, a sector of the economy, or a weapons system under development? The advice of scientists and engineers must be fed into the planning and policy-making network if society is to adapt itself to the rapid pace of technological evolution fostered by modern science.

There is emerging, then, in a modern scientific nation-state such as France is attempting to develop, a reciprocal relationship between science and state. On the one hand, the state is formulating a policy toward science so that research will have utility for national goals. The corollary of this is that scientific developments are increasingly taken into consideration. The French state is beginning to take account of scientific advance in the formulation of its policy goals. This reciprocal relationship is in its earliest stage of development, but the consequences of the integration of science into national policy-making will have great significance for the nature of French science and its role in society.

Though the Fourth Plan for research and development was the first one to be prepared by the present institutions for science planning, an analysis of the preparation of the Fifth Plan (1966-70) shows us how the French have tried to relate scientific planning and over-all national planning. The effort leaves much to be desired, but it is an important step forward.[13]

Formulation of the Plan

To understand French science planning one must know at least in outline the structure of French socio-economic planning. The responsibility for the preparation of the plan rests

[13] This discussion is based on interviews with staff of the Plan and DGRST, reports of the Planning Commissariat, and many articles, the key one of which is "La Préparation du Vème Plan de la Recherche," pp. 1-22. In addition, the writer found James Brian Quinn, "National Planning of Science and Technology in France," *Science*, CL, No. 3,699, Nov. 19, 1965, 993-1,003, to be helpful.

with the Planning Commissariat. Though the Commissariat has a small staff the burden of the work falls on two sets of commissions. The so-called vertical commissions deal with specific economic sectors such as chemistry, agriculture, or energy. The "horizontal commissions" are devoted to problems in research, manpower, and regional development, which cut across the areas of interest of the vertical commissions. The task of these two sets of commissions is to coordinate their plans to achieve the overall national objectives formulated by the Government.[14]

PLANNING FOR SCIENCE

With respect to the role of science in the planning process, the focal point is the *horizontal* Commission for Scientific and Technical Research which was first established during the preparation of the Fourth Plan. The Commission is composed of the 12 members of the Scientific Advisory Committee and representatives from important research sectors and organizations, and is charged with drafting a report for the Planning Commissariat on the incorporation of scientific and technical research into the plan. The chairman of the Commission is the chairman of the Advisory Committee; the General Delegation is the Secretariat to the Commission and is responsible for drafting the preliminary document which serves as the basis of the Commission's report to the Planning Commissariat. A result of this overlapping membership is a close liaison between scientific and socio-economic planning (see FIGURE 2).

The formal preparation of the Commission's report to the Planning Commissariat began in October 1963 with the establishment of three different sets of preparatory groups, constituted so as to give birth to "the most constructive dialogue possible between the representatives of pure science and those whose function is more directly tied to industrial expansion

[14] This relationship is concisely spelled out in *ibid.*, pp. 997-98.

Figure 2
BASIC ORGANIZATIONAL RELATIONSHIPS IN FRENCH SCIENCE PLANNING[a]

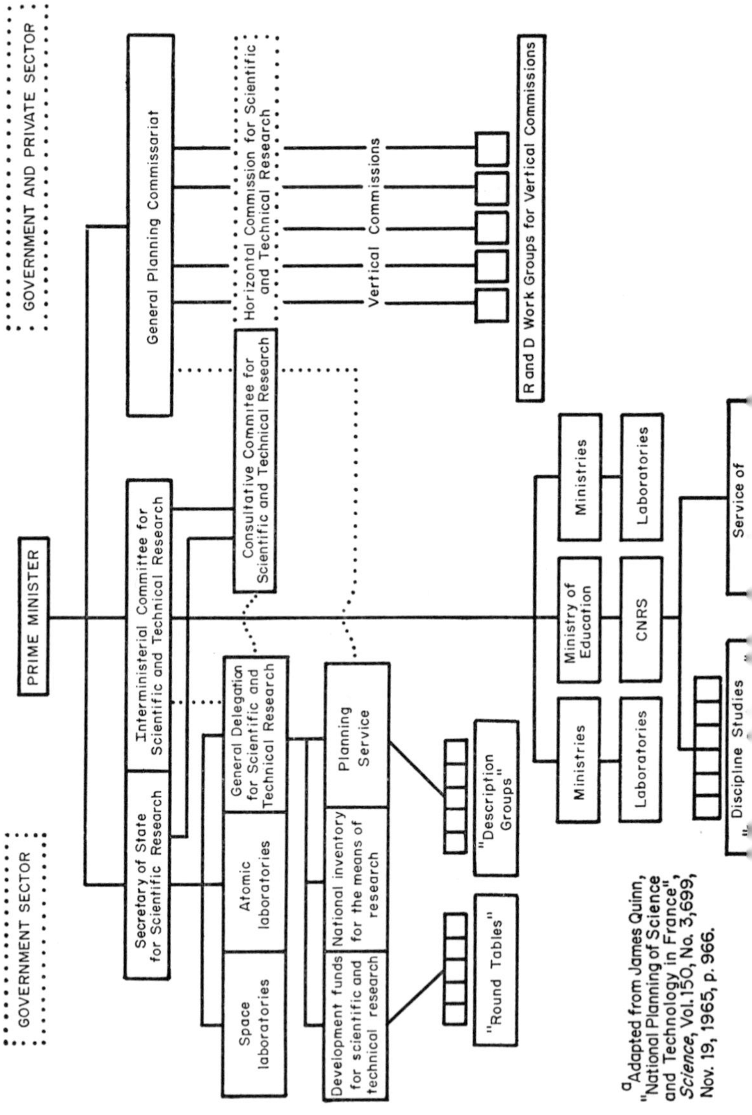

[a]Adapted from James Quinn, "National Planning of Science and Technology in France", *Science*, Vol.150, No. 3,699, Nov. 19, 1965, p. 966.

226

and related economic activities, to social welfare policies and to general policy."[15] In this fashion, it was hoped, scientific and over-all socio-economic planning might progress, each taking account of the other. In the immediate future, scientific planning would be influenced by economic, social, and political objectives of the plan; conversely, in the longer term the setting of the latter objectives would be influenced by the evolution of science and technology. Hopefully, too, by this mechanism the users of science could specify their demands for new science and technology to the university scientists, who in turn would inform the users of new and potential discoveries of interest to specific industries and other activities.

The first set of preparatory groups was organized by scientific disciplines or domains of research. Composed of representatives from different research sectors, the first phase of the groups' work was to survey the present status of the research within its domain, forecast its future development, and evaluate the reform, manpower, and financial needs of the fields. This work drew from the annual reports (*conjoncture scientifique*) of the CNRS; the long-term (1980-85) forecasts of scientific developments (*prospectives scientifiques*) prepared by the so-called description groups of the DGRST; and the research needs expressed by different economic sectors. On the basis of this work each group then (1965) examined the investment proposals of the ministries and, within the financial guidelines laid down by the Commission on Research, prepared a list of proposals for the development of its domain of research to be implemented during 1966-70.

The second set of preparatory groups was concerned with general problems related to scientific research. One group was responsible for examining indirect means for aiding scientific and technical research, such as patents, taxation, and fiscal policy. A second group sought to develop criteria of choice

---

[15] "Préparation du Vème Plan," p. 11.

with respect to the general orientation of French science and the allocation of resources among various domains. A third group was charged with the task of harmonizing French technical assistance abroad with domestic research programs. A fourth group worked with the official responsible for regional development on the problem of decentralizing the national scientific effort. And last, a fifth group on technical research and development was established to maintain liaison with other commissions concerned with research, such as those charged with manpower and education, and to coordinate and synthesize the work of the third set of preparatory groups.

The third set of preparatory groups were research and development work groups organized under those vertical commissions concerned with problems of production, e.g., chemistry, energy, and agriculture. The mission of each group was to analyze the current status of technical research in its sector (organization, level of effort, foreign competition, etc.) and to evaluate future prospects: possible scientific and technical developments which were the most promising, manpower needs, projection of public and private financial effort. Because a member of the Scientific Advisory Committee was appointed to each of these working groups, liaison was established between them and the Commission on Research.

These three sets of preparatory groups prepared their individual reports within the guidelines laid down by the Commission on Research. Notably, the Commission established budget ceilings for each group. The DGRST coordinated this work with the more general deliberations of the Commission on Research. On the basis of these preparatory reports, the Commission on Research prepared its preliminary report and submitted it to the Commissariat.

Following the submission of the reports of the various commissions, the preliminary plan was drafted by the Planning

Commissariat and submitted to the Social and Economic Council for criticism and debate. This Council is composed of representatives of social and economic groups throughout France, and though it has no legislative powers its influence is not negligible. From the Social and Economic Council the plan went to the French Parliament where the main options facing France over the next five years were debated. Throughout these latter stages of the preparation of the plan, the focus was on the share of GNP to be devoted to scientific and technical investment. In this matter, as in all others dealing with the plan, the final decisions rest with responsible public officials and take the form of a "law-program" voted by the National Assembly.

On the basis of the "law-program," further discussions take place among the Planning Commissariat, the Ministry of Finance, the Commission for Research, and other interested groups. The Commission on Research then completes its final report.[16] The report on the Fifth Plan, which was completed in January 1966, serves to guide the formulation of science policy through the early 1970s.

SCIENCE IN PLANNING

As indicated above, science is not merely an "output" of the Plan; scientific and technological developments are also "inputs" which affect all other sectors of the plan and must be taken into account. Consequently, the developing effort in France to formulate a rational policy toward science is complemented by the attempt to master the problems associated with the growing importance of science in policy formulation. For both practical and psychological reasons in a world in which science is constantly giving rise to novel and powerful

[16] Délégation Générale à la Recherche Scientifique, Commission de la Recherche, *Rapport Général pour le Vème Plan*, Jan. 1966.

technologies governments must deal with the implications of scientific advance for increasingly numerous areas of public policy. The acceleration of technological change necessitates that governments attempt to anticipate the short- and long-term effects of the growth of knowledge and new technology.

The notion that "to govern is to foresee" (*gouverner, c'est prévoir*) is at least as old as Richelieu. But there is a profound change in the psychological dimensions of the problem of *prévision*. In the past the future was assumed to be a continuation of the present; in the modern world change has become the accepted norm, and government is impelled for practical reasons to ascertain the ways in which change will affect present policies and what new problems it will create. And though scientific advance is not by any means the sole cause of this situation, its contributory role is a major one simply because of the potency of modern scientific technology. This changed situation is well summarized by one writer on French planning:

> The closely-knit structure of the modern world, which is partly the result of technological advances, enables us to make forecasts for consumption and production which would have been impossible in the past.
>
> Only fifty years ago, the idea of predicting the future trend of consumption of a particular product or group of products seemed completely utopian. . . . Today the factors determining consumption can to some extent be foreseen. Production is less dependent upon climatic variations or mere chance than it used to be, and more closely conditioned by technological discoveries; the appearance on the market of a new fertilizer or a new type of seed affects harvests as much as the climate. . . .
>
> Without exaggerating the extent of social determination, we have to admit that the increasingly close connection between all technological and economic phenomena, the re-

lationship of present to past and of future to present, facilitates forecasting on a scale that would have been unthinkable not so very long ago.[17]

A concern with forecasting and "predicting" the shape of the future has become an intellectual preoccupation in contemporary France. Though the systematization of social and economic forecasting was evident in the 1930s and under Vichy, an adequate methodology, sufficient data, and a strong commitment were missing.[18] The full flowering of this interest in the future took place after World War II and is perhaps one of the major manifestations of the psychological revolution which took place when Frenchmen began to look forward rather than backward. For its emergence as an important theme in modern French thought, much credit must be given to the late philosopher, Gaston Berger, who, through personal influence and his journal, *Prospective*, influenced important Frenchmen "to see the probable future, but to prepare for the hoped for future and even perhaps to try to make more probable the hoped for future."[19] In one form or another, this theme runs through the writings of many French writers and the activities of several important organizations.[20]

Before proceeding further, however, we must distinguish here between the impressive French effort to create the intellectual and organizational instruments for quantitative economic and population forecastings (*prévision*) and the broader and speculative endeavor to conjecture about the qualitative

[17] Bauchet, *Economic Planning*, pp. 15-16.
[18] For a brief history see Jacques Wolff, *La Prévision*, Éditions Berger-Levrault, 1963. See also Bertrand de Jouvenel, *The Art of Conjecture*, trans. N. Kita Lary, Basic Books, 1967, esp. pp. 200-30.
[19] Jean Meynaud, "À propos des Spéculations sur l'Avenir," *Revue Française de la Science Politique*, XIII, No. 3, Sept. 1963, 674.
[20] See *ibid.*, for a survey and appraisal of this movement in France. Meynaud himself is highly critical of what he considers to be a naïve optimism pervading the thoughts of the future.

implications of scientific and technological (*prospective*) advance. *Prévision* provides the necessary basis for the immense capital investments undertaken by private and public institutions, and for several years has been the responsibility of such agencies as the National Institute of Statistics and Economic Studies (INSEE) and the National Institute for Demographic Studies (INED), which are intimately associated with the economic planning aspects of the plan.[21] It is *prospective* activity that concerns us now.

In recent years an important new trend has commenced in this preoccupation with the shape of the future. While Berger had been interested in long-term changes (10-20 years), his writings and those of his associates were unofficial. Since the advent of the de Gaulle Government, and due largely to the influence of Pierre Massé and Bertrand de Jouvenel, interest in the need to make qualitative forecasting more relevant to national planning and to place it on a more scientific foundation has increased. By the mid-1960s important steps were being taken to integrate "futuristic" thinking into governmental decision-making on an official basis.

In the area of national planning the attempt to take into account the implications for the future of scientific and technological developments began in earnest with the preparation of the Fifth Plan. Several mechanisms were established to accomplish this goal. The General Delegation, as noted above, created a number of "description groups" to study development through 1985 of specific scientific disciplines (*prospective scientifique*), their potential contributions, and their needs if these contributions were to be realized.[22] The discussions of the description groups were fed via the preparatory groups into the report of the Commission for Research. In addition, since certain members of the description groups served also

[21] Cf. Bauchet, *Economic Planning*, Chap. 1.
[22] Quinn, "National Planning," p. 999.

on the research and development work groups of the vertical commissions and the round tables of the programs of concerted action, this "prospective" mentality ran through the over-all elaboration of the science plan and the over-all plan.

A second attempt to forecast long-term scientific, technical, and related developments took place in the vertical commissions and especially in the work of their research and development work groups. The most notable example of this was the report of the Commission on Energy for the Fourth Plan. Because "a five-year forecasting survey does not make it possible to plan adequately for one of the 'heavy' sectors, i.e., demanding considerable equipment and manpower," the Commission was obliged to foresee the French energy picture as it would be in 1975.[23] Among the parameters the Commission took into consideration were the rate of general economic expansion, the output of crude steel, and trends in relevant technologies such as steel production, atomic energy, and transport. The Commission's research and development work group concerned itself with the "state of the art," the promise of ongoing research programs, and the future technical manpower and research needs of the energy sector of the economy.

While the work of the Energy Commission was a heroic attempt to make long-term forecasts, its failings revealed the limitations of such efforts. It found that the number of uncertainties is so large and "the economic problem involved is so vast and complex . . . the means at present available are inadequate to rough out a suitable model, and . . . most of the data could not be expressed in the form of figures." Thus the Commission found itself in the dilemma that the normal period of the plan—five years—was too short for realistic technological forecasting, and 15 years (1960-75) was too long, given the rapidity of social and technological change. In addi-

[23] Commissariat Général au Plan, *Rapport Général de la Commission de l'Énergie*, 1961, p. 30.

tion, French industry continued to be extremely reluctant to furnish the Planning Commissariat with sufficient information on new products and improved technical processes.

This situation caused the vertical commissions in drafting their reports to tend to take little account of possible scientific and technological developments. Indeed, planning and projections of the National Institute of Statistics and Economic Studies (INSEE) for the French economy have tended to rest on the assumption that the present state of technology would prevail throughout the duration of the plan.[24] The large numbers of unknowns, the difficulty of measuring productivity change, and the inability to determine the rate at which new products will enter the market during the relatively short period covered by the plan forced this limitation. Even in this world of rapidly accelerating technical change, the implications of new technology tend to make themselves felt over a longer period than four or five years. Nonetheless, the research and development work groups of the vertical commissions served to make industrialists and planning officials sensitive to the possible long-term consequences of scientific-technological advance.

The most interesting attempt of the Planning Commissariat along this line was the creation of the 1985 Commission. The inspiration of Pierre Massé, the 1985 Commission was under the chairmanship of Pierre Guillaumat, former Secretary of State for Science, and was composed of a distinguished panel of scientists, scholars, and public officials. It was to envision the "probable and hoped for" France of 1985 and provide a framework for the general orientation of the Fifth Plan. As part of this inquiry the General Delegation, in its capacity as secretariat to the 1985 Commission, sponsored a number of meetings where scientists and other experts drafted reports on

[24] The Forecasting Directorate in the Finance Ministry, for example, does no technical forecasting.

the possible social and economic implications of scientific and technological advance. These confidential reports (*prospective scientifique*) provided background material for the work of the 1985 Commission and for the report of the Commission for Research of the Plan as well. The final report—*Réflexions pour 1985*, published in 1964—though subject to serious criticisms included valuable analyses and forecasts of such matters as the supply of raw materials, the needs of scientific research, and the problems of leisure and urban life in 1985.

Through these various instrumentalities, science, in theory at least, has been "integrated" by the Fifth Republic into the national plan for social and economic development. Science is becoming less isolated from the larger concerns of industrialization and modernization; it is more and more an integral part of France's *économie concertée*. As the planning purist would have it, the policy options which guide the formulation of the national plan are selected by public authority, i.e., the Social and Economic Council, the Parliament, and the Government. On the basis of the chosen options and necessary technical considerations the planning experts draft the national plan, taking into consideration relevant scientific and technological factors. On the basis of this plan the Commission for Research devises the science plan. Finally, through such policy instruments as the annual budget envelope, the program of development assistance, and the programs of concerted action, the state implements the plan for nonmilitary or civil science in both the public, and where appropriate, the private spheres.

Objectives of the Plan

Whereas the Third Plan was preoccupied with investment in manpower and the Fourth emphasized the development of the infrastructure for research and of university-industrial cooperation, the Fifth seeks to put into effect a "true strategy of research" that will place France at the level of other advanced

235

societies. By the end of the Fifth Plan in 1970 the French hope to double national expenditures for both research and development in the civilian sector, thus bringing this expenditure to 2.5 percent of the GNP. They also intend to increase the number of research workers from 33,000 (1963) to 70,000.[25] In addition to new programs of investment and concerted action the Fifth Plan emphasizes reorganization of the mechanisms for the coordination of research, decentralization of the total national research effort, and reform of scientific and technical organizations. Most important of all, a major emphasis is to be placed on the program of development assistance to help private industry finance technological innovations (see Chap. 10).

APPLIED AND TECHNICAL RESEARCH

The Fifth Plan follows the course set by the Fourth in emphasizing applied and technical research, which should narrow the technology gap between France and the scientific nation-states. The new set of concerted action programs concentrates on electronics (especially computers and automation), the physical sciences, and the earth sciences.[26] Total investment for the research envelope (of which 707 million francs, or 18 percent, is for the programs of concerted action) during the course of the Plan is 3.9 billion francs to be allocated according to TABLE 13. In addition, 600 million francs will be devoted to contracts for development assistance. Last, if one includes public expenditures not covered by the plan, such as those of CEA, the Ministry of Defense, and the Ministry of National Education, as well as expenditures by private industry, then the total French expenditure (investment and operations) on research and development during the course of the plans is assumed to be between 56 and 58 billion francs.[27]

[25] Commissariat Général au Plan, *Cinquième Plan de Développement Économique et Social (1966-1970)*, II, pp. 36-59.

[26] For a complete list see DGRST, Commission de la Recherche, *Rapport Général*, pp. 154-55.

[27] *Ibid.*, 146.

The French particularly hope to strengthen their position in several areas of immense economic and military importance. In the field of mathematics the plan puts special emphasis on modern systems of computation and automatic data-processing. Three big centers for computer and automation research are to be set up in Paris, Grenoble, and Toulouse, along with eight smaller centers elsewhere. These facilities will be linked by a communications network so that all France can be served by computers. In addition, several laboratories and programs of concerted action are to be established in the area of operations research. Much of this effort ties directly into the concentrated French effort to establish themselves in the computer field. (cf. *Plan Calcul*, discussed in Chapter 10).

A second important field in the Fifth Plan is oceanography. Funds are to be invested to develop special research centers, a program of concerted action, and eventually a National Center for the Exploration of the Oceans (CNEXO). The hope is

TABLE 13.

Research Envelope under the Fifth Plan[a]
(in millions of francs)

Mathematics	315
Physics	1,254
Chemistry	400
Earth sciences, water, atmosphere	284
Oceanography	150
Biology and Medicine	590
Agricultural research	390
Construction, public works, urbanism	162
Human sciences	120
Industrial property	10
Interdisciplinary operations and miscellaneous	225
Total	3,900

[a] DGRST, Commission de la Recherche, *Rapport Général*, p. 150.

that CNEXO would do for oceanography what CNES has done for space research—define a national program, coordinate the research of different laboratories, and administer large equipment.[28] The center would regroup the numerous but scattered French researchers in this area and create an institution with sufficient "critical mass" to be effective.

Though space research is not the responsibility of the Commission for Research, the funds allocated for it are included in the plan. During the period 1966-70 the French government intends to spend 2 billion francs on space research. Of this amount three-fourths is to be devoted to a national program of satellite research, use of sounding rockets, and construction of facilities; the other fourth goes principally to the two European space organizations—European Launcher Development Organization (ELDO) and European Center for Space Research (ESRO).[29]

COORDINATION

The Fifth Plan envisages the reorganization of structures for the coordination of research at the national, regional, and working levels. At the national level the science planners propose that each technical ministry designate an official to provide the liaison between the ministry and the DGRST. In ministries without a research program this official would evaluate the research needs of the ministry and the effect of ministerial decisions on the science plan. In those ministries with a research program the official would prepare an annual report on the research program of the department, coordinate the research activities of the ministry's technical bureaus, and ini-

[28] *Le Monde*, June 1, 1966.
[29] "La Recherche Scientifique et Technique Française (1966-1970): Les Grandes Lignes du Cinquième Plan," *Le Progrès Scientifique*, No. 89, Oct. 1965, p. 20.

tiate research programs within and without the ministry itself of interest to the ministry. In effect, the responsibility for research programs within an individual ministry would be vested in one official, and a government-wide mechanism centered around DGRST would be established for the coordination of the national research effort.

DECENTRALIZATION

At the regional level the decentralization of research is an important factor in the over-all strategy for the development of France. The objective is to stimulate the development of several metropolitan areas in order to counterbalance Paris and promote regional growth. Some of the proposed *métropoles d'équilibre* such as Toulouse already have important scientific and technical establishments around which industry can develop. As part of this objective, "laboratories will be built in such a way that the scientific potential will be spread over the whole country; at present this is concentrated around Paris (75 percent) and Lyon and Grenoble (10 percent). Decentralization will favor these areas."[30]

As in the United States and Great Britain, certain universities and laboratories throughout the country are to be selected to become "centers of excellence," places where a "critical mass" of research workers and equipment can be assembled. An eventual distribution of the national research effort (exclusively of the programs of concerted action) is foreseen along the following lines: 35 to 40 percent in Paris and Orleans; 50 to 55 in the *métropoles d'équilibre*; and 10 to 15 in the rest of France.[31] Furthermore, industrial investment is to be guided in terms of regional scientific and technical specializations.

[30] André Marechal, "Problems of Science Policy in France," *Discovery*, XXVI, No. 8, Aug. 1965, 14.
[31] "La Recherche Scientifique et Technique Française (1966-1970), p. 22.

The DGRST, through conferences and other methods, is to encourage the harmonizing of private and public efforts in accordance with regional specializations.[32]

ADMINISTRATION

At the working level the Fifth Plan proposes several major reforms of both public and private organizations. To improve the relationship between the CNRS and the universities the plan calls for a more precise definition of their respective missions and the establishment of mechanisms within the Ministry of National Education to harmonize the research and teaching programs of the two organizations with one another and with the program of DGRST. Also, an effort is to be made to improve the liaison between the Ministry of National Education and the Ministry of Public Health.

In several important sectors the plan recommends the creation of relatively autonomous and specialized institutes, which would have the responsibility of organizing the national research effort in the following areas:

Applied mathematics—a national institute on automation and information.
Physics—a national institute of nuclear and high energy physics.
Oceanography—a national center of oceanographic studies.
Earth sciences—a national geological service.
Economic and social sciences—a center of coordination and orientation of research on social and economic development.[33]

In the private sector the plan proposes that the technical research centers be developed through concentrating their re-

[32] *Ibid.*, p. 23.
[33] *Ibid.*, pp. 23-24.

sources on specific themes and projects; the centers should also utilize contracts for the first time to engage university and other laboratories on industrial problems. Furthermore, the centers are to be encouraged to regroup themselves in geographical areas near the industries they serve and to increase the exchange of information among themselves.[34]

Since a major emphasis of the plan is to facilitate the translation of new fundamental knowledge into new technology, steps are to be taken to improve university and industrial contacts through reform of the laws governing university-industrial relations. In particular, these changes will remove legal restrictions that have prevented university laboratories from accepting industrial research contracts. The patent system of the CNRS is to be modified to encourage cooperation with industry, and the programs of concerted action are to concentrate on industrial research. Most important of all, the Government is to expand its program of development assistance through which it helps private industry finance technological innovation.[35]

In Chapter 10 we will return to an evaluation of the implementation of Fifth Plan proposals. The question to be considered at the moment is the utility of science planning. Is this a valuable exercise? What are its merits? Dangers?

Critique

The evaluations of the French effort to plan science range from the harsh denunciation of one French scientist that fundamental science cannot be planned[36] to the enthusiastic endorsement by one knowledgeable American observer who has written:

---

[34] *Ibid.*, p. 24.   [35] *Ibid.*, pp. 24-25.

[36] Michel Magat, "La Recherche Scientifique: Réponse à Louis Armand," *L'Express,* Mar. 30, 1964. Magat is a professor at the Faculté des Sciences, Paris.

France is in the midst of an imaginative and dynamic experiment in the planning of civil science and technology (S&T) on a national scale. France has the most formalized structure for national planning in the Western World, and many countries expect her to lead in developing useful new concepts and techniques for integrating science and technology into national plans. French efforts and progress in this regard deserve the attention of thoughtful scientists and national policy makers throughout the world.[37]

From the viewpoint of this study both positions are partially correct but each overstates its case. The opponent of planning is supported by the history of science, which demonstrates the repeated introduction of novel and unanticipated discoveries into the corpus of scientific ideas. The many attempts to foresee exactly where important discoveries would lie, or lead, have met with almost universal frustration. Conversely, many of our most remarkable technologies have been the unintended consequences of the free play of scientific imagination. As Michael Polanyi has commented in criticizing the Marxist theory of planning science in the interest of social utility:

> What technical inventions were the discoveries of the Nobel Laureates Planck, Einstein, Perrin, Millikan, Michelson, Rutherford, Aston, Chadwick, Barkla, Heisenberg, Compton, Franck, G. Hertz, Rubens, Laue, Joliot, Fermi, Urey, Anderson, W.H. and W.L. Bragg, Schrödinger, Dirac, etc., unconsciously intended to produce? No one can tell— so the new theory of science must pass them over.[38]

On the other hand, the nature of the scientific enterprise today and the shortened lead time between discovery and application necessarily point to a greater role for the state in de-

[37] Quinn, "National Planning," p. 993.
[38] Michael Polanyi, *The Logic of Liberty*, Routledge and Kegan Paul, 1951, p. 82-83.

termining the purposes of scientific research. Changes in the scale and organization of scientific research necessitate that the state make long-range decisions with respect to huge capital investment in research facilities, the training of scientists and technicians, and the financing of research programs. The competition for funds among the huge number of disciplines and specializations spun off by scientific advance necessitates that the state, on the advice of its scientific advisors, establish priorities to guide investment in facilities, manpower, and programs. Without question, one of the criteria to be employed increasingly in all nations is that of social utility.

Of equal importance, however, is that the planning of science, in the sense of consciously relating ends and means, has been taking place for a long time. What is important to ask, therefore, is not whether science ought to be planned but by whom, for what ends, and how. To say categorically that science cannot be planned is actually to offer a defense of the existing methods for distribution of funds.

As Thomas Kuhn points out in his *The Structure of Scientific Revolutions*,[39] most scientific research is "normal science," in contrast to the revolutionary and unanticipated discoveries that change the evolutionary course of scientific ideas. Such normal research involves the "determination of significant fact, matching of facts with theory, and articulation of theory."[40] Though this requires competent men and may pave the way to important discoveries, the content and the problems of normal science proceed directly from existing scientific theories and postrevolutionary discoveries. Such an endeavor involves the extrapolation of the known into the realm of the unknown. Even though normal research may sometimes lead to the most revolutionary of discoveries, as occurred in Becquerel's discovery of radioactivity, this is not usually the case. Instead, the

[39] University of Chicago Press, 1962.
[40] *Ibid.*, p. 33.

problems of normal science lie open to all and wait to be "cleaned up" in order for science to move ahead.

Moreover, we even tend to exaggerate the mysteries of scientific discovery and revolution. Though novelty and creativity cannot be captured in a formula, one cannot help but be impressed by the degree to which scientists in any age concur with one another in their identification of the areas where revolutionary discoveries will be made. The high incidence of simultaneous discovery in the past[41] and the extent to which scientists in all countries today have "zeroed in" on such questions as the essence of the genetic code, the nature of matter, and the anomaly of the quasars in distant space, reveal their sense of where great discoveries will be found and where priority should be given. The question therefore is not "whether planning?" but "by whom?" and "how?"

In the past, decisions on the pursuit of science rested almost solely with scientists themselves. The cost of equipment, the operating expenses of laboratories, and the cost of individual experiments were not important determinants of specific decisions, though these factors influenced the over-all level of research. As a consequence of the change in the economics of research, in answer to the question—Who plans normal research?—one must answer "the state" as well as scientists. In all major scientific countries an uneasy partnership is developing between the state and its scientists for the planning and governance of science.

The second important change in the planning or policy-making for science is the matter of goals. Previously the interests of scientists almost entirely determined the direction of

---

[41] See Robert Merton, "Priorities in Scientific Discovery: A Chapter in the Sociology of Science," *American Sociological Review*, xxii, 1957, 635-59; Robert Merton, "Singletons and Multiples in Scientific Discovery: A Chapter in the Sociology of Science," *Proceedings of the American Philosophical Society*, cv, 1961, 470-86.

scientific research.[42] But today the influence of external, or social, needs on the direction of scientific research seems to be greater. One can only say "seems" because almost any research supported by the state would also be favored by some group of scientists, and who is to say which group truly speaks for science? For this reason what exists in France and elsewhere is in reality an alliance between the "progressive" elements in science and those in the state.[43] The representatives of the scientific establishment in the government are the atomic physicists, electronic specialists, and biologists whose fields are at the frontier of scientific advance and are also held to be most significant for the affairs of state.

There have been changes in the aims of science policy and in the loci and method of decision-making for science policy. As we have seen in France and in the United States, the focus of decision-making for science is becoming more formalized and concentrated in the agencies of the state. In addition, the search for more rational and efficient means to determine the allocation of resources for science has gained momentum. This longing for "criteria of scientific choice"[44] and the development of a "science of science"[45] have been stimulated by the immense and still increasing discrepancy between available scientific resources and unanswered scientific questions on whose answers rest the solution of important social or technical problems.

[42] Robert Merton, "Science and Military Technique," *Scientific Monthly*, XLI, Dec. 1935, 542-49. Merton estimates, for example, that about 10 percent of the research of the Royal Society in seventeenth-century England was directly influenced by military needs.

[43] Abraham Moles, "La Cité Scientifique en 1972," *Bulletin SEDEIS, Futuribles*, No. 41, 1962.

[44] Cf. Bruce L. R. Smith, "The Concept of Scientific Choice: A Brief Review of the Literature," RAND Report P-3,156, June 1965.

[45] See the writings of Stevan Dedijer, Derek de Solla Price, and Stephen Toulmin. Maurice Goldsmith and Alan MacKay, eds., in *The Science of Science*, Souvenir Press, 1964.

What is taking place in France, the U.S., and other Western societies is in effect a Keynesian revolution in the relationship of science and state. Rejecting the laissez-faire-*laissez–rechercher* philosophy of the past, the science planners seek a role for the state in science affairs that can balance the need for central direction against the need for scientific freedom and initiative. But it is a Keynesian revolution without a Keynes, for no one has or can formulate the appropriate magnitude and direction of state intervention. Nonetheless, the science plan provides a forum where conscious consideration can be given to the needs of French science and long-term goals can be established.

If the conservative critics of French science planning are too disparaging, its extollers tend to exaggerate the successes of the plan. There can be no doubt that the innovation of a national science plan has enhanced the position of the science planners and has done much to modernize French scientific and technological institutions and pursuits. Yet the weight of the past continues to lie heavily on French science. The inability of plan and planners to alter the situation is due to the nature of the French polity and of science itself.

Three aspects of the plan which reflect French political life reveal the limitations of the plan. In the first place, though in theory the plan is a means to achieve social cooperation and consensus, in practice it is a device by which the state seeks to mobilize the French people in the direction *it* believes to be correct; as such this *étatisme* frequently thwarts and seldom stimulates initiative. Secondly, though the forecasting activity surrounding the formulation of the plan is no doubt a beneficial exercise, it really is not sufficiently integral to the policy-making process. This can be seen if one contrasts the French plan with the planning and policy-making process of large American corporations. In the latter, the five-year plans are continually updated, and forecasts are revised on the basis of current information. Planning and forecasting are part of the yearly budget cycle. As a consequence, whereas the French plan remains relatively unchanged throughout its lifetime, the corporate five-year plan begins anew each year in the light of past decisions and new prospects.

The separation of the plan from policy-making is a function of French administrative structure. What is too frequently neglected in assessing the efficacy of the plan is the fragmented structure of the French state. Power over the various sectors of the plan is distributed among the several ministries which enjoy considerable autonomy within their respective spheres. Though the Ministry of Finance and the Planning Commissariat can exercise a negative function, they have too little positive influence over the activities of the sovereign ministries.

The science plan seeks, in effect, to transform the power structure of French science, but has little leverage for doing so. The two main policy instruments of the planners—the budget envelope and the programs of concerted action—are, as was pointed out in Chapter 7, weak. The budget envelope, and therefore the science plan, cover a small fraction of the total French expenditures for science and does not cover important areas like atomic energy. Even in areas covered by the budget envelope, such as the CNRS, the plan has too little influence on the determination of research priorities. As for the programs of concerted action, though they have been significant in themselves, they are too small to give the planners much control of the direction of French science.

The science planners are successful insofar as they are able to persuade government and private enterprise to cooperate in the formulation of the science plan and to conform to its objectives. As agencies directly responsible to the Prime Minister, both the Planning Commissariat and the Minister for

Science have some, though not much, influence over the technical ministries and the nationalized industries. The Government, in turn, can gain some adherents from private industry through its control of credit, licenses, and purchases. It also influences the direction of private science through its own investment of funds and research contracts. More will be said of this in the next two chapters. In general, however, what power the science planners have is essentially one based on gentle persuasion and not the exercise of real administrative or political power.

Another weakness of the French science plan is one inherent in the nature of science itself. Though much can be done to improve the "rationality" of decision-making with respect to the allocation of resources for scientific research, the critics, in a profound sense, are correct in asserting that basic science cannot be planned in order to maximize its social and economic return. The most compelling example of "useless" research which proved to be of great technical significance is atomic energy, which was judged by Ernest Rutherford, the discoverer of the neutron, to be of no practical consequence whatsoever. Similarly, vast sums have been invested in scientific fields believed to be of imminent technical significance that proved to be dead ends. The U.S. crash program in the early 1950s to harness the fusion energy of hydrogen is an example. In the area of science planning, as distinct from economic planning, the fact that the essence of science is the discovery of novelty makes it exceedingly difficult to specify goals and the means to achieve them.

Aware of the above and skeptical France can compete on a broad front with the U.S., Raymond Aron has suggested that she follow Japan's example. He has condemned the current French tendency to "sprinkle" its scarce research funds over many areas trying to duplicate American science. Instead, he and others argue, France should concentrate in the several areas where the French can hope to establish a place in the world market.[46]

The difficulty in following Aron's course of action, from the viewpoint of French leadership is that it runs counter to its political objectives of reducing French dependence on the United States in advanced technologies and of establishing French hegemony in western Europe. Acceptance of Aron's position would undoubtedly entail French withdrawal from some high prestige areas of research and development and some related most directly to national power: supersonic aircraft, computers, atomic energy, and many others. France, it is believed, would have to remain dependent on the U.S. for these technologies at the risk of sacrificing her independent military capability and foreign policy. Such a strategy, based primarily on economic criteria, would insure the continued hegemony of the United States in western Europe. Parenthetically, a Gaullist might add, Japan's science policy will become more like France's as Japan becomes increasingly concerned over its total dependence on the United States for military security and seeks to play a more forceful role in world affairs.

The dilemma facing France in formulating her science policy has been expressed by Louis Villecourt: "Any major orientation not conforming to the directions taken by the Soviet Union or the United States would lead to specialization and the giving up to these nations a quasi-monopoly of advanced research. Furthermore, a large part of the research budget is determined in advance by the options established on the other side of the Atlantic or the Iron Curtain."[47] Yet few funds are left over for independent lines of research with

[46] Raymond Aron, in *Le Figaro*, Nov. 21-22, 1964.
[47] "Politique Scientifique et Dimensions Nationales," *Nouvelle Frontière*, No. 8, Oct.-Nov. 1964, p. 29.

which to advance France to the front rank in those areas of science and technology neglected by the United States and other major scientific societies.[48]

Faced with the choice between (1) carving out a niche for themselves through specialization at the risk of dependence on other nations for vital technologies, or (2) competing against the scientific states with all the risks entailed in being forever the follower—the French have chosen the latter. These risks, as the British experience reveals, include a brain drain of researchers to the centers of advanced research in the United States, a declining competitive position, and a deficit balance of technological payments for the technologies needed to follow in the steps of the large scientific states.[49] Nevertheless, the French are confident that they can succeed in this endeavor. This confidence is based on their conviction that French ingenuity, assisted by national planning, can overcome American superiority in manpower, money, and organization.[50]

France can never hope to surpass the Americans in the number of computers, reactors, or aircraft placed on the world market, but French officials believe that she can, through wise husbanding of limited resources, maintain a French presence in these important fields. Similarly, though France may not be able to match the great powers in scientific research, it is believed imperative that she maintain a national capability in those fields of great scientific and technological significance. In this way France could avoid compromising completely her economic and political independence to one or another of the scientific giants. At the most she may regain her former scientific and technological preeminence.

In this effort the French suffer one overwhelming disad-

[48] *Ibid.*

[49] This is the conclusion of Villecourt in *ibid.*, p. 30.

[50] It is interesting to note that French works on scientific discovery tend to emphasize individual creativity and intuition, whereas American works stress external social forces and organization.

vantage vis-à-vis the more wealthy U.S. The United States can afford to pursue a broad and adventuresome program of basic and applied research. Cost enters into the picture, but the hard choices come primarily at the advanced stages of the development process, when risks, costs, and opportunities can be most easily calculated. The French, on the other hand, with their much smaller scientific and engineering establishment, cannot cast their net wide; priorities must be established at a much earlier stage—that of fundamental research where the uncertainties are greatest.

The increase in general knowledge of the economics of research and the improvement of French statistics on research and development should remedy this situation somewhat. It is extremely doubtful, however, that France or any other nation can develop completely satisfactory techniques by which to allocate resources for science in an optimum manner.[51] The very essence of science is the emergence of novelty. If one knew the results of research, there would be no need to do the research in the first place. Moreover, there is an inherent danger in tying research too closely to social utility. A science keyed to immediate social needs will lead to marginal improvements in technology, but it won't produce the revolutions which effect immense transformations in man's technical capabilities. One cannot escape the paradox that the most useful science in the long run is that scientific research which has no useful end as its intended goal.

In the absence of any accepted rational technique by which to determine scientific priorities, the French science plan is, in the final analysis, the outcome of a number of conflicting political pressures and aspirations. First, the plan reflects the struggles and compromises among the numerous ministries

---

[51] This subject is treated by Richard Nelson, Merton J. Peck, and Edward Kalachek, *Technology, Economic Growth, and Public Policy*, The Brookings Institution, 1967.

and economic sectors engaged in its preparation; its content is as much a result of the persuasiveness of various scientists and ministerial spokesmen as it is a reasoned statement of France's scientific and technical needs. Second, the plan emphasizes those fields of research, such as space, electronics, and atomic energy, which are in rapid advance abroad and which are regarded by the present French Government as having great prestige, military utility, and economic value. Warranted or not, the French belief is that they must establish themselves in these costly and advanced fields if France is not to be a backward nation in a world increasingly dominated by the scientific powers.

The science plan, however, is but one aspect of the French effort to establish themselves in these "strategic" scientific-technical areas. As important as the area of civilian research covered by the plan may be, it is overshadowed in scale and importance by the French emphasis on atomic energy, space research, and the modernization of military technology. These programs account for over 70 percent of the total French expenditure for scientific research and development (37 percent for military modernization; 37 percent for space and atomic energy).[52] For this reason, no account of science and state in contemporary France can neglect an analysis of these crucially important subjects.

[52] *Le Monde*, June 24, 1965.

Chapter 9 · Defense, Space, and Atomic Power

Today the scientific research of a modern country contributes in the highest degree to its defense: to its defense on the economic plane in permitting it to fight against a technical and economic invasion, but equally to its defense on the military plane. In all times the weapons utilized have incorporated the results of research. But the rapid evolution of science and technology has reinforced and made more direct than in the past this relationship between armament and defense, on the one hand, and the results of research, on the other hand. The actual rapidity of scientific and technical progress means that henceforth armies can no longer content themselves with utilizing the results of research itself and buying or ordering the materials; they must promote research themselves by participating directly or indirectly in advanced work in the domains which most interest them: the choice of the major options of armament and strategy must take into account all factors in order to avoid being brutally outmoded: it is not continuous, slow, and foreseen evolution which poses a problem but the appearance of true discontinuities issuing from scientific discoveries which put into question from time to time the truths, the best accomplishments; atomic energy or the laser are good examples of this. Armies not only must do or have done for them technical research which is directly related to their immediate needs, but they also must maintain themselves abreast, in the most disinterested fashion, of fundamental research in a certain number of sectors, even when this research has no visible direct lines with the armament programs.

—Le Progrès Scientifique, *March 1966*

The commitment embodied in the military law-program (1960-64) to modernize the French armed forces and create a nuclear striking force, or *force de frappe,* had profound implications for the welfare of French science and its relationship to the state. The development of complex command and control mechanisms, sophisticated weapons systems, and advanced auxiliary technologies has posed major challenges for numerous areas of French science and technology. Consequently the French military after considerable neglect has begun to take an interest in scientific research and its place in weapons innovation. Conversely French scientists have become involved in defense-related research and now occupy important advisory and administrative positions in the Ministry of Defense and other agencies concerned with problems of national security.

The purpose of this chapter is to assess the impact of the defense program on French science and technology; I offer no judgment of the wisdom of the French decision to create a nuclear striking force. Whether this military program and its technical components are militarily, politically, and economically sound is not at issue here; these questions have been discussed extensively elsewhere.[1] What is of interest here is the role of this defense-related effort in the modernization of French science and technology and in the transformation of the relationship between science and state in France.

For several reasons an examination of the interaction between science and defense in France is difficult. There is the problem of secrecy. It is difficult to obtain the reliable information necessary before making definite assertions about the precise ways in which defense monies and actions are impinging on French research and development. One does not even have

[1] Edgar Furniss, Jr., *De Gaulle and the French Army,* The Twentieth Century Fund, 1964, Chaps. 7-9; Raymond Aron, *The Great Debate,* trans. Ernst Pawel, Doubleday, 1965.

solid information on the amounts devoted to specific subjects or the exact groups to whom the funds have been dispensed.[2] Though interviews are revealing, knowledgeable Frenchmen are reluctant to speak openly. For example, a recent nonofficial survey of French scientists on the impact of defense funds on French science was conducted only after the surveying organization agreed not to make its findings public. One has to rely, therefore, more than he would like, on inference and the comparable experience of other countries, especially the United States and Great Britain.

Another problem is the difficult one of separating civil from military science and technology, and of distinguishing between institutions which support one or the other. While this problem exists anywhere today it is especially acute in France, where "defense" is defined in the broadest possible terms. For example, as the history of the French atomic energy program in the postwar period reveals, the line between civilian- and military-related research and development can be a thin one. The CEA, especially through its Division of Military Applications, which is responsible to the Ministry of Defense for the development and production of atomic warheads, is as much a military as a civil organization. The same ambiguity is found with respect to the civilian space agency, the *National Center of Space Studies* (CNES). For though it is by no means primarily a defense institution, and although it serves important scientific and economic goals, its ultimate justification at the present level of funding is national security and international prestige. It is appropriate, therefore, to include a discussion of these two agencies in this chapter, along with the research and development programs of the Ministry of Defense.

[2] One unclassified summary is contained in "Recherche et Développement au Sein du Ministère des Armées Pendant le Ve Plan," *Le Progrès Scientifique*, No. 94, Mar. 1966, p. 22.

Science and Defense

THE WORLDWIDE REVOLUTION IN SCIENTIFIC-MILITARY RELATIONS

Prior to World War II military technologies in all countries were generally adaptations of civilian technology. The automobile, provided with armor plating and guns, became the tank; the airplane, fitted with machine guns and bombs, became a potent weapon; the machine gun itself was a faster firing hunting rifle. Though the military services might at times give support and encouragement to such innovations, the function of military research and development was conceived as merely the improvement of existing technologies, so as to meet recognized military requirements—more speed or durability, for example.

This "requirements approach" to research and development was hostile to the innovation of radical technologies. Both the mentality of military leadership and the scarcity of resources made research and development subordinate to the immediate, foreseeable needs of production and the improvement of existing technologies. The military lacked an appreciation of what unfettered research and development could do, at the same time they had the responsibility of insuring that the weapons at hand were brought to their highest peak of efficiency. It was these circumstances as much as anything else that made the military officer of the past conservative toward scientific research and technological development.

In the Second World War the traditional relationship between science and military technology was radically altered. Belligerents for the first time employed scientists on a massive scale to develop novel technologies. In the United States, scientists and engineers were placed at the head of research organizations and given the responsibility of innovating new technologies by exploiting fundamental science. As was mentioned in Chapter 5, in most cases the scientists remained within the university or industry-administered laboratories, and thus a new institutional relationship was established between government and private research.

The shift from an "engineering" to a "scientific" way of thinking regarding the place of research in weapons development brought about revolutionary technologies that transformed the war at both tactical and strategic levels. Of equal importance, this wartime science-military alliance led to a partial yet significant reversal of the relationship between civilian and military technology.

In the postwar period the science-military liaison was retained in the United States, Soviet Union, and Great Britain. At first it existed at a greatly reduced level; then, under the stimulus of the arms race, the collaboration was extended much further than during the war. Of even greater significance, the character of the relationship changed. The wartime task of scientists was essentially that of applying existing theory to the innovation of new technologies. Scientists had not really carried out basic research, in its truest sense, in promising but undeveloped areas of military importance. Instead, they had functioned as engineers and applied researchers in exploiting the basic knowledge already available, even though in many cases it had been discovered just prior to the war. Now after 1945 there was recognition of the utility of basic knowledge.

Under the pressure of the cold war and the qualitative arms race between the Soviet Union and the United States, the military could no longer depend on the normal rate of scientific advance. Just as military demands for new technology outdistanced the pace of civilian innovation during the war, now in the late 1940s the military appetite for the scientific knowledge underlying modern technology was far greater than the "normal" production of civilian science. Consequently the military establishment in the U.S. and many other nations changed

257

its mind about the value of basic research and became the foremost patron of the nation's scientific and technological effort.

This development inevitably has led to the appointment of scientists to important administrative and advisory positions within the military establishment and related institutions. The scientists' task has been not only that of helping to manage the multibillion-dollar research and development program of the military but also advising the government on the implications of scientific-technological advance for military strategy and policy. The result in the U.S. has been a union of universities, industries, and the military in an intricate mechanism for the advancement and exploitation of scientific research. A similar development is presently unfolding in France.

THE TRADITIONAL RELATIONSHIP OF SCIENCE AND
DEFENSE IN FRANCE

Until the late 1950s the cleavage between science and defense in France was almost total. Though highly skilled engineers were produced for the armed services by the *grandes écoles*, they—like engineers everywhere—were trained in current engineering practices rather than basic sciences. They were especially weak in the modern fields of electronics, nuclear energy, and space technology. Though competent and resourceful, French military engineers tended to have a traditional "engineering" mentality toward innovation, and not a modern, "scientific" one. Therefore they have not been energetic in the application of modern scientific theory to technological innovation.

At the same time, a great cleavage has long existed between the academic world and the military establishment in France. This "alienation" has its source in the deeper *Armée-Nation* division and the political differences between university and military over decolonization and communism.[3] Occasionally

[3] Furniss, *De Gaulle*, Chap. 1.

the two have joined forces. During national emergencies the French military, in its search for anything that might win the war, has turned to scientists for help and scientists have searched for ideas that might have military value. This was so in the dark period in World War I, when Paul Langevin tried to develop a method for submarine detection and came up with a prototype sonar.[4] This war-born alliance, however, ceased with the end of hostilities. Twenty years later, in the somber days of December 1939, the story is told that the French Commander-in-Chief, General Gamelin, sought to reestablish this relationship and addressed the following question to the CNRS: "Is there to your knowledge, an original discovery or invention, realized by ourselves or our adversaries, which, immediately or in the near future, could change radically the conditions of war?"[5] The CNRS replied that "it does not appear probable that a completely original discovery has been realized which could change radically the conditions of war in the near future."[6]

The CNRS made a few minor contributions to French military technology in the short time before France's collapse. The French, for example, developed radar independently of the U.S. and Great Britain. Interestingly, the Minister of Supply, Raoul Dautry (the future first Administrator General of the CEA), engaged Joliot-Curie and his codiscoverers of the concept of the chain reaction to help adapt atomic energy to military purposes.[7] The fall of France, of course, brought this work to a close, forestalling the evolution of the close contact be-

[4] Frédéric Joliot-Curie, "Le Professeur Langevin et L'Effort Scientifique," *La Pensée*, Oct.-Dec. 1944, p. 32.

[5] Henri Laugier, *Service de France au Canada*, Éditions Bernard Valiquette, 1941, p. 57.

[6] *Ibid.*

[7] Lawrence Scheinman, *Atomic Energy Policy in France under the Fourth Republic*, Princeton University Press, 1965, pp. 3-4; Bertrand Goldschmidt, *The Atomic Adventure*, trans. Peter Beer, Pergamon Press, 1964, pp. 13-15.

tween academic science and the military establishment which developed during the war in the U.S., Great Britain, and the U.S.S.R.

After the war French scientists had little to do with the military. A great number of the leading scientists, especially in atomic energy, were opposed to policies regarding such matters as the Soviet Union, rearmament, and the French colonies. The French military had not been forced by the war, or by the postwar arms race, to undertake extensive research and development activities. It had in fact been much too preoccupied with colonial wars to adapt itself to the scientific age. Influential officers discouraged interest in advanced weapons lest it detract from the immediate needs of the nation. Furthermore, the unstated policy of successive French Governments was that the French military should rely on American weaponry rather than spend the vast sums required for French-designed arms.[8] As a result, aside from a few notable exceptions such as aircraft, the French under the Fourth Republic were little involved in military research and development, particularly in highly advanced technologies. French military institutions reflected the disinterest.

By a decree of May 24, 1948 the French Government established the Committee for Scientific Action for National Defense (CASDN).[9] Placed under the authority of the National Defense Council and composed of scientific leaders such as the secretary of the Academy of Sciences, the High Commissioner of CEA, the Director of CNRS, and *faculté* deans, the committee was given the responsibility for advising the military on its R and D program.[10] However, this attempt to unite science and defense was of little consequence. The CASDN was not given

[8] Furniss, *De Gaulle,* p. 18.

[9] Général Guerin, "Politique Scientifique et Défense Nationale," in *La Défense Nationale,* Presses Universitaires de France, 1958, p. 423.

[10] For a complete listing see Général Guerin, "Les Officiers Polytechniciens Dans les Organismes Scientifiques et Techniques de la Défense Nationale," in *L'École Polytechnique en 1960,* p. 82.

the funds necessary to support an effective research program and was placed outside the military administrative hierarchy; the result was that it had no financial means and little administrative authority with which to influence military R and D.

The military R and D effort itself was fragmented among the technical agencies of the three armed forces, and was under the direction of military engineers. The Minister of Defense had little authority to coordinate these programs and increase their effectiveness, though some steps were taken in this direction under the Fourth Republic. A decree on March 10, 1956, for example, established the Technical Committee of the Armed Services Programs, but like all previous interservice committees it could not provide the leadership and direction essential to an ambitious and truly innovative research and development effort.

The decision to create a nuclear striking force and modernize the armed services made the traditional organization of military R and D obsolete by 1960. Centralization of decision-making for R and D became necessary in order to meet several pressing needs: coordination of work of the three armed services on the atom, missiles, and electronics; programing of modern technology for years in advance; and the establishment of priorities among numerous competing projects because of the cost of modern research and development.[11] Of equal importance, industrial, government, and academic research had to be integrated with that of the military services into an immense and united effort leading to weapons development.

REORGANIZATION OF MILITARY R AND D UNDER
THE FIFTH REPUBLIC

The centralization of executive authority over the armed forces evident in the United States and Great Britain is due primarily to the nature of modern warfare and weapons tech-

---

[11] Général Lavaud, "La Délégation Ministérielle pour l'Armement," *Revue Militaire Générale*, Dec. 1961, p. 617, Jan. 1962, pp. 103-14.

nology.[12] In France this universal concern over the need for effective command and control of fast-acting, highly destructive weapons, was reinforced by the experience of the army officers' revolt against de Gaulle's Algerian policy and the recognition of the need to transform a colonial army into one oriented to the modern world.[13] The result of these pressures may be found in the major reforms of 1959, 1961, and 1962, which greatly strengthened the powers of the Prime Minister and the Minister of Defense over the three competing armed services. Also, a General Secretariat for National Defense was created to coordinate defense policy, and the Committee for Scientific Action for Defense (CASD) lost the "national" from its name and was strengthened to advise the Prime Minister on "defense problems in the field of scientific and technical research."[14] The chairman of CASD was made the scientific adviser to the Chief of the General Staff, and was also "associated, as representing the National Defence, with the formulation of national research policy, and in this capacity maintains contact with the Delegate-General for Research, whose services and means are at his disposal."[15] Though primarily an advisory and coordinating body, CASD does have limited funds to initiate R and D projects.

Most important of all, from the viewpoint of this study, several new agencies were established at this time which were assigned various responsibilities, including the integration of science and defense: (1) the Ministerial Delegation for Armaments (DMA); (2) the Directorate of Research and Test-

[12] Charles Hitch, *Decision-Making for Defense*, University of California Press, 1965, p. 77.

[13] Raoul Girardet, ed., *La Crise Militaire Française, 1945-1962*, Cahiers de la Fondation Nationale des Sciences Politiques, 1964.

[14] OECD, *Reviews of National Science Policy—France*, 1966, p. 25; F. Ridley and J. Blondel, *Public Administration in France*, Routledge and Kegan Paul, 1964, pp. 80-81; Furniss, *De Gaulle*, Ch. 7.

[15] OECD, *Reviews of National Science Policy—France*, p. 25.

ing (DRME) within the DMA; and (3) the Consultative Committee on Forecasting, and the Center for Forecasting and Evaluation (*Centre de Prospective et d'Évaluation*) (attached to the Minister of Defense).[16] In addition, the Minister of Defense began to take the necessary steps to change the weapons R and D practices of the services themselves.[17]

In short, France began on a much smaller scale its own McNamara revolution. Administrative and military authority were centered in the Minister of Defense. The military research and development program was reorganized and brought directly under the Minister's control. Finally, the Minister was given the assistance of scientists and other civilian experts to carry out his responsibilities.

THE MINISTERIAL DELEGATION FOR ARMAMENTS[18]

The DMA, established originally in 1961 and subsequently reorganized, is directly responsible to the Minister of Defense for the management and coordination of the over-all armaments program.[19] Headed by the Minister Delegate for Armaments, the agency was placed at the same governmental level as the chiefs of the military services (*états-majors*). Under its jurisdiction there are several administrative bureaus, six technical agencies including the DRME, and one technical service. In addition, the DMA, on behalf of the Minister of Defense, main-

[16] "Recherche et Développement," p. 12.

[17] For a discussion of other important reforms see Albert Boyer, "Aspects Scientifiques et Économiques de la Construction d'une Armement Nucléaire par la France," *Revue de Défense Nationale*, Oct. 1963, pp. 1,535-56.

[18] The following discussion is based on a number of interviews with French officials and scientists. Two documents were especially helpful: "Recherche et Développement," and Ministère des Armées, *L'Orientation Nouvelle de la Recherche de Défense*, Feb. 1963.

[19] Several important categories of research were left outside DMA. Biological and medical research of military interest remained the responsibility of the Service de Santé des Armées, as did the oceanographic research of the Service Hydrographique de la Marine.

tains close liaison with the Division of Military Applications of the CEA, the agency responsible for the fabrication of nuclear warheads for the *force de frappe*.[20]

The reform of the French military R and D effort, however, is not restricted to official governmental institutions. In France, as was largely true in the U.S. prior to 1940, all military research and development have been conducted in government arsenals or laboratories, though *production* contracts have frequently been given to private industry. The weakness in this approach is that the military cannot take full advantage of the skills and resources of private enterprise; nor can military research and development benefit the private economy (the spinoff or spillover effect). To remedy the situation, through research and development contracts, France, like the U.S., is rapidly creating a scientific-industrial complex closely allied with her military establishment. For this reason, several of the more important components of the defense-related industrial establishment should be mentioned. Of the private and quasi-public industrial firms that are intimately associated with military and technological modernization the most important is the Company for the Study and Manufacture of Ballistic Missiles (SEREB), which was created in 1959 to construct missile-launching vehicles for the *force de frappe*, and particularly since 1962, intermediate range land-based and polaris-type missiles. In addition, there are numerous aerospace firms such as Sud Aviation, SEPR, and SNECMA which do research and development work for the military. Increasingly, French military research, development, and production will be carried out in private firms under contract rather than through the traditional arsenal system.

The *Directorate of Research and Testing*. Directly responsible to the Armaments Minister, the DRME is the most important new agency involved in the modernization of the French

[20] "Recherche et Développement," p. 14.

armed forces and the integration of scientific research and weapons development.[21] In contrast to the other military R and D institutions which actually conduct research and tend to focus their activity on immediate and short-range military requirements, the DRME is an advisory, coordinating, and activating agency. It does little R and D in its own laboratories. Instead, it has the responsibility of promoting in other agencies advanced scientific technologies "susceptible of orienting over the long term the armament policy of the nation."[22]

The DRME grew out of the need to remove research from a subordinate position to problems of production and the short-term military requirements of the services.[23] As was pointed out above, the traditional research agencies of the military services have been dominated by engineers with little experience in modern scientific research and little knowledge of how to work with the basic researchers in the *grands établissements* and the universities.[24] To overcome the gap between fundamental science and military technology, the DRME was placed under the leadership of distinguished academic scientists. From 1961 to 1965 the Scientific Director—and the man most responsible for effecting a rapprochement between science and defense in France—was Professor Pierre Aigrain of the *Faulté* of Science of Paris and the *École Normale Supérieure*.[25]

In an attempt to facilitate liaison between basic science and weapons development the Government took the unusual step of permitting the scientific leaders of DRME to retain their university chairs. Also, the Ministry of Finance gave permission

---

[21] "Organisation et Fonctionnement de la Délégation Ministérielle pour l'Armement," *Revue de Défense Nationale*, Oct. 1961, pp. 1,678-81.

[22] Ministère des Armées, *L'Orientation Nouvelle*," p. 3.

[23] Général Lavaud, "Promotion de la Recherche pour les Besoins de la Défense," Association de Cadre Dirigeants et Économique, Bulletin No. 175, Jan. 1963, p. 6.

[24] *Ibid.*, p. 7.

[25] "Recherche et Développement," p. 18; *Le Monde*, Jan. 23, 1965.

for DRME to hire university consultants to assist on a part-time basis while possessing full administrative responsibility for the elaboration and management of research programs. Contact with the "hardware" side of DRME's mandate was provided by the assistant director of technical research and his assistants, who were engineers and military officers well acquainted with military technology and requirements. So for the first time, university scientists, engineers, and military officers were brought together within one organization to advance scientific research for military purposes.

There are several interesting tasks of the DRME. In scientific research it functions in the area of defense science, much as the DGRST and its associated agencies do in nonmilitary science. It maintains an inventory of scientific resources and projects of interest to the armed services. Furthermore, the DRME advises the Minister Delegate for Armament on researches to be undertaken. On behalf of the Armaments Minister the DRME assists in the formulation and coordination of the research programs of the other technical agencies and has the responsibility of harmonizing these programs with the research activities of agencies external to the military, such as the DGRST, CNRS, CNET, and other institutions for civilian science.

The DRME has direct control over two important research institutions—the National Office of Aerospace Study and Research (ONERA) and the *Institut Franco-Allemand* (IFA) at Saint Louis. ONERA, founded in 1946 and first attached to the DTCA, came under the control of the DRME in 1961. It was originally devoted to research in classical aeronautics but in 1963 it began to engage heavily in space research. Its primary task is advanced research on long-term military projects, though it also works closely with CNES, the civilian space agency. The IFA was created in 1959 by France and Germany. Its specific responsibility is to provide a bridge between theoretical scientific research and armaments, with researches in the area of theoretical and experimental physics, aerodynamics, and bal-listics. Needless to say, the original hopes for the collaboration in weapons research and development have not yet materialized.

The DRME activity most relevant to this study is its role in academic and industrial research. Through the employment of the contract mechanism the *Directorate of Scientific Research* (DRS) and the *Under-Directorate of Technical Research* (SDRT) of the DRME are assuming an increasingly important respon-sibility for the orientation and direction of fundamental and technical research in France. By the selective awarding of re-search grants and contracts DRME is seeking to stimulate and give priority to those researches and developments believed to be of highest military utility. In effect, it is elaborating and executing a national policy toward scientific and technical research.

The working out of a research policy for DRME takes place within the framework provided by the Center for Forecasting and Evaluation. On the basis of the center's long-term fore-casts of France's strategic and technological needs the DRS se-lects a number of research areas which, in the combined judg-ment of scientists, engineers, and military officers, promise long-term military utility. On the basis of the research areas, or themes, the scientific divisions organized by disciplines se-lect specific scientists and laboratories for research grants. As was mentioned above, an unusual feature of this system is that the chairman of each division is a university professor but who nevertheless assumes administrative responsibilities for the sci-entific program associated with his discipline. In this way sci-entists can keep abreast of the rapid development of their disci-plines and at the same time have a sense of responsibility for the success of the DRME's commitment to advance research of potential interest to defense.

The research themes of the DRME are fairly broadly defined.

And almost a third of the DRME's funds is not tied to the established themes but is free money to be distributed to interesting projects in scientific and technical research. In fundamental research, nearly half of DRME funds go to universities; the rest is allocated to industry and state institutions.

In technical research a similar elaboration of research projects in terms of the over-all research themes takes place. The programs of the Under-Directorate for Technical Research are intermediate researches between the fundamental research sponsored by the Directorate of Scientific Research and the actual prototype development work of the other Technical Directorates responsible to the Armaments Minister. The greater part of the research contracts awarded by the divisions of SDRT —e.g., those in telecommunications, propulsion, and fluid mechanics—go to industrial corporations. Some applied research, however, is carried out for DRME by the universities, thus involving universities in military research on a permanent basis for the first time.

Support provided by DRME to research it favors in universities and industries is not exhausted by its awarding of research contracts. Like the CNRS, the DRME has approximately 270 scientists it makes available to laboratories throughout France.[26]

DRME, through its Under-Directorate of Testing, is responsible to the Armaments Minister for the establishment of testing facilities and the evaluation of prototypes. Directly related to this responsibility, the DRME advises the Minister on the status and merits of technological developments. As a consequence, in France as in the United States, the great change in the role of scientists in the area of defense is due not just to the use of the end product of scientific research but to the realization that one has to know the state of scientific knowl-

[26] "Recherche et Développement," pp. 25-26.

edge to make policy decisions of all types. This is especially true with respect to the investment of vast resources in the development or purchase of particular weapons systems. It is essential to know whether a weapon to be programed is the best available or will soon be made obsolete. For this reason DRME, with its extensive contacts in the scientific world and its Center for Operation Research, is the principal advisor to the Armaments Minister and the Minister of Defense on technological developments.

Organizations for Forecasting and Evaluation. In national defense, as in the civilian sectors, the French have sought to establish methods and institutions for "forecasting" the implications of scientific, technological, and other important developments. Because of the scale and power of modern science and technology this concern over implications is shared by a number of policy planning and advisory agencies such as the CASD. In addition, more analytical and professional types of organizations such as the Inter-Service Center for Operations Research under the CASD and the Group for the Mathematical Study of Political and Strategic Problems in the *École Pratique des Hautes Études* also do research on questions related to the advance of science and technology.[27]

Undoubtedly the most significant organizations in this connection are the Center for Forecasting and Evaluation and the Consultative Committee on Forecasting. Originally these agencies, under slightly different names, were part of the DRME. But at that level they lacked the leverage to have much influence on defense policy. They were transferred to the Minister of Defense at the time of the preparation of the second military law-program in 1965. The purpose of this law-program was to set the course of French policy for the next five to 10 years; therefore it was believed necessary to begin reflection on

[27] Institute for Strategic Studies, London, *The Growth of Strategic Studies Outside the United States,* Adelphi Papers, Dec. 1963, p. 9.

the short- and long-range options of French military policy.[28]

The CCP is presided over by the scientific director of the DRME and is composed of representatives of the chiefs of the French armed services and the technical agencies of the Ministry of Defense in order to "study the reciprocal influence of the perspectives of scientific development and the concepts of military strategy and tactics."[29] In this manner communication is assured among scientists and technicians, on one hand, and the military services on the other.[30] The background for these discussions is proposed by the DRME and the CPE, which serve as permanent secretariat and catalogue developments in the scientific, technological, economic, and geopolitical realms. The center also evaluates weapons systems for the Minister of Defense; it employs such methods as systems analysis and cost-benefit analysis which have been used so extensively in the United States. Special "prospective," or study groups of scientists, engineers, and military officers are established to envisage all the military applications of a scientific concept such as superconductivity or to consider all the possible technical solutions to a military problem.[31] What is important, therefore, is not mere forecasting but the attempt to make "prospective" serve policy planning and execution.

In order to carry out this "prospective" function the CPE, under the guidance of the CCP, conducts its own program of research on such questions as the strategic implications of technological advance, evaluates alternative systems for performing various tasks, and advises the Minister of Defense on the long-

[28] This discussion is based principally on several interviews with French officials and on "Le Centre de Prospective et d'Évaluation du Ministère des Armées," *Bulletin d'Information du Ministère des Armées*, Feb. 1965. Reprinted in *Le Progrès Scientifique*, No. 94, Mar. 1966, pp. 32-35. See also *Le Figaro*, Jan. 5, 1964.

[29] "Recherche et Développement, p. 10.

[30] These relationships are discussed in detail, *ibid.*, pp. 32-36.

[31] *Ibid.*, p. 10.

term implications of proposed courses of action. It evaluates the forecasts of the individual armed services and provides them with an over-all framework within which to carry out these speculations.

The significance of CPE's work for this study is that it works closely with the DRME in the formation and evaluation of the annual research programs of DMA. The projections and analyses of the CPE provide an important framework for the annual research themes of the DRME. Reciprocally, the CPE prepares an annual report which synthesizes the long-range impact of DRME research on French military policy, and undertakes studies of the short-term impact of research and development programs on the other technical agencies of the DMA. Additionally, the CPE, in cooperation with the DRME, awards research contracts in areas of advanced science and technology, especially where radical discontinuities could disrupt military planning. The CPE constitutes another mechanism with which contemporary France can reorient her scientific research to serve the state both as an object and determinant of national policy.

The General Orientation of Military R and D

While the specific end products of the French defense R and D effort and the programed composition of their nuclear striking force are of little direct relevance for this study, an awareness of them provides a necessary background for a discussion of the general orientation of military research and development in France. For this reason the first part of this discussion is to be devoted to a consideration of the French six-year military law-program (1965-70).

The dominant and most interesting feature of the military program is the construction of the *force de frappe*, which will absorb $5.4 billion of the projected $11 billion to be spent on the military over the course of the next six years; the remaining $5.6 billion is to be spent on advanced types of conventional weapons systems (SEE TABLE 14).[32] Although the nuclear striking force makes the greatest demands on French science, the general modernization of conventional military forces also may have important implications for the future of French science and technology. But the most significant aspects of military modernization for our present purpose are those most vital to the creation of the *force*—aerospace, electronics, and atomic energy.

The nuclear striking force is to be composed of three basic components, to be phased in over the course of the six-year program. The first is composed of approximately 60 *Mirage IV* bombers, initial units of which became operational in November 1964. The second component of the force will be approximately 75 land-based ballistic missiles on "hardened" sites, to be operational by the late 1960s. Last, the French are planning a Polaris-launching, nuclear-powered submarine fleet. The first of these submarines—without its missile complement—is scheduled for the 1965-70 nuclear force; the missiles themselves (16 per submarine) are to be ready by 1970. Two or three additional nuclear submarines are expected to be allocated in the early 1970s.

To meet the objective of modernizing their military forces the French have undertaken an ambitious R and D program with which numerous university laboratories, industries, and civilian government agencies, as well as the technical military agencies, are associated.[33] But the significance of DMA's, and especially DRME's, expenditures during the Fifth Plan (TABLE 15) lies not so much in their total amount as in their concen-

[32] "French Continue Nuclear Delivery Buildup in 6-Year Plan," *Aviation Week and Space Technology*, LXXXII, No. 11, Mar. 15, 1965, 27.

[33] For a discussion of this research program see "Recherche et Développement," 26-30.

TABLE 14.

France's Six-Year Military Program, 1965-70[a]
(in millions of dollars)

General R & D	172
General studies	300
Production of nuclear material	1,341
Studies and production of nuclear armaments	1,093
Arms testing	688
Nuclear propulsion studies	55
Studies, production and deployment of strategic missiles	
common studies	152
ground-to-ground	203
sea-to-ground	252
Missile fuels	160
Missile test vehicles and infrastructure	198
Space military studies	106
Aircraft general studies	684
Mirage IV	586
Mirage III	226
Mirage III VTOL program	480
Supersonic trainer-fighter program	140
Transall program	220
Air Force special missiles, ground-to-ground and ground-to-air	150
Navy *Breguet* Atlantic ASW program	122
Navy ASW *Super-Frelon* program	43
Navy service and trainer aircraft	13
Army helicopters—*Alouette 3* and *SA-330*	213
Army DRONE missile program	19
Army ground vehicle equipment	1,787
Army tactical and anti-aircraft missiles	622
Navy fleet equipment	609
Navy nuclear submarine program	334
Total authorizations	10,984

[a] Adapted from *Aviation Week and Space Technology,* Mar. 15, 1965, p. 27.

tration in a number of important fields (TABLES 16 AND 17) and in the discretion enjoyed by officials in distributing them. In contrast to the CNRS, for example, where decision-making

TABLE 15.

*DMA Financial Projection for R and D During the
Fifth Plan, 1966-70*[a]

	Program authorization (millions of francs)	
	Research	Development
DRME	1,143[b]	912
Atomic energy	2,564	1,585
Rockets	200	2,100
Land weapons	202	1,018
Navy	250[c]	470
Air		3,810
Munitions	230[d]	397
TOTAL	4,589	10,292
R & D TOTAL	14,881	

[a] Adapted from "Recherche et Développement," p. 22.
[b] Of which 251 is basic research.
[c] Of which 40 is basic research.
[d] Of which 25 is basic research.

authority for science still remains highly decentralized and distributed among too many researchers committed to the status
quo, the officials of the DRME can give priority to various scientific and technical fields through awards of research grants and
contracts. In effect, decision-making for science, including basic
research, has become more highly centralized in the DRME than
anywhere else in French society. As a consequence, the DRME,
which during the Fifth Plan will allocate over 230 million
francs to basic research via contracts, can by itself and through
cooperation with the DGRST, play a major role in the reorienta-
tion of French science and technology.

The Space Program

The French space program is the third largest in the world.
Following the lead of the United States and the Soviet Union
the French are motivated not merely by disinterested scientific

TABLE 16.

Basic Research Supported by DRME, 1966-70[a]
(millions of francs)

Mathematics	12.3
Physics	
Solid State	28.5
Nuclear	22.8
Electronics	48.2
Thermodynamics and mechanics	11.2
Other	36.0
Chemistry	37.3
Earth sciences and oceanography	15.3
Biology	14.2
Education	10.0
Total	236.0

[a] Adapted from Délégation Générale à la Recherche Scientifique et Technique, *La Recherche Scientifique et Technique* (1966-1970), p. 237.

TABLE 17.

Technical Research Supported by DRME, 1966-70[a]
(millions of francs)

Mechanics of fluids	28.8
Fluid propulsion	40.4
Energy, motors	35.4
Measuring equipment	56.5
Telecommunications, geophysics	44.0
Materials, structures	39.4
Behavioral sciences	4.5
Prototype	61.0
Total	310.0

[a] Adapted from Délégation Générale à la Recherche Scientifique et Technique, *La Recherche Scientifique et Technique* (1966-1970), p. 238.

curiosity but by the desire for national prestige and the belief that there is an intimate connection between space research and technological advance in the modern world. In contrast to these nations, however, the French have foregone the development of an expensive man-in-space program, which is the most costly component of the American and Russian space programs. Furthermore, unlike the U.S. and U.S.S.R., the French space effort is not a completely autonomous program but is dependent on European programs such as the European Launcher Development Organization (ELDO) for some of its essential components (see Chapter 12).

The rationale for France to enter the expensive business of space research was supplied in March 1963 by then Minister of Science, Gaston Palewski:

> History clearly shows that the independence of nations and their ability to survive are intimately bound up with their scientific efforts and the intelligence with which these efforts are carried out. . . . There is scarcely any branch of science from which, either alone or in association with other countries, we can stand apart. Our resources are undoubtedly limited. Neither France nor Europe can at the moment bear the considerable financial effort that sending men into space represents for the United States and the USSR. Consequently we must forego this. But we must not use the modesty of our contribution as an excuse for dissociating ourselves from space research itself. That is why we are apportioning our resources between our national program and our contribution to the European organizations that have just been created. . . . France and Europe are convinced that they have something to say on space research. . . . They also feel that the technological progress necessitated by space exploration is fruitful and often has other applications in practical life on this planet. Under these circumstances it would have been a mistake to do nothing. This mistake has been avoided.[34]

[34] Ambassade de France, New York, *France Air and Space*, Sept. 1963, p. 21.

ORGANIZATION

Prior to 1957 France had undertaken little research related to space exploration. Though the Telecommunications Center (CNET) had been doing important work of a preliminary nature in electronics and the military had a program of ballistic missile studies, crucial areas of a space program such as rocket development had been largely neglected. In the time before the Soviet *Sputnik* and the French decision to create a nuclear striking force no need was envisioned for France to conduct expensive space research.

The first major change of attitude came in 1959 when the French government decided to give priority to space research in its first programs of concerted action. At the same time, in order to formulate space policy and coordinate the developing space activities outside the defense area, the Government created a special committee for space research attached to the office of the Prime Minister and administered by the General Delegation. Under the chairmanship of Pierre Auger, the Committee was made responsible for assessing France's position in space exploration and, in collaboration with the Ministry of Defense, for proposing a program of action to the Prime Minister. In addition the military research agencies, under the policy guidance of CASDN were reorganizing the military side of the developing French space effort.

The principal outcome of the Auger committee's work was the founding in March 1962 of the *National Center of Space Studies*, responsible to the Prime Minister through the Minister for Science for the civilian side of the total French space effort. The CNES was given the responsibility for developing scientific and technical aerospace research, to prepare and execute programs in its establishments or through research contracts, and to follow all questions of international cooperation in conjunction with the Ministry of Foreign Affairs.[35]

Several features of the French space program as it subsequently developed are noteworthy. In contrast to the American civilian space program conducted by the National Aeronautics and Space Administration (NASA), the CNES program is much more closely affiliated with the military space program. NASA has its own launchers, manpower, and facilities; CNES is dependent on the military. By a 1961 agreement between the Minister of Defense and the Minister for Science, all rocket research in France was made part of the military missile program under the direction of the DMA. The CNES rocket launcher, the Diamant, is actually a three-stage missile originally developed for the *force de frappe* by SEREB. Similarly, the military supplies the bulk of the engineering manpower and the launching facilities. In effect, therefore, the civilian space program of CNES is but the tip of an iceberg, nine-tenths of which lies hidden in the military programs administered by DMA and under the policy guidance of CASD.[36]

Another interesting aspect of both the civilian and the military French space program is the extensive involvement of universities and private industry. The French have quite consciously sought to duplicate the American experience of using the space program as a means to stimulate selected fields of scientific research and sectors of the economy such as electronics and propulsion.[37] SEREB, for example, is the prime contractor for building the Diamant launcher. Other French aerospace firms, such as Sud Aviation, Nord Aviation, and MATRA, have contributed to the research and development of France's satel-

[35] La Documentation Française, "La France et la Recherche Spatiale," No. 195, Mar. 1964, p. 7.

[36] Ray Battersby, "French Eyes on the Future," *Survival*, VII, No. 6, Sept. 1965, 222.

[37] Maurice Ponte, "Recherche Spatiale et Industrie," *L'Expansion Scientifique*, No. 4, Dec. 1959, pp. 17-18.

lites and launchers. Space competition, according to a prevalent French view, has replaced war as a stimulus to technological advance and French industry must be made to share in the rewards.[38]

In essence, CNES is a contracting and coordinating agency at the center of a complex network of universities, industry, French government agencies, and international space programs. Through the use of research contracts and joint programs it has sought to use its own funds as seed money to stimulate a much greater sphere of French science and technology. In the words of one official, one of the aims of the CNES is "to make the space industry the research and development shop of all French industries."[39]

Similarly, the CNES intends to make a major impact on French universities. Through research contracts to university professors and the awarding of fellowships to graduate students (about 40 a year in 1965), the CNES seeks to stimulate an interest in space-related sciences within the academic world. Most ambitious of all, CNES and the military space agencies hope to establish space research complexes around the Universities of Paris, Toulouse, and Aix-Marseille.

GENERAL ORIENTATION

The French civilian space program has shown a remarkable growth rate since it began in 1961. From an initial funding of eight million dollars in 1961 it had reached approximately 58 million in 1965.[40] In terms of manpower CNES itself grew from 75 technical personnel in 1963 to approximately 500 in 1966.[41]

---

[38] Battersby, "French Eyes," p. 219. Cf. *Le Monde Diplomatique,* Feb. 1966.

[39] Quoted in *International Science and Technology,* Sept. 1965, p. 75. For an evaluation of the space program on French industry see *Le Monde,* Dec. 20, 1966.

[40] *International Science and Technology,* p. 75.

[41] *Ibid.*

Some of the most important programs are:[42]

The Diamant Launcher. France's first satellite launcher, this is a three-stage rocket capable of orbiting a 175-pound payload. All three stages were first tested successfully on November 26, 1965. A more powerful version, *Diamant-B*, will considerably increase French space capabilities.[43]

Space Research Program. The heart of any space research program is its satellite research program. France's first satellite, the A-1, was launched on November 26, 1965. It was an experimental capsule of 88 pounds, carrying radio and radar transmitters. The primary mission was to test the *Diamant* launcher. A second satellite, the FR-1A, was launched on December 6, 1965; it was a research satellite launched into a polar orbit by an American rocket under a cooperative agreement with NASA. A third French satellite, D-1A or Diapason, was launched February 17, 1966, to test equipment including the *Diamant* launcher. Through 1969-70 the French have programed about two satellite launchings annually.

Ground Stations and Launch Sites. In order to launch and utilize their satellites, the French have constructed, or begun to construct, a number of launching sites and a network of ground stations. The two initial launching sites were Colomb-Bechar and Hammaguir in the Sahara. To replace them the French have constructed a $70-million launch site at Kourou, in French Guiana.[44] The site is scheduled to be fully operational in early 1969, and will be in a highly advantageous lo-

[42] This information is a composite from several sources: Ambassade de France, *France Air and Space; International Science and Technology*; La Documentation Française, "La France et la Recherche Spatiale"; Ambassade de New York, "The French Space Program," *French Affairs*, No. 191A, Apr. 1966; "La Programme Spatiale Française," *Le Monde*, Sept. 14-15, 1965.

[43] *Le Monde*, Apr. 7, 1967.

[44] For the financial breakdown of French space expenditures see *International Science and Technology*.

cation, as it will permit the French to place satellites in both polar and equatorial orbits. Initially, the Guiana Space Center will handle only the *Diamant* launcher. Later, new launching sites will be constructed for more powerful rockets, such as the advanced rocket being developed by the ELDO program.[45]

Communications Satellite Program. Though the French plan to use satellites for weather forecasting, navigation, and other commercial purposes, of greatest interest to them is satellite communications. They are determined, in particular, by one route or another, to prevent the United States from attaining a monopoly of global satellite communications. In part, the basis of the concern over American domination of world communications is commercial. More importantly, the French fear its political consequences, as "the transmission of radio and television programs is one of the most supple and diversified means to assure a presence and influence abroad."[46]

French plans for a communications satellite system have been plagued by a number of uncertainties: the rapid advance of satellite technology, the indefinite status of the European satellite program, and the uncertainty of having a suitable launcher to place satellites of differing capabilities into orbit. Originally France conceived of a simple, earth-circling satellite to relay telephone and telegraph communications between France and, especially, French-speaking Africa (Project SAFRAN, "Satellite Africa–France"). As more sophisticated satellite technology has become available from the U.S., and there are more powerful launchers through the European Launcher Development Organization and France's own strategic missile program, the French have raised their sights with Project SAROS TWO.[47] This program entails the development of a geostationary communications satellite which would carry radio

---

[45] The status of the ELDO program and its importance for France are discussed in Chap. 12.
[46] *Le Monde*, Jan. 29-30, 1967.
[47] *Ibid.*

and television programs as well as telephone and telegraph messages. At the least, it is believed, SAROS would serve to maintain French interests and influence in Africa, the Middle East, and the less developed countries. At the most, it could become the basis of an independent European satellite communications system. A step in this direction is the agreement between France and Germany to build by 1970 two experimental SAROS-type satellites.[48] Whether SAROS will ever materialize, however, is dependent on a number of political, financial, and technical considerations, which will be treated in Chapter 12.

International Space Cooperation. In addition to this national space program France cooperates actively with other nations on a bilateral and multilateral basis. She has bilateral arrangements with both the Soviet Union and the United States, and is a member of the various European space organizations and principal global space organizations. (See Chapter 12.)

The Atomic Energy Program

As in space research, contemporary France has undertaken a major effort to exploit the advanced scientific technology of atomic energy for commercial and military purposes. The French atomic energy program is the largest in western Europe and in certain respects rivals that of the British. This program lies at the core of French military modernization. In a country deficient in sources of energy and concerned over economic independence, it is basic to her long-term economic development. For the French, being "nuclear" is being modern, and modernization is a theme which runs through all phases of French life today.

ORIGINS

The French nuclear program was not the result of a systematic and rational calculation but it evolved step by step in a

[48] *Le Monde,* Apr. 30-May 2, 1967.

logical progression from scientific to industrial to military stages long before de Gaulle returned to power. As Scheinman concludes, "the apparent political advantages which accrue to a nuclear nation [and] the general inclination toward a *grandeur* which characterized most leaders of the Fourth Republic" led the French to push atomic energy development toward the obvious culmination. The hallmark of de Gaulle's nuclear policy has been its continuity with the policies of his predecessors.[49]

In retrospect, a remarkable aspect of the French nuclear program, both nascent and developing, is the relative absence of controversy surrounding it, compared, say, to policies regarding the Indochinese War, the Algerian War, and the proposal for the European Defense Community. Though natural scientists, politicians of the far Left, and independent critics have criticized the immorality or folly of French nuclear policy, that policy has never become a major issue of party controversy and there has been only limited public debate on its wisdom—at least compared to controversies over other major policy questions and the agitation nuclear weapons policy has engendered in the United States and Great Britain.

The French entered the military phase of their nuclear program via many small incremental steps, none of which in itself triggered a mass protest: (1) the decision of November 1951 to construct two high-power-plutonium-producing reactors; (2) the creation in late 1954 of a nuclear weapons planning unit, the *Bureau d'Études Générales* (BEG) in the CEA; (3) the incorporation in the CEA's Second Five-Year Plan of a decision taken in July 1957 to build an enriched uranium plant (the Pierrelatte plant) which would benefit electricity production, nuclear propulsion, and military weaponry.

Another factor is that by the time the formal decision to build an atomic bomb was made by Prime Minister Félix Gail-

---

[49] Scheinman, *Atomic Energy Policy*, p. 216.

lard in April 1958, France had expended most of her protest energy on the Algerian war. Frenchmen subsequently have been too tired to protest nuclear weapons and have preferred the calm and relief brought about by peace and relative prosperity. The scant attendance at anti-bomb rallies attests to the absence of a profound concern over the *force de frappe*.

A far more speculative reason for the absence of vociferous dissent with respect to the French nuclear weapons program is the tacit assumption made by many groups in France that a nuclear weapons capability is not merely a prerequisite for political independence but an essential attribute of modern nationhood—indeed, that advanced nuclear and space technologies are necessary for any people that wishes to maintain and express its unique national genius and retain a position of influence in the world. Certainly this was the conclusion drawn by many influential Frenchmen in the wake of their impotency before Soviet nuclear threats and their abandonment by the United States at the time of the Suez crisis in 1956. Scheinman has even gone so far as to suggest that it is "probable that if the Gaillard Government had presented to the National Assembly the question of whether France should make an atomic bomb it would have received a favorable response."[50] Whatever the soundness of this observation, the course has been set and it will be difficult for subsequent governments to alter it substantially.

ORGANIZATION

As was pointed out in Chapter 6, the organization of the French Atomic Energy Commission is unusual in three ways: a high degree of administrative and financial autonomy; a bicephalic administrative structure; and a broad range of responsibility reaching from basic research to the commercial and military development of atomic power. The scientific research infrastructure of the CEA is composed of four major, nonmili-

[50] *Ibid.*, p. 191.

284

tary nuclear research centers in addition to other research establishments responsible to CEA's Directorate of Military Applications. Two of these centers are near Paris, at Saclay and Fontenay-aux-Roses; the other two are in southeast France, at Grenoble and Cadarache. In total, as of 1960, the facilities of these establishments included 18 nuclear reactors and critical assemblies, 20 accelerators including a synchrotron, and numerous laboratories. In addition, the French have created a vast industrial empire around atomic energy which encompasses uranium mines, refineries, and production. Among these facilities the most important are the Marcoule Plutonium Complex on the lower Rhône, the Mazingarbe heavy water plant begun in 1964, and the Pierrelatte plant for the production of enriched uranium by the gaseous diffusion method.

Almost all of these research and industrial centers conduct scientific and technical research. While the greater part of the research is in nuclear physics and engineering the growth of atomic energy has provided opportunities for the development of other fields—fundamental biology, the medical sciences, electronics. What is interesting here, however, is the technological exploitation of this research effort, particularly in two areas: the development of nuclear power; and the nuclear weapons program.

THE NUCLEAR POWER PROGRAM

Though the beginning of the French nuclear power industry may indeed be dated from the decision to construct two natural-uranium, graphite-moderated, compressed-air-type reactors for producing plutonium at Marcoule, emphasis on the exploitation of atomic energy for electricity began only in 1957 with the Second Five-Year Plan for atomic energy. At this time the decision was made to equip France with the necessary infrastructure for the commercial exploitation of atomic energy, including the construction of Pierrelatte. To carry out this program Électricité de France (EDF), a nationalized industry, took over the construction and operation of nuclear power stations, while the CEA retained its responsibility for research, development, and design. In contrast, therefore, to the United States, where the commercial exploitation of atomic power has resulted from an alliance between private industry and the AEC, France's atomic industry is controlled almost entirely by two public concerns.

By 1962 the first nuclear power plants to contribute substantial amounts of electricity to the national grid operated at Marcoule.[51] Around these plants a large industrial complex soon developed. Subsequently, other nuclear power centers were constructed; more are under construction. Of these the most impressive are those at Chinon in the Loire valley, which were constructed by Électricité de France. Its three reactors EDF1, EDF2, and EDF3 are expected to have a total power of 5,000 megawatts by 1975, at which time it is expected that nuclear kilowatts will have become economically competitive in France. Other nuclear power centers are at Saint-Laurent des Eaux on the Loire River, Saint-Vulbas in Ain department, and Brennilis in Brittany.

The distinguishing feature of the French nuclear power program is its emphasis on natural uranium reactors, whereas the United States has based its nuclear power industry on enriched-uranium reactors. Such a course was dictated by France's decision to go into power production at such an early stage in its atomic program, its unwillingness to be dependent on American supplies of enriched-uranium, and its own inability to produce enriched-uranium.[52] (France could not produce enriched-uranium because it lacked necessary financial resources and technical information which the U.S. would not make available.)[53]

[51] Goldschmidt, *Atomic Adventure*, p. 98.
[52] *Ibid.*, pp. 160-62.   [53] Scheinman, *Atomic Energy Policy*, pp. 65-67.

This French policy of *l'indépendance énergétique* vis-à-vis nuclear power has been summarized by Nicolas Vichney:[54]

> This quite legitimate ambition depends for today and tomorrow on a "family" of reactors studied by the CEA (the graphite-gas moderated, natural uranium fueled); for the immediate future on the reactors where graphite is replaced by heavy water; for the long-distance future on the breeder reactors, those installations which can produce more fuel than they consume. At the same time that they produce electricity, the graphite-gas and the heavy water reactors produce the plutonium indispensable for fueling the breeders, which will give to us in their turn more plutonium, in order to produce more breeders.
>
> Thus, in following this process—which has already been called the "plutonium way"—France can develop atomic energy without having to construct a very costly plant for producing enriched uranium necessary for a civil program, nor must France obtain enriched uranium from the United States and become dependent upon another country. Encouragingly Great Britain follows the same course.[55]

THE NUCLEAR WEAPONS PROGRAM

The French nuclear weapons effort is part of the modernization program of the armed forces legislated in the law-program of 1960 and expanded by the law-program of 1965. Included in these programs were the funds necessary for the construction of an isotopic separation plant at Pierrelatte to produce fissionable uranium-235.[56] By 1964 the CEA budget amounted to five percent of the state's total expenditure and three-fourths

---

[54] *Le Monde*, May 10, 1966.

[55] Actually Great Britain has started to shift from reliance on natural- to enriched-uranium fueled reactors.

[56] Goldschmidt, *Atomic Adventure*, p. 123. Total cost of Pierrelatte is estimated by Goldschmidt at $800 million (p. 155).

of this was devoted to the military program.[57] In addition it should be noted that 60 percent of CEA's budget comes from the Ministry of Defense.

The first French atomic explosion based on plutonium and produced by the Marcoule reactors took place on February 13, 1960 at the Saharan Military Experiment Center. The perfected plutonium weapons were tested in May 1962 and delivered to the French Air Force in 1963.[58] R and D have also continued on the production of hydrogen weapons based on the U-235 produced at Pierrelatte. It is anticipated that hydrogen weapons will be ready in 1968-69.

At the same time that the CEA has been engaged in the development of nuclear warheads the DMA, through its technical directorates, has been conducting related R and D activities. The Military Atomic Studies and Research Center (CERAM), for example, carries out studies on nuclear radiation detection and protection. Of greatest significance is the development at the Cadarache Nuclear Research Center of the nuclear propulsion system for the future Polaris-type launching submarines which are to be the third phase of the French nuclear deterrent force. The propulsion system is an enriched U-235 reactor whose fuel element was supplied by the U.S. on condition that it be used only for land-based experiments.[59] The enriched uranium for the operation of this propulsion system will be supplied eventually from Pierrelatte.[60]

The Impact of Military Modernization and the Space Program

The impact on French science and technology of the efforts to modernize the armed forces and become a space power

[57] *Ibid.*, p. 155.

[58] Pierre Messmer, "Our Military Policy," *French Affairs*, No. 155, May 1963, p. 1.

[59] Goldschmidt, *Atomic Adventure*, p. 156.

[60] Victor McElheney, "The French Bomb: How Much Technical Fallout?" *Science*, Vol. 147, No. 3,653, Jan. 1, 1965, p. 36.

raises important questions to which there are no definite answers available in the 1960s. The difficulty in evaluating the situation is due, in part, to the secrecy surrounding French military affairs. In addition, too little time has elapsed since the inauguration of these programs for anyone to form a well-informed judgment. Even in the U.S., where information is much more readily available and there is more experience to rely on, a satisfactory evaluation of the scientific and technological spinoff of the military and space programs does not exist. In this situation, therefore, one can do little other than consider the pros and cons that have been argued from both sides of the issue.

ARGUMENTS OF PROPONENTS

The position of the French Government and its supporters is that these prestigious military and space programs provide the state, in a democratic and free enterprise society, with a vital mechanism for influencing the rate and direction of scientific-technological advance. Acting in the name of national security the state can award research contracts and grants in order to provide selective stimulation to important industries and fields of research. Research and production in such varied fields as aeronautics, chemistry of metals, and plastics, can, as the head of the Senate's Finance Committee pointed out to his colleagues, "play the role of accelerator as much in the development of techniques as in increasing production."[61] In short, national defense is the prime propellant of scientific and technical progress, "because in a society dominated by the power of money, only the military and its research are not submitted to the criterion of profit-making in the short or medium range."[62]

There are many writers in France and the U.S. who argue that military-space programs inhibit the progress of science and

[61] Quoted in Furniss, *De Gaulle*, p. 184.
[62] Quoted in *ibid.*, p. 216.

useful technology. But the defenders of the French effort make the opposite claim: that such programs are the motor of the modern, science-based economy, and that they set a pace which forces all industrial sectors to higher levels of achievement. Piganiol and Villecourt have expressed this view very well:

> ... among the justifications for the French *force de frappe*, few have recognized an essential one. To the pressure of needs of normal human life which create progress, is added a pressure which issues from the collective and competitive life in which humanity is engaged: pressure born of the contracts of research, but also stimulating to contracts of increasing size for prototype development or simply pilot studies to determine the real possibilities of industrialization. A country which renounces a stimulant of this order—regardless of its military nature—will not possess on its soil an exceptional source of technical progress.[63]

For the de Gaulle Government the lesson to be drawn from the American and Russian experiences is that the route to modernization is through massive armament and space programs. Such programs enable the Government to build up underdeveloped sections of the country and provide support for those areas of the economy in which scientific research and technology meet, for example, electronics, aviation, and nuclear energy.[64] These areas are the most vivid ones in determining the standing of a nation in the world today. In effect, France, though it may remain weak in many areas of scientific and technological development, can leapfrog ahead into the areas most important to her well-being.[65]

Perhaps the most important way in which the military-

[63] Pierre Piganiol and Louis Villecourt, *Pour Une Politique Scientifique*, Flammarion, 1963, pp. 88-89. See also Michel Drancourt, *Les Clés du Pouvoir*, Fayard, 1964, pp. 48-53.

[64] Furniss, *De Gaulle*, p. 184.

[65] Boyer, "Aspects Scientifiques," p. 1,545.

space program is expected to influence French industry is through the spinoff of new technological products and processes and by setting an example of high technical achievement for the rest of the economy. From numerous areas of militarily related research the French Government anticipates a flow of important technologies with valuable social and economic applications. Most frequently mentioned in this regard are developments in nuclear engineering, oceanography, new materials, new motors, propulsion techniques, and advanced aeronautical techniques.[66]

The French Government traditionally has been reluctant to aid private industry directly through the awarding of contracts for research and development but has now recognized the potential benefits of such aid. "In France," according to one survey, "as in the United States, about 60 percent of private technical work is in fact subsidized by credits of military origin."[67] Between 1965 and 1970 the French military program will devote about 7.8 billion francs to research, development, and testing, much of which will go to private, competitive industry.[68] In electronics, for example, approximately 10 percent of the 31 billion francs destined for the *force de frappe* will go to the largely private electronics industry.[69] In the development and construction of Pierrelatte, 90 percent of the work was carried out by private companies.[70] It is hoped that such governmental support will not only stimulate research and technological development, which will spill over into the civilian competitive economy, but also that it will accelerate the concentration movement within French industry.

[66] "Recherche et Développement," p. 31.
[67] Pierre Lelong, quoted in Boyer, "Aspects Scientifiques," p. 7.
[68] Assemblée Nationale, Séance du 30. Novembre 1964, *Journal Officiel*, p. 5,738.
[69] Commissariat au Plan, Commission Permanente de l'Électronique, "Situation de l'Électronique en France," Mar. 1962, p. 12.
[70] Furniss, *De Gaulle*, p. 216.

If the modern, research-based industries such as electronics and chemistry did not receive large governmental subsidies via military and space programs, it is argued, they could not survive on their own because the civilian market is not sufficiently large to support the high costs of R and D. Given the importance of these industries for the modern state and its political independence, they must therefore become essentially quasi-public enterprises, supported by military and space contracts. It is one attribute of a modern nation, the French Government reasons, that huge governmental subsidies should support the frontier areas of R and D. Out of such support for military programs will come many of the most important products for the civilian market and a force for the modernization of French society. "To abandon the atomic effort," Prime Minister Pompidou has argued, "is to condemn France to becoming an underdeveloped country within the next ten or fifteen years."[71]

Responding to the argument that funds could be employed more effectively through direct investment in backward areas of science and technology, the supporters of the military program retort that this alternative is illusory. For them it is precisely the nationalistic and security aspects of the military and space programs which induce Frenchmen to spend millions of francs on science and push aside tradition when it provides obstacles to modernization. While investment in military and space programs may not be an efficient way, in terms of cost-benefit analysis, to modernize a nation's science and technology, in a democratic nation like France it is the only way to subsidize science and technology at the required level.

Furthermore, as one highly placed scientist has argued, military programs actually do not have the effect of diverting funds and personnel from important civilian areas. Even if the

[71] Quoted in Raymond Aron, *The Great Debate*, pp. 112-13.

force de frappe were to disappear, he pointed out, French re-search could not expand very much. The basic problem for France is not lack of money but lack of researchers; the great-est area of need for more money is in education.

Another official has made an additional argument against the "diversion theory": "While the CEA's military effort is cer-tainly in some respects at the expense of the civilian pro-gramme, it has the immense advantage of creating the same broad technological base in the fields of special materials and reactors from which all the great atomic powers have been able to launch their industrial development of nuclear energy."[72]

Proponents of the *force de frappe* argue that the psycho-logical spillover of the military program may be just as im-portant as the scientific and technological. The heart of the whole nuclear weapons program—construction of the Pier-relatte plant for the separation of the nuclear bomb material (U-235)—will not only bring financial aid to private industry in advanced technological sectors including metallurgy and nuclear power, but it represents a technological-scientific under-taking unsurpassed in French history. The organizational and industrial scale of the project cannot help but have an impor-tant psychological effect on the thinking of French industry, and perhaps even on a large section of French society, with respect to the importance of research. The Frenchman's image of France and of the relative importance of scientific and tech-nical matters in French life will almost certainly be changed under the influence of such technological achievements. If so, French intellectual and social life might be pervaded by an attitude more conducive to scientific research and technological innovation than that which is presently dominant in France.

[72] Goldschmidt, *Atomic Adventure*, pp. 156-57.

ARGUMENTS OF OPPONENTS

Critics of the present French military program argue, on the other hand, that scarce resources needed for basic research and the civilian economy are being diverted to the development of technologies which have no economic or scientific and perhaps not even military utility.[73] In constructing Pierrelatte, for example, they point out that billions of dollars and thousands of technicians are being used to build a technology developed several decades earlier in the United States. Consequently the Government is weakening rather than strengthening France's scientific and technological position in the world and is making France increasingly susceptible to American economic imperialism.

These critics estimate that 50 percent of France's total number of researchers and 80 percent of her young researchers are working on the *force de frappe*. One source gives 4,000 as the number of scientists and engineers being diverted from teaching and research.[74] Therefore, they reason, the production of new scientists and the growth in basic knowledge required for the long-term future are being sacrificed for the immediate development of technologies of little practical use.

With respect to the alleged spillover from the military program in forms of new scientific knowledge and new civilian technologies, critics point out that the amount of spillover is a function of the scope of the military R and D program and of the capacity of the economy to take advantage of new concepts and technologies. The payoff for science and the economy of the American military and space programs (to the extent that there has been such a return), is asserted to be due to the rather wide-ranging character of the programs themselves and to the capacity of American industry to take advantage of them. In

[73] "La Force de Frappe," *Esprit*, Dec. 1963.
[74] "Les Besoins en Hommes pour la Force de Frappe," *Les Cahiers de la République*, No. 54-55, Apr.-May 1963, pp. 304-305.

American military and space research several alternatives of a fundamental nature are frequently investigated in the attempt to solve a problem; indeed, long-term projects with relatively small probability of immediate return have been supported. In this process science and technology are advanced over a broad front, even though at times little may be contributed to the immediate missions of the supporting agencies. As in American research industries, the interests of the military and space agencies are sufficiently broad to encourage oriented fundamental research programs on the assumption that any new item of knowledge may prove to be of practical importance to one project or another.

The argument of the French Government, that American experience proves military and space programs have great utility for a nation's scientific and technological standing, is believed by some to be contradicted by a closer look at the American situation. Critics point out that the amount of spillover has been decreasing as military and space technology have become more sophisticated, specialized, and divorced from civilian technology. For example, it has been argued that the relevance to the civilian economy of the missile programs is far less than was the case of the aircraft programs being displaced by missiles.

The French effort, the critics argue, is far too narrowly defined and short term to spill over to any significant degree into new areas of science and technology. French resources must be concentrated on a relatively few developmental projects and research must be oriented toward them, because of the difference in scale between France's effort and that of the great powers. The total budget of the *force de frappe*, according to the estimates of one author, is approximately equal to the annual research (excluding development) budget of the United States or the Soviet Union.[75]

[75] Alfred Grosser, *French Foreign Policy under de Gaulle*, trans. Lois Ames Pattison, Little, Brown, p. 154.

In field after field, critics point out, close inspection and analysis show that the spillover of the military program into civilian applications will be negligible, if not actually detrimental. In the two areas of civilian technology where claims of spillover have been most emphasized—atomic energy and electronics—they point out the following:[76]

Atomic Energy. In the opinion of Nicolas Vichney the two atomic projects most likely to have spillover are the production of tritium by the Celestin reactor and the Pierrelatte isotope-separation plant. While French science, technology, and industry can derive some benefit from both, these advantages are held to be limited and not commensurate with the costs. As presently conceived, it is argued, these materials production facilities contain few innovations. A great problem, as another detailed analysis brings out, is that the technologies of military reactors and civilian power reactors are substantially different.[77]

Vichney doubts that the U-235 to be produced at Pierrelatte will substantially advance the French nuclear power industry. For a considerable period the total supply will be absorbed in the production of nuclear warheads for the *force de frappe.* The amount of uranium Pierrelatte could produce for power production is inadequate to meet France's ever increasing needs for electrical power. Finally, the cost of the enriched uranium produced at Pierrelatte will be approximately three times the price of American enriched uranium; even if Pierrelatte were expanded the French price would never be competitive on the European market with the American product.

[76] In addition to a number of interviews, this discussion is based primarily on a series of articles in *Le Monde,* written by Nicolas Vichney, its distinguished science writer: Feb. 22-24; Nov. 28-30; Dec. 1, 1964. For a review of some of Vichney's views see McElheny, "The French Bomb," pp. 35-36.

[77] "Incidence du Programme d'Armement Sur le Développement Nucléaire Française," mimeo. n.d.

Furthermore, Vichney points out, the future of nuclear power lies with breeder-reactor technology which consumes relatively small amounts of enriched uranium. On the other hand, he concedes, the military atomic program will benefit the economy in several ways. In particular, the development of new alloys will advance materials science in France and make new materials available to French industry. Given the place of materials technology in the modern industrial economy this potential benefit may be of long-term significance. Again, it is a matter of the high cost of such spillover.

Electronics. In contrast to the U.S. where military research and development contracts did much to launch the transistor and computer industries, the French military has done little to advance either technology. The military emphasis has been on immediate needs. As a result the necessary computation equipment has been purchased from the United States; the computer work undertaken has been the elaboration of American techniques, with little impetus given to indigenous technology such as that of integrated circuits. In any case, the development of the French computer industry into a competitive position with American computers is seen to be a major undertaking in itself, far beyond the effect of any spillover from military programs.

In other areas the development of a high-speed camera for recording nuclear explosions, of radar and other electronic equipment for the *Mirage IV*, and of an inertial guidance system for missiles, it is argued, will have some civilian application. The state of electronics will no doubt be advanced, but except for the high-speed camera none of these developments is considered significant for the economy for the moment.

In assessing the nuclear program's alleged impact on French science critics point out that the building of the *force de frappe* is largely an industrial and engineering task. It is involved more with the application of existing knowledge and technologies than the discovery of new scientific concepts. The scientific and technical research necessitated by the effort is directed more to the answering of specific questions such as the measurement of nuclear cross-sections than the advancement of any branches of science. As such, it is an affair of *Polytechniciens* and other engineers, rather than scientists. Thus it is argued that the impact on science of the effort is essentially the negative one of decreasing the amount of funds spent on basic research and on the training of the next generation of scientists.

For the critics of the *force de frappe* the experience of Britain reveals the folly of a small country's trying to keep up with great powers. The possession of a nuclear striking force not only failed to give the British political independence from the United States, it actually helped to increase British dependence. By overcommitting their resources to military research and development the British weakened their own civilian technological effort.[78] Also, to the argument that only a military program rationalized in nationalistic terms will induce the French people to make the financial sacrifice for long-term scientific and technological benefits, Raymond Aron comments:

Are we to assume that the National Assembly would vote down appropriations for peaceful uses of atomic energy and that therefore it takes the H-bomb to make them approve these funds, so that all research becomes an integral part of the French deterrent? In the reign of Charles de Gaulle the

[78] Louis Villecourt, "Politique de la Science," *Nouvelle Frontière*, No. 8, Oct.-Nov. 1964, p. 30. Actually the British error, after World War II, as P.M.S. Blackett, President of the Royal Society and Chief Advisor to the Minister of Technology, has written, was to put all R and D in government laboratories rather than contracting out the responsibilities to private industry. (*Science*, Vol. 155, No. 3,770, March 31, 1967, p. 1,656.) This arrangement minimized the spillover of military programs into the civilian economy; the French intend to avoid this mistake.

mere possibility of such parliamentary intractability could not be seriously entertained for even one moment.[79]

Aron's statement focuses on the crux of the issue: setting aside the question of the military and political value of the French military program, one's position on its scientific, economic, and technological utility is determined in large part by his judgment of what would be taking place in French scientific, technological, and economic affairs if the military program did not exist. Would the French be undertaking the immense effort required to improve their scientific and technological situation, or wouldn't they? Indeed, would support for scientific and technical research be increased several-fold? Would efforts be made to transform the traditional structure of French scientific institutions and to encourage cooperation among government, university, and industrial laboratories?

The history of the Fourth Republic, though impressive with respect to scientific reform, does not give one confidence to respond positively, at least without strong qualification. The liberal democratic leadership of de Gaulle's predecessors was not adequate to formulate the policies and bring about the cooperation among social groups necessary in the modern scientific state. A powerful force is required to smash the Napoleonic system and the interlocking relationships which have held back reform.

The Fifth Republic has chosen to use the motive power of nationalism to force the pace of modernization of French society, including its scientific and technological institutions. However, without its military utility, de Gaulle would not have been interested in science to the extent of giving it such strong financial backing and supporting broad-scale reform of traditional scientific-technical institutions.

Perhaps the most beneficial aspect of the French military

[79] Aron, *The Great Debate*, p. 113.

and space programs is their psychological impact. The development of a domestic nuclear striking force and space technology is symbolic of France's commitment to become a modern scientific-technological society. Furthermore, by making great demands on French managerial and technical skills, the effort forces society to set a higher standard of performance and expectation for itself. Certainly the American space-military research program has had an incalculable yet profound effect on a broad sector of American science and technology.[80] In France these ambitious and prestigious programs have indeed undermined the psychology of dependence on American science and technology which had dominated French thinking for the past several decades.

More concretely, the military R and D program provides reformers with a much needed lever for overturning the power structure and the attitudes which have held back the advancement of French science and technology for a century and a half. New organizations have been created and new fields of study have been launched, which will increase the pace of change in French science and industry. In this connection it is instructive to note that when the accelerator was constructed at Saclay in the early postwar period, France had few theoretical or experimental physicists and many argued that it was folly for France to undertake such a project. The success of Saclay in changing the attitude of Frenchmen toward modern physics and the traditional pattern of French scientific institutions is being repeated by the Directorate of Research and Testing and the National Center for Space Studies.

On the other hand, the price France is paying for these gains is a high one. The financial burden of the investment of many

[80] Frederick Seitz, "Science and the Space Program," *Science*, Vol. 142, No. 3,730, June 24, 1966, 1,719-21. Seitz, President of National Academy of Sciences of the United States suggests a number of ways in which the space program is altering the style and attitudes of industrialists and scientists.

billions of dollars in the nuclear striking force is readily apparent. A high political cost may yet be paid if France stimulates other nations, especially West Germany, to follow a similar strategy of modernization. Furthermore, it would appear that the emphasis on the *force de frappe* has contributed, as its critics assert, to the decline (at least for the moment) of the French position in civilian technology. The emphasis on military and prestige projects has caused the diversion of resources from important areas of civilian technology to military R and D work; as yet there has been little spillover into the economy. Perhaps of even more significance in the long run is that the emphasis on a national solution to the alleged imperialistic threat from the United States may impede a successful European cooperative effort in science and technology.

Map 1 Distribution of Research Workers in the Private Sector, 1963 (full-time equivalent)[a]

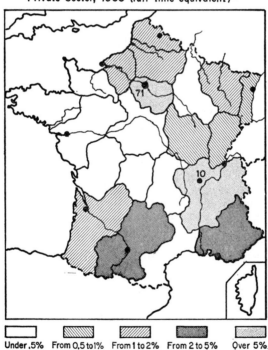

Under .5%   From 0.5 to 1%   From 1 to 2%   From 2 to 5%   Over 5%

Total number of research workers: 16, 653

[a]Adapted from OECD, *Reviews of National Science Policy - France*, 1966, p.70.

Total number of research workers: 16,653

Chapter 10 · The Balance Sheet of Modernization: Scientific and Technical Institutions

No French Government has done as much for research as the present Government. . . . If this is so, it is because the first concern of the Fifth Republic has been to set the country on its feet again and make it independent; hence the virtually parallel and similar efforts it has made for both research and defence.

> —GASTON PALEWSKI, *Minister for Science,*
> *Speech to the National Assembly,*
> *June 19, 1964*

As de Gaulle acknowledges in the quotation that opens this book, there is a profound conflict between the character of traditional France and the nature of the modern scientific-industrial society. The Napoleonic pattern of institutions, the tenacity of group privilege, and the French personality stand as obstacles to the development of French science, technology, and industry. These impediments are giving way to the forces of modernization but slowly in a society as tradition-bound as that of France. Disturbed though many Frenchmen may be with the status of their technology and the problem this poses for France, the predominant mood remains essentially one of complacency, when what is required is a social revolution.

Judging from the scientific reforms of the initial years of the Fourth and Fifth Republics, it would appear that the pace of reform had slowed by the mid-1960s. Some suggest that this hiatus can be explained by de Gaulle's alleged indifference to basic science, and Prime Minister Pompidou's long-standing hostility to science and scientists; he is, after all, French scientists point out, an *ancien élève* of the literary section of the *École Normale Supérieure.* "Research," he is reputed to have said, "does not form part of the options of the government."[1]

More likely, however, the change in the pace of reform is due to the fact that the dramatic and easy-to-do things have already been done. Ahead lie the difficult tasks of changing long-established attitudes and institutions. Above all, what must change is the belief that France can adapt to the contemporary world without ceasing to be eternal France. Such an inhibiting attitude toward change runs throughout the reformist movement in France today. In the economic sphere the state seeks growth and innovation but only if it can be tightly controlled and France can be prevented from becoming a *civilisation du gadget*. The Government wants the mass education of scientists and engineers but it refuses to alter the privileged status of the *grandes écoles* or the system of *concours*. France desires the rapid expansion of scientific research and the development of close ties between the university and industry but fails to reduce the prerogatives of the professor, create truly autonomous and competitive universities, or remove the restrictions preventing close university-industry liaison. In short, Frenchmen wish to avoid the obvious logic of their situation: to meet the American challenge and to be powerful in the modern world, they must be willing to pay the price of becoming more like the United States.

With too few exceptions the French elite tend to believe they can resolve the technology gap through borrowing from abroad a new managerial technique here or making an institutional reform there. It is as though they were looking for the secret formula of American scientific and technological success. Though specific managerial techniques or policies are important in explaining the rise of the United States to scientific-industrial preeminence, the underlying necessary conditions are those features of modern America which the mem-

[1] Jacques Monod, "Pourquoi la France est Scientifiquement Sous-Développée," *Le Nouvel Observateur*, No. 49, Oct. 26, 1965, 4.

bers of the French elite in their hearts reject as the "American way of life"—the competitive market economy; mass education; social and geographical mobility; a new concept of the university's role in society; the entrance of scientists, economists, and professional managers into the ruling elite. It is on the basis of these social and economic conditions that the United States has built its dynamic scientific and technological civilization.

It would be wrong to conclude from this harsh judgment that the Napoleonic system described in Chapter 4 remains wholly intact. The reforms undertaken by the Fourth and especially the Fifth Republics have indeed been significant and far-reaching. While the present chapter cannot and need not evaluate the consequence of recent reforms for all those features of traditional French society which are inhibiting scientific and technical advance, several areas are crucial and reveal the successes and failures of the reformers.

Before entering this discussion it is important to realize that the forces of change continue to act in France; by their direction and magnitude they are undermining the obstacles to the modernization of France. Whether it will be these new forces or traditional France that will ultimately prevail will determine in large measure the future of France and Europe.

Forces for Change

Three powerful forces for change are acting to move present-day France in the direction of a scientific nation-state. These forces may yet bring about that social, economic, and political revolution which must precede the emergence of a strong, modernized French state and economy—the program of military modernization (including space research); the impact of the European Economic Community (Common Market); and the demographic revolution.

MILITARY MODERNIZATION AND THE SPACE PROGRAM

The nuclear striking force and prestigious space program are having a profound impact on French science, technology, and industry. Their influence on the structure of scientific and technical institutions cannot be denied even by those who believe that these programs in the long run will actually harm French science and technology. If the programs are doing nothing else they are at least bringing young, reform-minded scientists into positions of influence within the Government, and enabling the Government to give priority to advanced areas of science and technology.

The question arises whether military modernization and space research will continue as forces for change after de Gaulle leaves the scene. It has already been noted that French interest in nuclear weapons long antedates de Gaulle's return to power. As Scheinman concludes, the development of the atomic bomb by France was probably inevitable given the state of French opinion even under the Fourth Republic.[2] There is nothing in recent French political experience to indicate that de Gaulle's opponents will repudiate nuclear armaments if and when they regain power. As one Frenchman put it: "It is silly to expect France to abandon modern arms and return to archaic ones." On the contrary, it may be expected that the constant improvement of these arms will make ever increasing demands on French science and technology.

THE EUROPEAN ECONOMIC COMMUNITY

France's decision in 1957 to ratify the Rome Treaty, creating the European Economic Community, or Common Market, and substantially abandon her historic protectionism has produced perhaps the greatest force for change in contemporary

[2] Lawrence Scheinman, *Atomic Energy Policy under the Fourth Republic*, Princeton University Press, 1965, pp. 216, 219.

France. The creation of a vast European market to which French firms possess free access and, reciprocally, the challenge of foreign competition in home markets necessitate a vast reorganization of the French economy and the demise of traditional attitudes toward research and development.

Though newspaper headlines may emphasize the difficulties and crises which have been generated by the movement for a common European economy, a more remarkable feature is the speed with which the Common Market is altering the European and world economy. The structure of the European economy is being transformed by an accelerating corporate concentration movement within Europe, the decline of governmental controls over such matters as the capital market, and the "invasion" of Europe by American corporations with their huge financial resources, advanced technical know-how, and managerial skills. There is every reason to believe that these forces will continue.

THE DEMOGRAPHIC REVOLUTION

Since the end of World War II France has undergone a demographic transformation with significant implications for French science. After a long period of stagnation and decline, the French population has begun to grow again. Due mainly to the birthrate increase after 1945, France today, as Frenchmen constantly point out, is the youngest nation in Europe. This population explosion has become at once France's most vexing current problem and her greatest future hope. It is said that President de Gaulle's basic strategy toward European unification has been to hold back until the French and German curves of active population (ratio of productive citizens to total population) crossed, to France's advantage, in 1968. Of more immediate concern here is the fact that by the 1960s the French population explosion was flooding the educational system with students, causing a crisis for France's facilities, while presenting her with the prospect of increased numbers of scientists and engineers.

There is also a shift in the location of the French population; Frenchmen are moving in ever greater numbers from rural areas to the cities. While the greater part of this population movement is swelling Paris, other urban areas are also beginning to grow. For the first time in recent French history the prospect looms ahead that other urban centers may develop which could to some extent counter the domination of Paris over French life and become nuclei for regional scientific, economic, and social development.

The character of the French school population is changing as the proportion of working class and, to a lesser extent, peasant children attending the *lycée* and institutions of higher education increases.[3] This process of democratization is due in part to the growing affluence of French society and the rising expectations of the long underprivileged classes. Equally important have been the reforms of the Fourth and Fifth Republics (particularly the latter), which, for social and economic reasons, have sought to raise the educational and skill levels of the French population.[4] In effect, these educational reforms of an essentially conservative French government are contributing, though slowly, to a "social revolution" in France.[5]

At the level of higher education an unprecedented expansion is taking place in the universities and, to a much lesser extent, in the *grandes écoles*. At the beginning of the century there were approximately 30,000 university students in France;

[3] Stanley Hoffmann, ed., *In Search of France*, Harvard University Press, 1963, p. 418.

[4] For a discussion of the many issues see W. R. Fraser, *Education and Society in Modern France*, Routledge and Kegan Paul, 1963.

[5] Laurence Wylie, "Social Change at the Grass Roots," in Hoffmann, *In Search of France*, pp. 180-81. The immensity of the problem facing France in making education more democratic is examined in detail in P. Bourdieu and Jean-Claude Passeron, *Les Héritiers, les Étudiants et la Culture*, Les Éditions de Minuit, 1964.

by the end of the Second World War, there were three times as many; and in October 1966, there were fifteen times that many (460,000).[6] With the student population doubling every seven and a half years it is estimated there will be 750,000 students in higher education by 1972.[7] This is the highest growth rate in western Europe. In contrast to West Germany, where only about four percent of the school age population will graduate from institutions of higher education in 1972, the French figure will be nine percent, the American 20 percent.[8] Though the attrition rate among the entrants into the university system remains high, the numbers are unprecedented, especially in Paris, and are having an impact on the nature and organization of the French university and the availability of potential scientists and engineers.

A major consequence of the demographic pressures is a steady undermining at the university level of many long-standing obstacles to the full development of French science. Attitudes and institutions that are the product of an earlier historical era are being destroyed by the simple pressure of increased numbers. As Raymond Aron has observed, the growing school population may yet end the subordination of research to the training of secondary teachers:

> ... the degradation of secondary education and the inflation of the number of students are in the process of provoking the reforms which ministers, high officials and professors, separately or together, have been and remain incapable of doing: more clear separation of higher and secondary education, continuity of primary and secondary, acknowledgement that the training of *lycée* teachers is only one of the

[6] OECD, *Reviews of National Science Policy—France*, 1966, p. 54; *Le Monde*, Oct. 13, 1966.

[7] *Le Monde*, July 13, 1966.

[8] Raymond Poignant, *L'Enseignement Dans les Pays du Marché Commun*, Paris, Institut Pédagogique National, 1965, pp. 260, 267.

tasks, and not necessarily the most important, of the faculties, introduction of the nontraditional disciplines whose development is tied to the development of an industrial society.[9]

Supported by these three powerful sets of forces: military modernization and the space program, the European Economic Community, and the demographic revolution, the reform of scientific and technical institutions has proceeded in two directions. First, there has been a considerable expansion of scientific-technical organizations and facilities within the industrial sector and within the four broad categories of official research establishments—the Ministry of National Education; Technical Ministries; Ministry of Defense; and Ministry of Science. Since the origins and characteristics of the most important of these institutions have already been discussed, no further elaboration seems appropriate, other than to present the over-all structure as of 1964 which is shown by FIGURE 3. The second aspect has been the reform of existing scientific and technical organizations and the policies which guide them. While an exhaustive treatment of these reforms and developments cannot be undertaken here, several areas which are important for the future of French science and technology should be discussed even though they are much too recent to permit a conclusive evaluation.

The Reform of Scientific and Educational Institutions

In the scientific state of the second half of the twentieth century the core set of institutions is the university and related organizations for basic scientific research. In the French case this includes the *grandes écoles*, the *grands établissements*, and the CNRS. To improve its performance the French system for higher education and basic research is being reorganized and re-

[9] Raymond Aron, "La Crise de l'Université," *Preuves*, May 1964, pp. 18-19.

Figure 3
THE ORGANIZATION OF SCIENTIFIC RESEARCH IN FRANCE

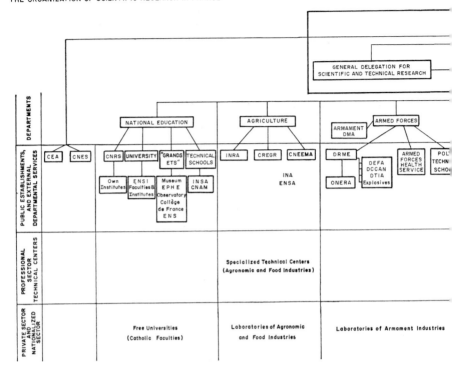

KEY TO ABBREVIATIONSa

B.R.G.M. Bureau de Recherches Géologiques et Minières (Geological and Mining Research Office).

C.E.A. Commissariat à l'Energie Atomique (Commissariat for Atomic Energy).

C.E.R.C.H.A.R. Centre d'Etudes et de Recherches des Charbonnages de France (Research Center for French local industry).

C.N.A.M. Conservatoire National des Arts et Métiers (National School of Arts and Crafts).

C.N.E.E.M.A. Centre National d'Etudes et d'Expérimentation du Machinisme Agricole (National Centre for Study and Testing of Agricultural Machinery).

C.N.E.S. Centre National d'Etudes Spatiales (National Centre for Space Studies).

C.N.E.T. Centre National d'Etudes des Télécommunications (National Centre for Telecommunication Studies).

C.N.R.S. Centre National de la Recherche S[c]ientifique (National Centre for Scientific [Re]search).

C.R.E.G.R. Centre de Recherche et d'Ex[péri]mentation du Génie Rural (Research and [Ex]perimentation Centre for Agricultural E[ngi]neering).

C.R.U. Centre de Recherche d'Urbanisme ([City] Planning Research Centre).

C.S.T.B. Centre Scientifique et Technique[du] Bâtiment (Building Construction Rese[arch] Centre).

D.C.C.A.N. Direction Centrale des Cons[truc]tions et Armes Navales (Central Depart[ment] for Naval Construction and Armament).

D.E.F.A. Direction des Etudes et Fabrica[tions] d'Armement (Department of Armament S[tudies] and Construction).

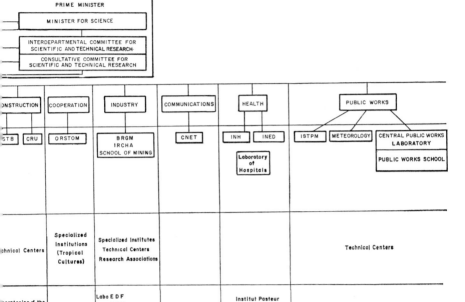

M.A. Délégation Ministérielle à l'Armement (Armament Ministerial Delegation).

R.M.E. Direction des Recherches et des Moyens d'Essais (Research of Testing Methods Directorate).

T.I.A. Direction Technique et Industrielle de l'Aéronautique (Technical Industrial Department for Aeronautics).

D.F. Electricité de France

N.S. Ecoles Normales Supérieures (Higher Training Colleges).

N.S.A. Ecoles Nationales Supérieures Agronomiques (National Higher Agronomical Colleges).

N.S.I. Ecoles Nationales Supérieures d'Ingénieurs (Practical School of Higher Studies).

P.H.E. Ecole des Hautes Etudes

D.F. Gaz de France

I.A. Institut National Agronomique (National Agronomic Institute).

I.E.D. Institut National d'Etudes Démographiques (National Institute for Demographic Studies).

I.N.H. Institut National d'Hygiène (National Hygiene Institute).

I.N.R.A. Institut National de la Recherche Agronomique (National Institute for Agronomical Research).

I.N.S.A. Institut National des Sciences Appliquées (National Institute of Applied Sciences).

I.R.C.H.A. Institut de Recherches de Chimie Appliquée (Applied Chemistry Research Institute).

I.S.T.P.M. Institut Scientifique et Technique de Pêches Maritimes (Fisheries Scientific and Technical Institute).

O.N.E.R.A. Office National des Etudes et Recherches Aérospatiales (National Office of Space Studies and Research).

O.R.S.T.O.M. Office de la Recherche Scientifique et Technique Outre-Mer (Overseas Scientific and Technical Research Office).

S.N.C.F. Société Nationale des Chemins de Fer Français (French Railways).

a OECD, *Country Reports on the Organization of Scientific Research—France*, 1964, pp. 84-85.

formed at three different levels. The mechanism for the administration and coordination of higher education and scientific research at the level of the Ministry of National Education is being revamped. The university system, and to a lesser extent, the *grandes écoles* are being expanded and decentralized. And the internal organization of the university is beginning to develop and fill the gap at the intermediate level between the Ministry and the individual faculty members.

COORDINATION OF RESEARCH, EDUCATION, AND THE PLAN

The existence of two structures—the CNRS and the *facultés*—with similar responsibilities for fundamental research but with different responsibilities with respect to teaching, poses a serious problem for planning and coordination. In laboratory construction and the expansion of facilities, for example, the different perspectives of the two organizations can lead to over-expansion of some scientific disciplines and the underdevelopment of others. Frequently the researchers CNRS makes available to the universities are not appropriate for the latter's programs, and the awarding of university chairs does not necessarily take into account the research programs of the CNRS. In addition, there are problems concerning the division of tasks between research and teaching, the management of research careers, and the transfer of personnel between the CNRS and higher education.[10]

In order to close the gap between educational planning and general planning for fundamental research, the French Government issued a series of decrees on March 31, 1966 which created a Coordinating Committee for Scientific Research. Under the chairmanship of the Minister of National Education this Committee has the responsibility of developing and coordinating the scientific research and teaching effort within

[10] "La Recherche Scientifique au Sein du Ministère de l'Éducation Nationale à la Lumière des Récentes Réformes du CNRS," *Le Progrès Scientifique*, No. 95, Apr. 1966, 7.

the Ministry of National Education and maintaining a close liaison with the research activities of other agencies of government.

While the effort to coordinate research and teaching will no doubt be of some benefit, its effectiveness is severely limited by the structure of the *facultés* and the CNRS. In both cases many of the important decisions over the activities to be coordinated are made by administrative levels over which the top administrators have little control—the professors in the case of the *facultés*, and the sections in the case of CNRS. The coordinating committee will help, but it cannot overcome what is essentially a problem of decentralization of authority.

EXPANSION, DECENTRALIZATION, AND RATIONALIZATION
OF HIGHER EDUCATION AND SCIENTIFIC RESEARCH

Two interrelated policies are guiding the reform of higher education. The first policy is to decentralize the system of higher education and reduce the domination of Paris over French scientific-intellectual life.[11] The second policy is to build up regional centers of specialized research and education, in contrast to the Napoleonic system of a uniform curriculum. In this way, France seeks to consolidate her highly dispersed and limited scientific resources and concentrate them at places where there is a sufficient "critical mass" to insure their effectiveness.

The effort to decentralize French higher education and reduce the hegemony of the University of Paris is manifest in and around Paris itself, as well as throughout the provinces.

---

[11] There are 136,000 students at the University of Paris, one-third of the total in the university system. *Le Monde*, Nov. 23, 1966. See Gérald Antoine, and Jean-Claude Passeron, *La Réforme de l'Université*, Calmann-Levy, 1966. The statistics on the student-faculty ratio in Paris and elsewhere give one an appreciation of the situation; see *Le Monde*, Feb. 16, 1959: University of Paris, 269 to 1; the provinces, 99 to 1; the United States and Soviet Union, 15 to 1.

Undoubtedly the most important new science *faculté* is that at Orsay, located near Saclay outside Paris. Conceived in the early 1950s, Orsay has been formed around the nuclear studies that were first established there.[12] Despite the resistance of the original science *Faculté* of the University of Paris, Orsay became an independent *faculté* on January 1, 1965. In addition, two new science *facultés* are to be established at Nanterre, just to the east of Paris, and at the old *halle aux vins* in Paris proper; several other new *facultés* are under study.[13] As a consequence, the pinnacle of French science is now shared by two (soon to be more) science *facultés* in Paris whose competition should increase the vigor of French science.

Throughout France old provincial universities are being renovated and new *facultés* founded. A number of *facultés*, such as Strasbourg, Dijon, and Grenoble, are moving partially or completely from their ancient quarters in the center of the city, and in several cases, are being established on American-style campuses in the suburbs.[14]

A major goal of the expansion of provincial universities is to establish specialized scientific-industrial complexes throughout France as a means to integrate university research with regional industrial development.[15] At Toulouse, as we have already seen, a great complex of technical institutes, military installations, and industries directly linked to the aerospace industry is being created. Other regional, specialized centers

---

[12] Nicolas Vichney, "Concentration d'Artillerie Dans la Vallée de Chevreuse," *L'Expansion Scientifique*, No. 2, Apr. 1959. Symbolic of the change in French science education represented by Orsay is the fact that professors will have offices where they can meet with their graduate students. The writer remembers an interview he had at the *Faculté* of Science in Paris with one of France's most distinguished mathematicians, who shared an office with a half dozen other faculty members.

[13] *Le Monde*, Nov. 23, 1966.   [14] *Le Monde*, Apr. 29, 1966.

[15] Olivier Guichard, *Aménager la France*, Laffont-Gonthier, 1965, pp. 159-60.

include those at Grenoble in electro-chemistry, low-temperature physics, and nuclear physics which have formed around the new science campus of the University of Grenoble.[16] Strasbourg is specializing in macromolecular studies; Orleans is establishing itself in high-temperature chemistry, Nancy in solid state physics, and Bordeaux in tropical biology.

Unfortunately the decentralization of research outside Paris and its consolidation into large, specialized centers and laboratories has not proceeded very far.[17] Scientists resist large laboratories and projects because of their fear of external control. Paris continues to attract scientists; understandably many prefer to live there and commute to the provincial universities where they have their chair. Industry, too, prefers to keep its laboratories in or near Paris and the *grandes écoles* resist leaving Paris.[18] As a consequence, between one-half and two-thirds of the French scientific effort remains in the Parisian region (see MAP 1). But the base of French research is beginning to expand and a competitive system similar to that of nineteenth century Germany and twentieth-century America may yet come into existence.

INTERNAL REFORM OF THE UNIVERSITIES AND FACULTÉS

In 1965, when the brilliant and outspoken Jacques Monod was awarded the Nobel Prize for Medicine, he used the occasion to deliver a bitter and scathing attack on the complacency of French science and academic life. Reading Monod's

[16] Robert Trékin, "Links with Industry at the University of Grenoble," *Impact of Science on Society*, xv, No. 1, 1965, 27-39.

[17] Some of the proposals and problems are discussed in Conseil Économique et Social, "Possibilités de Décentralisation des Laboratoires de Recherche Scientifique et Technique," *Rapport* No. 3, Feb. 2, 1962.

[18] The movement of the *grandes écoles* out of Paris and closer to the industries they serve is one of the most important recommendations of the so-called Boulloche Report. "Les Conditions de Développement, de Recrutement, de Fonctionnement et de Localisation des Grandes Écoles en France," La Documentation Française, 1964.

indictment as recorded in the Leftist journal, *Le Nouvel Observateur,* one is impressed by how little the fundamentals of the university system have really changed since Napoleon— profound conservatism, bureaucratic overcentralization, the stultifying examination system. As Monod asserts, the university continues to play a "retarding role of great importance" in French science because of its self-satisfaction and complacency.[19] What was required, he argued, was a revolutionary transformation of the French university system.

To prepare for such a revolution a second *Colloque de Caen* was held on November 19, 1966, which brought together several hundred scientists and many prominent Frenchmen, including Science Minister Peyrefitte, Education Minister Fouchet, former Finance Minister Giscard d'Estaing, and former Prime Minister Mendès-France.[20] Its purpose was to draft a program for the reform of the university, much as the first *Colloque de Caen* in 1956 had been concerned with the lack of adequate financial support for scientific research. What the participants wanted were those features of the American system of higher education which account for the *efficacité américaine*: (1) the organization of teaching and research according to disciplinary departments rather than by autocratic chairs and small inefficient *laboratoires de chaire*; (2) the selection of professors on the basis of competence in research (but without *publier ou périr*) rather than through the system of cooptation; and (3) the integration of the *facultés* into medium-sized universities with a large degree of financial

[19] Jacques Monod, "Pourquoi La France est Scientifiquement Sous Développée," p. 2. Raymond Aron, for example, has made some valuable observations explaining why, despite all its objectionable features, neither the government nor the professors do very much to reform the system of higher education. Aron, "La Crise de l'Université."

[20] On the other hand, the conference drew the wrath of nonscientists who resented the presumption of the scientists in taking it upon themselves to propose a program of university reform.

316

autonomy and flexibility to determine curriculum,[21] develop specialized areas of teaching and research, and seek research support from many sources.[22]

"Throughout old Europe," Bertrand Girod de l'Ain wrote in *Le Monde* of the Caen meetings, "one witnesses today a kind of 'heartrending reassessment': the university elite dazzled and alarmed by the extraordinary dynamism of higher education and research in the United States estimate that the European *facultés* are often paralysed by their own privileges which prevent some competition for discovery, the rapid adaptation to the mutations of knowledge, and the fruitful exchange of personnel."[23]

The strength of the American university system is its highly competitive nature; competition among professors for priority of discovery, research grants, and professional advancement, competition among autonomous, flexible universities for funds and prestige. In the absence of such intense competition among professors, laboratories, and educational institutions the French system remains sluggish and backward.[24] But a high price must be paid for the stimulus of competition. The professor must suffer the anxieties of "publish or perish" and give up his many privileges. The state must relinquish its strict controls over the universities and permit a competitive "market" to come into existence, at the same that it increases its support

[21] The inflexible statutes governing scientific finances and other matters have certainly harmed French science. On the other hand, French scientists have developed many ways by which to get around the regulations. The writer in his interviews with French scientists encountered a certain circumspection toward discussing such matters.

[22] An extensive account of the Colloquium, including a list of its 15 recommendations, appears in *Le Monde*, Nov. 15 and 16, 1966; a detailed report is contained in Association d'Étude Pour L'Expansion de la Recherche Scientifique, "Colloque National de Caen," *Bulletin Quotidien*, No. 4, Nov. 14-15, 1966.

[23] *Le Monde*, Nov. 11, 1966.

[24] OECD, *Reviews of National Science Policy—France*, p. 94.

of higher education and research. The available evidence indicates clearly that neither the professors nor the state is prepared to pay the price of the *efficacité américaine.*

"In the eyes of the Government," one French journalist quipped in a report on plans to reform the CNRS, "the end of research is not to search but to find."[25] From the perspective of the Government CNRS has not fulfilled its potential with respect to scientific research or the innovation of new technologies. If one accepts this criticism, then the situation is serious, because such a large percentage of France's research force are employed by CNRS.[26]

The Government has implemented a number of reforms aimed at overcoming the alleged conservatism of the CNRS. For example, in late 1964, it passed a decree restricting tenure on the disciplinary sections to two terms. This was immediately hailed in France as a victory for the young scientists over the older men who have long dominated the organization and discouraged expansion into newer specializations.[27] While this and related reforms were important, the problem of the overdecentralization of decision-making at the level of the sections of the National Committee remained.

By the same set of decrees of March 1966 which established the Coordinating Committee in the Ministry of National Education, the Government sought to strengthen the authority of the Director and the administrative structure of the CNRS.[28] The Director and two assistant directors were replaced by an administrative structure similar but not identical to the dyarchical authorities of the CEA. The Director-General of the CNRS continues to be a scientist but he is now assisted by a civil

[25] *Le Monde*, Mar. 5, 1965.
[26] "La Recherche Scientifique," p. 2. [27] *Le Monde*, Oct. 14, 1964.
[28] "La Recherche Scientifique," pp. 9-11, 14-23.

servant responsible for the administrative and financial aspects of CNRS's operations. In addition, a *collège des directeurs scientifiques* (about five in number) of distinguished scientists was created to assist the Director-General in the elaboration of the research program. Together these officials constitute the Administrative Committee which is responsible for all "decisions relative to plans and research programs and to putting them into operation."[29] Hopefully, through this centralization of decision-making authority in the hands of the Director-General and making the Directorate a fulltime, appointed body, the development of a coherent research policy will be possible.

At the same time that the Director-General's authority was strengthened vis-à-vis the sections, the decrees of March 1966 sought to increase CNRS's financial autonomy from the Ministry of Finance. Prior to this reform the CNRS, like the universities and any other public agency (except CEA), had been subject to the slow, complicated "red tape" of the Ministry of Finance. It was very difficult to shift resources from one area of research to another in the light of new discoveries and opportunities. In the words of one government report this situation was a "brake on the development of the work of the researchers and a sterilizing factor in international competition."[30] To correct the situation the Director-General was given authority to modify the CNRS budget within rather broad limits and a modest fund was made available to him, whose expenditure could be accounted for on an *a posteriori* basis. Hopefully, these financial reforms will increase the flexibility of the management of the CNRS and enable it to exercise more initiative.

In addition to the attempts to strengthen the administration of the CNRS the decrees of March 1966 opened the way to immense changes in the operation and responsibilities of the CNRS. By far the most ambitious reform affecting its future is the proposal for the creation of national institutes.[31] This con-

[29] *Ibid.*, p. 10.   [30] *Ibid.*   [31] *Ibid.*, p. 12.

cept is similar to one of the original reforms proposed by the Scientific Advisory Committee to the Interministerial Committee in the early days of the Fifth Republic; its defeat at that time was a serious blow to science reformers. The basic idea is that the institutes would be given considerable financial and administrative autonomy and would have the responsibility of reorganizing, coordinating, and developing the national effort in high priority areas of science and technology requiring a heavy investment in equipment and manpower. In part, through the use of research grants and contracts, the institutes would coordinate research among CNRS, university, and other researchers, as well as bringing together university and industrial scientists in the application of new scientific knowledge to technological innovation. One institute is to be concerned with the evaluation of the technical worth of new knowledge.[32]

Along with the reform of higher education, the establishment of national institutes is crucial for the scientific and technical future of France. If successful, these institutes could provide leadership for the development of specific fields and provide a bridge between basic scientists from the universities and the utilizers of scientific knowledge from industry. Industrialists would be able to make their needs known to scientists and scientists could inform industrial representatives of the new technical possibilities opened by scientific advance. While some of this type of exchange already takes place in the commissions of the Planning Commissariat, it is at the working levels where it is most necessary and most lacking. Unfortunately there is little basis for confidence that the institute concept will succeed. The placement of the institutes *within* the CNRS may actually represent a defeat, as the institutes were originally proposed by the science reformers precisely because the CNRS was too conservative scientifically and unresponsive to the problems of industry. Furthermore, the Ministry of

[32] *Le Monde,* Dec. 16, 1966.

Finance continues to resist the principle of financial autonomy essential to the institute concept.[33]

Doubtless the fundamental cause of the conservatism of the CNRS, and of the universities as well, is the system of allocating resources to professors, laboratories, and CNRS researchers regardless of the merits of the research to be undertaken. Unless CNRS and the universities shift to the project-grant system employed by the U.S. priority cannot be given to research of the highest scientific or practical merit. By forcing scientists to compete for financial support, the project-grant system creates an incentive for them to undertake those researches which in the judgment of the leadership of the CNRS and the universities would do the most to advance French science and technology. The need for this type of reform was stressed by Jacques Monod in contrasting the CNRS's method of allocating resources to that of the project-grant employed by the programs of concerted action:

> In our discipline, the method of financing which appears to me to be the best, but which unhappily has not yet been adopted by the CNRS, is to finance small teams. Rather than distribute credits or technical aid to a professor, without reference to his program or research team, I prefer much more financing by programs, that is, the mode of financing that we have adopted in the General Delegation for molecular biology: support is given to a responsible person, generally one responsible for a small team to carry out a program for a period of, say, three years. This support covers personnel, equipment, and operations.[34]

Such a reform, of course, would be greatly resisted because it strikes at the privileges of the university professors and career researchers of the CNRS.

[33] *Le Monde*, June 23, 1967.
[34] *Le Monde*, Nov. 23, 1966.

The Balance Sheet of Modernization:

THE REFORM OF MEDICAL-BIOLOGICAL RESEARCH

Though French doctors and scientists were preeminent in the founding of modern medicine and biology, these subjects have been in a disreputable state in France for over a century. In order to remedy the situation in medical education, practice, and research, a special interministerial committee was formed in 1956 under the chairmanship of Professor Robert Debré, president of the Academy of Medicine and one of France's most distinguished doctors.[35] By a fortuitous circumstance, Dr. Debré's son, Michel Debré, had become Prime Minister by the time that the committee proposed its radical recommendations for the reform of French medical education and research. Together father and son overrode the strong opposition of the medical *facultés* and saw the committee's report become law on December 30, 1958.

The basic objectives of the Debré reform were to remove the long-standing cleavage between the medical *facultés* and the hospitals and to force the medical professor to devote more time to teaching and research and less to his lucrative private practice. To overcome the cleavage between the hospitals and the universities, which are administered by separate ministries, and improve the coordination of medical education, the reformers borrowed the British and American concept of the university-hospital center (CHU) which combines the responsibilities for research, teaching, and patient care.[36]

Perhaps the most significant aspect of the reform was the introduction of basic research laboratories into the new CHU's. If successful, this innovation will lessen the traditional gap between the basic bio-medical sciences and medical practice and education in France. In a sense, therefore, the Debré reform

[35] Dr. Debré's ideas are contained in *Les Cahiers de la République*, No. 5, Jan.-Feb. 1957, 124-26.
[36] Because the reform infringes on the liberty of professors to have a private practice it has been greatly resented.

seeks to bring about in the realm of medicine that integration of theory and practice which is also being sought in the industrial and military spheres.[37]

Though important, the Debré reform left untouched the larger problem of the organization and support of bio-medical research in France.[38] After 1945 the responsibility for the support of medical research rested with the National Institute of Health (INH). In several respects, however, the research program of the INH was very inadequate: (1) it supported essentially clinical (applied) research in the hospitals and gave little assistance to the basic biological sciences such as genetics and microbiology that have been revolutionizing medical practice; also, (2) the INH operated on a budget several times less than that spent by the British Medical Research Council and many times less than its American equivalent, the National Institutes of Health;[39] (3) the personnel statutes of the INH discouraged doctors and scientists from taking up medical research as a career; and (4) medical research was fragmented among a number of institutions that had little to do with one another; applied clinical research was the province of the hospitals administered by the Ministry of Health while basic research (such as it was) was located in the medical schools and the CNRS under the Ministry of National Education.

The INH was replaced in July 1964 by the National Institute for Health and Medical Research (INSERN) whose essential responsibilities are two-fold. INSERN was given much the same responsibility in the area of bio-medical research that the CNRS has in the over-all structure of French basic and applied research. This advance over the INH has been made possible by the improvement in organization and a great expansion in

[37] "La Recherche Scientifique," p. 3.

[38] For an evaluation of medical research in France see *Le Progrès Scientifique*, No. 83, Apr. 1965.

[39] U.S. National Science Foundation, *International Science Notes*, No. 8, August 1963, p. 5.

manpower and funds.[40] Secondly, INSERN has the responsibility of coordinating and developing the whole realm of the biological-medical sciences in France.

INSERN is modeled after the American National Institutes of Health. Like the Institutes, INSERN is organized by disease categories and multidisciplinary problems rather than by scientific disciplines. In contrast to the old French INH, the new organization supports fundamental research. Following a long-established practice of the U.S. Institutes of Health, scientific advisory panels have been appointed to guide the distribution of research and training grants to scientists in universities and other research institutions. Furthermore, the Minister of Health has created a scientific advisory committee of eminent scientists to advise him on medical research and the health problems of the nation.[41] The significance of this innovation is that in the area of medicine and biology, as in so many other areas, younger scientists representing the basic sciences and committed to a transformation of scientific institutions have come into positions of influence and power.

The changes in medical research represent an important departure, but the problems remaining are large. The medical *facultés* have been largely untouched by recent scientific and educational reforms. Whether the CHU will develop into relatively autonomous organizations, free of the burdensome and inflexible control of the ministries and with a capability of providing leadership for the research effort, remains to be seen. Though the French are founding important new laboratories, chairs, and institutes in modern areas, problems remain: the creation of a satisfactory infrastructure for biomedical research, the selection of medical professors on the basis of merit, and the allocation of research funds according

[40] OECD, *Reviews of National Science Policy—France*, p. 41.
[41] *Le Monde*, Oct. 27, 1964.

to scientific priorities, have only begun.[42] In short, in medical research and practice one sees in microcosm (only exaggerated) the problems that limit French science and the translation of new knowledge into new techniques.

The Reform of Technical and Industrial Institutions

The French economic revival after World War II, and especially after 1950, was based on a stronger technological spurt than that of any other European state.[43] Her nationalized industries, technical ministries, and private firms were outpacing other European enterprises in technological innovation. After 1960, however, French industrial research and development began to lose its momentum and her technological balance of payments ran more of a deficit each year. Though the industrial sectors that show the greatest deficits tend to be ones in which research activity is slight, the relative decline in the technological position of France is also evident in those research-intensive industries (*industrie de pointe*), such as electronics and chemicals, where the French have concentrated their efforts.[44] Trying to overcome this deterioration in their position, the French Government is carrying out reforms in three areas.

THE RAPPORT BETWEEN BASIC RESEARCH
AND TECHNOLOGICAL INNOVATION

The first problem to which the French are turning their attention is the absence of rapport between the source of new scientific knowledge (especially the university) and the industrial user. One approach to the problem is the creation of na-

[42] For a report on the status of medical reform see *Le Monde*, Jan. 26, 27, and 28, Nov. 16, 1966.

[43] Charles Kindleberger, "The Postwar Resurgence of the French Economy," in Hoffmann, *In Search of France*, pp. 148-50.

[44] OECD, *Reviews of National Science Policy—France*, p. 80.

tional institutes in various technical areas which will bring together basic and applied scientists from universities and industries. Another is the easing of the rules governing industrial research contracts to university laboratories and permitting professors to be industrial consultants. A third approach is to increase the number of scientists teaching in the *grandes écoles* and train engineers in the *facultés*.[45]

Another reform area is that of state assistance to R and D in the private sector. In contrast to the United States, where nearly three-fourths of the total amount of Federal funds allocated for R and D goes to private, competitive industries, France until recently has given few R and D contracts to private industry.[46] Prior to 1958 nearly all R and D work in connection with atomic energy or military weaponry was carried out in government laboratories.

In a world where R and D are determinant factors in economic competition, the fallacy of ignoring the private sector became apparent as France's technological position began to slip. The challenge facing France was stated bluntly in October 1963 by Minister for Science Palewski in a speech to the National Assembly:

> The state cannot be unaware that the public authorities in the most powerful and highly industrialized countries do not hesitate to finance through contracts a substantial proportion of the research done by private firms. The diversity of assistance provided for so-called private research, which is on a small scale in the case of France and on a massive scale in the case of the United States, gives rise to a new form of unequal competition in international economic relations.[47]

[45] *Ibid.*, p. 108.

[46] *Ibid.*, p. 40. The Government has of course given indirect aid such as tax incentives and support for the cooperative research associations.

[47] *Ibid.*, p. 84.

The state has begun to "nationalize" industrial research and, in effect, form a partnership with private industry. In both fundamental and applied research the contract mechanism is being used extensively by DGRST and DRME to aid French industry. In the case of DGRST the aid has been dispersed primarily through the programs of concerted action. Initially devoted almost entirely to fundamental research in the university, the proportion of these monies allocated to applied research and to private industry has been mounting steadily.[48] Under the Fourth Plan 291 million francs (about $60 million) was provided to launch research which included mechanical engineering, building and public works, and macromolecular chemistry (plastics); under the Fifth Plan 707 million francs (about $140 million) has been called for to support programs of concerted action on computers, automation, metallurgy, and others.[49] The DRME distributed 61.5 million francs to French industry in 1965 in the areas of its research interests; during the course of the Fifth Plan the total amount to be distributed under contract will be approximately 710 million francs.[50]

These measures, however, do not attack directly what the French themselves view as the nub of their problem—the inability of French firms to develop good ideas or inventions into new technological innovations. As Joseph Schumpeter first pointed out, it is not enough to do research; a firm must have the incentive and funds to develop and test the inventions and concepts to which its research gives rise.[51] Without this innovative capacity the French fear they cannot participate successfully in international economic competition. "In brief," the

[48] *Le Progrès Scientifique*, No. 97, June 1966, p. 3.
[49] *Ibid.*, p. 14.
[50] *Ibid.*, p. 4.
[51] The distinction between the conception (invention) of a new technology and its commercial development (innovation) was first suggested by Schumpeter, *The Theory of Economic Development*, Harvard University Press, 1934.

Minister for Science told the National Assembly in October 1963:

> It is as though the findings of our fundamental and applied research were not sufficiently exploited by our own industry. For reasons which are often very understandable, industry hesitates to advance the cost of research that is often expensive and hazardous. It seems more attractive in the short run to use foreign licences, even if in the long run this may compromise the chances and even the very independence of the firm.[52]

At the same time, French firms find themselves in competition with American firms which not only have immense resources of their own but frequently are subsidized through government programs (FIGURE 4). "The American method of subvention for industrial innovations, very simply, but very costly, consists in supporting nearly the total of the sums for research and development on the basis of noneconomic development themes, e.g., space and military. Free economic play is somewhat nullified."[53] On the other hand, the French Government reasons that France with her more limited resources, cannot depend entirely upon atomic, space, and military programs to subsidize industrial innovation. Instead she must select for support many technological developments that are tied directly to essential economic needs.[54]

To achieve this goal the Government established in 1963 a program of development assistance which seeks to accomplish in the area of technological development what the program of concerted actions of DGRST and the research contracts of DRME attempt in the area of basic and applied research. A number of "round tables" composed of scientists, engineers, and other

[52] OECD, *Reviews of National Science Policy—France*, p. 81.
[53] *Le Progrès Scientifique*, June 1966, p. 57.
[54] *Ibid.*

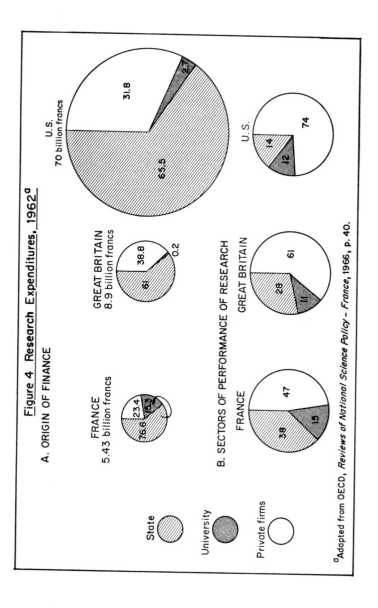

Figure 4 Research Expenditures, 1962[a]

A. ORIGIN OF FINANCE

U.S.
70 billion francs

31.8
65.5
2.7

FRANCE
5.43 billion francs

76.6
23.4

GREAT BRITAIN
8.9 billion francs

61
38.8
0.2

B. SECTORS OF PERFORMANCE OF RESEARCH

U.S.

74
14
12

FRANCE

47
38
15

GREAT BRITAIN

61
28
11

State

University

Private firms

[a]Adapted from OECD, *Reviews of National Science Policy – France*, 1966, p. 40.

experts have been established to study under the guidance of DGRST the feasibility of initiating "research-development" programs in designated industrial sectors.[55] Employing a set of criteria such as the state of the art, the importance for economic and military independence, and the market conditions, several areas, or themes, for concentration are selected. These developmental policies are then put into effect by a technical committee composed primarily of representatives from the Ministry of Finance, the Ministry of Industry, and DGRST.[56] The committee then selects projects from those submitted by industry.

In essence this is a program that seeks to encourage technological innovation in specially selected industrial sectors through the socialization of risks. Under its terms the state finances approximately half the cost of a firm's developmental project. If the innovation is a success the firm repays the loan to the state; if not, the loan is cancelled in its entirety.

The first program of development assistance was begun in 1965 and was devoted to two industrial sectors: mechanical construction, and electrical and electronic construction. To advance developments in these areas the state set aside 10 million francs ($2 million). For 1966 two new sectors, metallurgy and chemistry, were added and 59 million francs was authorized for the total program. In 1967 the amount was raised to 125 million francs and a new concept of "horizontal themes" was introduced.[57] The purpose here is to tie together technological advances in the primary sectors of the economy, with the secondary sectors depending on them. In this way the development of a new primary material such as a plastic, for example, can stimulate innovations in textiles.[58]

[55] *Ibid.*, p. 57.
[56] *Ibid.*, p. 58.
[57] *Le Monde,* July 16, 1966.
[58] *Le Progrès Scientifique,* June 1966, p. 60.

330

This program of development assistance is a major change in the state's attitude toward the economy. In the past the Ministry of Industry gave minimal support to developmental projects through its Fund for Social and Economic Development, but the state has been reluctant to expand its role much beyond the provision of research contracts. The Ministry of Finance, in particular, has resisted the assumption by the state of the financial burden involved in promoting technological development. At the same time, science planners have insisted on this extension of the state's role in the economy. At a May 1965 meeting of the Interministerial Committee for Scientific and Technological Research, attended by General de Gaulle, the advocates of expanding the program carried the day. The directing role of DGRST in the program was enhanced and increased funds were allocated.[59] Within the framework of the Fifth Plan a major emphasis is placed on the program of development assistance.[60] Yet, it should be appreciated, the sums involved are really very modest.

But in formulating the program of development assistance one vital area of scientific technology was not included: computers, automation, and data processing. No aspect of modern technology is of greater interest to the French and arouses in them more anxiety concerning American technological hegemony. But though there has been much agitation and talk little has been done. Machines Bull "fell" to General Electric; the remainder of the industry (15 percent of the French market) has been fragmented among several ineffective firms more interested in feuding among themselves than in cooperating against the common foe, the U.S. The Government, for its part, has stood aloof from the plight of the industry and has done little significant work in its own laboratories.[61]

[59] *Le Monde,* May 16-17, 1965.
[60] *Le Progrès Scientifique,* June 1966, p. 58.
[61] Raymond Saint-Paul, "L'Automation: Peu de Recherches en France," *L'Expansion Scientifique,* No. 9, Apr. 1961.

In 1965, discussions began within the Government to elaborate a national program to create a viable French computer industry and provide France with her own information-handling and automation capabilities. One year later, on July 20, 1966, *Plan Calcul* was announced. The essence of the plan[62] is as follows:

1. The government is to encourage the fusion of two French computer companies, Compagnie Européenne d'Automatisme Électronique (CAE) and the Société d'Électronique et d'Automatisme (SEA). The new company, Compagnie Internationale Pour l'Informatique (CII) is to produce a "French" line of computers. A second new company, named Sperac (Systèmes et Périphériques, Associés aux Calculateurs), is to supply auxiliary equipment.

2. The government will provide funds and contracts to support the merged firms.

3. The government will appoint a general delegate for data processing attached to the office of the Prime Minister who would be responsible for the elaboration of the *Plan Calcul*. He will have funds to support scientific and technical research and will coordinate the national information and computer program both within and without the Government. In addition, there is to be founded an Institute for Automation and Information Research (IRIA) to conduct research and train engineers and scientists in computer and information sciences.

The goal of the *Plan Calcul* is to develop and produce in a relatively few years a computer which will capture a place for France in the growing world market for computers and, at the least, decrease French dependency on the United States. Initially, however, CII is to produce under license a computer

---

[62] *Le Monde,* July 21, 1966.

model of the American firm, Scientific Data Systems. While this will give the French additional experience, the long-term success of CII will be dependent on basic research to develop new approaches to computer logic and design radically different from those chosen by the Americans. Though this strategy is more risky than that of following American experience it could lay a sounder foundation for a possible French leadership in future generations of computers.

There is an irony in the efforts of the French state to play a greater role in industrial R and D—namely that the United States, the world's foremost free enterprise nation, is forcing traditionally *dirigeant* France to socialize the basic resources of the modern economy—scientific R and D. In a situation where an economy, two-thirds of whose firms are relatively small (a total work force of less than 1,200 employees), is competing in a world market with industrial giants, the French government believes it must assume more of the burden of the industrial R and D effort.

PROMOTION OF INDUSTRIAL CONCENTRATION

The third area of concern regarding industrial R and D is the relatively small scale and dispersed nature of French industry and its consequent inability to finance long-term basic or applied research and ambitious development programs. "A comparison with four other European countries shows that in 1962 research activity and its financing in [French] firms were below the average of all countries considered. Although in 1963 French industrialists considerably stepped up their efforts (by 11 percent) they do not yet seem to have caught up with their European colleagues. . . ."[63] This failing is attributable in part to the attitudes of French business, but the basic limitation is the scale of French corporations and their meager financial resources.

[63] OECD, *Reviews of National Science Policy—France*, p. 116.

333

In a free, competitive market small French firms tend not to invest their limited resources in long-term basic, or even applied, research where the results in new knowledge are available to competitors at home and abroad. Though larger French firms invest a higher proportion of their revenues in R and D than do American competitors, the difference in scale leaves the French firm at a disadvantage in absolute terms and exposes them to a greater risk. The problem they face was stated by a leading French businessman in the following example:

> A firm with a turnover of F15 million cannot spend F3 million on development without considerable risks. These F3 million represent 20 percent of its turnover; allowing for the time needed for tooling up, development and subsequent profits, it will take at least six years to amortize the cost. . . . If the venture failed it would mean catastrophe. On the other hand, for a firm with a turnover of F150 million, development work costing F3 million, i.e., 2 percent of its turnover, raises no problem. In large firms, . . . there is a considerable concentration of research resources. . . . However, even the big French firms are often smaller than their competitors in other countries.[64]

In response to this situation, and in anticipation of the lowering of tariff barriers due to the Common Market and the Kennedy Round of tariff liberalization, the French Government is actively encouraging corporate mergers and industrial cooperation. In the opinion of the formulators of the Fifth Plan, if French industry is to "counterattack" the entry of foreign firms into the French economy then "in most of the large sectors of the economy (aluminum, steel, mechanical, electrical construction, electronics, automobile, aviation, chemistry, phar-

[64] Quoted in *ibid.*, p. 78.

macy, etc.) the number of these groups must be very limited, often even reduced to one or two."[65]

In effect, the French are marshalling and reorganizing their industrial forces for the gigantic economic struggle they foresee as the Common Market and tariff liberalization come into operation. Through the removal of legal inhibitions to corporate concentration and the creation of positive inducements, the French Government is seeking to force the pace of industrial concentration. Both the Fund for Economic and Social Development (FDES) and the award of research contracts, for example, favor and encourage corporate merger. More potent, however, are the economic forces coming into play with the advent of the Common Market, the squeeze on corporate profits over the past couple of years, and the belief of French businessmen that size is a prerequisite if they are to overcome the advantages of American and European competitors.

As a result of these influences the French economy is undergoing a rapid change and corporate concentration is proceeding at a rate three times faster than it was only a decade ago. Already the concentration movement has led to the elimination of many hundreds of small industrial firms and the regrouping of established firms into larger enterprises such as Thomson-Brandt (electronics, appliances) and Dassault-Bréquet (aviation).[66] In addition, important agreements for cooperation in R and D are taking place, such as that of Renault and Peugeot in automobiles, and the Compagnie Générale de Télégraphie sans Fil and Schneider in specialized computers. While these mergers and cooperative arrangements are by no means sufficient, they are obviously a necessary pre-

[65] Commissariat au Plan, *Cinquième Plan de Développement Économique et Social (1966-1970)*, 1965, I, 68-69.

[66] Jacques Houssiaux, "Les Tendances de la Concentration des Entreprises en France," *Service Direction*, Jan. 1961, pp. 51-56. For a listing of some of the more important recent mergers see *France Actuelle*, XVI, No. 7, Apr. 1, 1967.

requisite for a greater research and development effort by French industry.

ADVANCED SCIENTIFIC TECHNOLOGY:

EMPHASIS AND WEAKNESS

Following the lead of the U.S., the Soviet Union, and Great Britain, the French R and D effort has emphasized primarily advanced scientific technologies which are of military significance or are believed to be the growth sections of the modern economy. As TABLE 18 reveals, nearly 80 percent of the total French R and D effort is being devoted to four industrial sectors—aeronautics, energy, electronics, and chemicals.[67] Fur-

TABLE 18.

Concentration of Industrial Research, 1963[a]

Industrial Sector	Percentage of:	
	R & D finance	Total research workers
Electronics and electrical engineering	25	28
Aeronautics and space	24	21
Energy, nuclear engineering, and oil	14	12
Chemicals and pharmaceutical products	14	15
Total	77	76

[a] Adapted from OECD, *Reviews of National Science Policy—France,* p. 79.

thermore, though the French state provides only one-third of the funds for industrial R and D, 89 percent of these funds go to three sectors only—aerospace (73 percent financed by the state), nuclear energy (81 percent), and electronics (36.5 percent). All other sectors receive only about 90 million francs in state aid, which is only two percent of the state science budget. This Government support is limited to a few large firms; 10

[67] OECD, *Reviews of National Science Policy—France,* p. 79.

firms in 1963 received three-fourths of the funds paid out by the state to the competitive sector.[68]

Despite the rather impressive concentration of the total national effort, the French position in each of the above areas is in peril. In aeronautics French experts are in general agreement that the French aviation industry, along with that of the rest of western Europe, is in a state of crisis because of American competition.[69] The industry, one of the country's foremost earners of foreign exchange, is finding it increasingly difficult to compete against the American aerospace industry. As one report has pointed out, the American aerospace industry's domestic civilian market enabled Boeing and Douglas to sell over 400 aircraft between June 1964 and June 1965, compared to the fewer than 50 civilian aircraft sold domestically by the entire French and British industries.[70] The Plowden Report on the plight of the British (and by implication the French) aircraft industry considered the American advantages of size to be overwhelming:

> In spite of the scale of American [aircraft] exports, their home market is nine times larger than their export sales. The corresponding British ratio is 3½ to 1, and the French 2 to 1. With such a vast home market completely assured for civil aircraft, the Americans have a solid base for overseas operations.[71]

With respect to R and D, of the $12 billion spent by the American aerospace industry in 1964 90 percent came from the Federal Government through defense and space con-

[68] *Ibid.*, p. 76.

[69] An excellent survey of the industry is "La Construction Aéronautique et Spatiale Française," *Entreprise*, Apr. 4, 1964, Supplement au No. 447.

[70] Christopher Layton, *Trans-Atlantic Investment*, The Atlantic Institute, 1966, pp. 96-97.

[71] The Report of the Committee of Inquiry into the Aircraft Industry Appointed by the Prime Minister, Cmnd. 2,853, 1965, p. 5.

tracts.[72] In no other industrial sector is the spinoff of military research into the civilian economy more apparent, with the result that both American military and civilian aircraft frequently can be priced under comparable French aircraft on the export market and can thereby outsell both their British and French competitors. The principal French military aircraft, the *Mirage IV,* for example, is not holding its own against its American equivalent in the military market, the *F-III.* In the civilian area, France's showpiece, the *Caravelle,* has not matched the sales of its American counterpart, the Boeing 727; in seven years of production, only 216 *Caravelles* have been sold, against the sale of 494 Boeing 727's in less than three years.[73] As 40 percent of the income of the French aviation industry comes from its exports this poor performance poses a serious threat.[74]

With the phasing out of *Caravelle* production, and excepting the *Concorde* project, the French aviation industry has become heavily devoted to military aircraft. Two-thirds of the export orders in 1965 were for military equipment (fighter aircraft, helicopters, antitank missiles).[75] A large proportion of the resources of the industry is being devoted also to the production of planes and equipment for the *force de frappe,* severely limiting for the time being design work on civilian aircraft.[76]

The situation suggests the vast changes taking place in the area of aviation technology and their implication for the French. Prior to 1950 the French aviation industry was successful largely because design and ingenuity were all important. With the increasing complexity of aircraft and especially of supersonic aircraft, heavy investment in research, develop-

[72] Layton, *Trans-Atlantic Investment,* p. 96.
[73] *Le Monde,* May 13, 1966.
[74] *Le Monde,* Apr. 8, 1965.
[75] *The Economist,* July 9, 1966, p. 169.
[76] *Le Monde,* June 13-14, 1965.

ment, and prototype-testing has become crucial. Significantly the only French aircraft since 1945 that has really paid off is the *subsonic Caravelle*. With the coming of the supersonic era the French—like the British—find their future in aviation threatened.

It is for these economic and technical reasons that the *Concorde* project is so important to the French. Though condemned by many as a worthless search for prestige, it is in the area of aeronautics the functional equivalent of the space and nuclear weapons programs—namely, an instrument by which to modernize the French aviation industry. In the words of one of France's top aeronautical engineers, "The project has been very important for us, very stimulating. It was a unique occasion to have money to push ahead on all these technical fronts. All was permitted for *Concorde*. 'It is for *Concorde*? Okay.' "[77]

Turning to another major area of advanced technology—atomic energy—one encounters apprehension among the French. At the least, the French atomic energy industry, based on natural uranium reactors, appears to have reached a crucial point in its development. Though technically successful, natural uranium power plants (except perhaps those of immense scale) cannot compete economically against American and British enriched uranium reactors, which are about 10 percent cheaper. The French have sold only one reactor abroad to Spain, under an arrangement whereby the French agreed to purchase back part of the electricity.

Of greater significance, France herself may have to import enriched uranium reactors to meet her own growing energy requirements. By 1975 90 percent of the increased demand for electricity must be met by atomic energy and apparently if

[77] Interview with Philippe Poisson-Quinton, *International Science and Technology*, Apr. 1967, p. 80.

Électricité de France has its way, this energy will be supplied by the less expensive enriched uranium reactors.[78]

France stands alone today against the United States, Great Britain, and the Soviet Union in supporting the value of natural versus enriched uranium. Great Britain, which also originally chose to develop natural-uranium reactors, abandoned the effort when it proved uneconomic, and Britain is now converting its uranium separation plant from military to peaceful uses.[79] Looked at solely from an economic viewpoint France would appear to be facing an increasing burden in the pursuit of her policy of *indépendance énergétique*.

According to the Commission on Electronics for the Fourth Plan the French electronics industry is in a serious condition.[80] As we have already seen, the French have suffered a large deficit balance of technological payments in electronics, and their computer industry is in a state of crisis. In the case of computers the magnitude of the French problem of "catching up" is readily apparent. While the French Government has selected one of their top engineers and managers—Robert Galley, the builder of Pierrelatte and Marcoule—to put the *Plan Calcul* into effect, the problems he faces are enormous. Can the French, for example, realistically hope to match IBM's new *System 360*, which cost $5 billion to develop? During the course of the Fifth Plan the French Government has provided only about $130 million for computer development. Furthermore, the French firms whose very limited resources and talents must be combined to compete with the American computer firms, are highly resistant to any diminution of their individual identity; and management resists bringing in new blood. Although novel basic concepts and much fundamental

[78] For a survey of the French atomic power industry see Nicolas Vichney, *Le Monde*, May 10, 1966.

[79] *Le Monde*, Dec. 11, 1965.

[80] Commissariat au Plan, Commission Permanente de l'Électronique, "Situation de l'Électronique en France," Mar. 1962.

research are necessary to overtake the Americans, French universities have no chairs devoted to computer logic and theory and there are relatively few researchers in industry.[81] Moreover, the intention of the French Government is to overcome France's low standing in the computer field *by 1968*. And even if the venture succeeds—which is highly doubtful—there is serious concern whether there will be a sufficient market for the projected French design.[82]

Similarly, the French chemical industry is judged to be in a dangerous position by virtue of its highly dispersed character, the relatively small size of its many firms, and the absence of state aid.[83] A meeting of high civil servants called together by the Prime Minister to assess the status of the industry found it, along with the mechanical and aluminum industries, to be on the "red" list of industries menaced by international competition.[84] The report of the chemical commission for the Fifth Plan came to the same conclusion.[85]

In the areas of advanced scientific technology the scale of French industry and of the nation herself is inadequate to the task that the French have set for themselves. France finds it increasingly difficult either to support the broad basic research in all the areas judged to be important or to develop the concepts that *do* emerge from French academic and industrial research. To meet these problems the French are turning increasingly to international cooperation in R and D. The nature and probable success of these efforts will be the concern of Chapter 12.

[81] *Electronic News*, Sec. 2, Nov. 7, 1966, p. 18.

[82] *Le Monde*, Dec. 9, 1966.

[83] In France 60 chemical firms share 50 percent of the sales, compared to Italy where one firm controls 40 percent and in Germany 3 firms control 30 percent. Cf. Victor McElheny, "Europe Considers Industrial Mergers," *Science*, Vol. 142, No. 3,721, Apr. 22, 1966, 486.

[84] *Le Monde*, Apr. 18-19, 1965.

[85] *Le Monde*, Mar. 22, 1966. For an excellent survey of the French chemical industry see *Le Progrès Scientifique*, No. 73, June 15, 1964.

Chapter 11 · The Balance Sheet of Modernization: The Professionalization and Governance of Science

The reform of structures such as laboratory consolidation, the establishment of research priorities, and financial reform are very little advanced. The professors continue to run the committees empowered to do the reforming, and the professors are too set off from the rest of society to see its needs. Even the Comité des Sages *is strongly university controlled.*

—A FRUSTRATED SCIENCE REFORMER, *1965*

The emergence of science as a social institution in the modern world is dependent on the establishment of an infrastructure of research facilities, the professionalization of research, and the achievement of an effective governing mechanism for the scientific enterprise. In the preceding chapter the development of scientific and technical organizations was discussed. The concern of this chapter is the extent to which present-day France has eliminated those aspects of the Napoleonic system which have been impediments to the professionalization and effective governance of science.

The Professionalization of Research

Though France may be credited with originating the concept of scientific research as a form of livelihood, the professionalization of research advanced very little between the time of Napoleon and World War II. Several of the most important causes of this retardation have already been discussed: the underdevelopment of research as a career; the relatively small production of scientists and engineers; and the absence of formal training of scientists and engineers in scientific research. Since 1945, and especially after the advent of the Fifth Republic, a number of important developments have begun to improve the quality and quantity of the scientific-technical elite in France.

RESEARCH AS A CAREER

In founding the CNRS scientists like Jean Perrin foresaw the establishment of scientific research as one of the *grands corps de l'État* which would take its place along with the *Conseil d'État*, the *Inspection des Finances*, and the university professors. The original statutes of CNRS, however, did not elevate research to such a secure and attractive status. To correct this the Scientific Advisory Committee proposed in 1959 that steps be taken to enhance the appeal of research as a career. On the basis of this recommendation the Government on December 9, 1959 issued three decrees altering the status of CNRS personnel. Although the improvement in the situation of the technicians left much to be desired, the scientific career within CNRS was placed on a relatively sound basis for the first time. Either by being incorporated into the civil service, as was the case with the upper ranks, or by receiving the benefits of civil service status through renewable contracts, the researchers in CNRS were offered the possibility of much more attractive careers.

In the university, too, the opportunities for a career have been increasing, largely because of the expansion in teaching positions caused by the student population explosion. Between 1928 and 1963 the number of professorships in the science *facultés* almost tripled, from 192 to 498; even more significant, the number of lower level positions was expanded approximately 19 times during this same period (see TABLE 19).[1] With the expansion in the number of chairs it has been possible to establish newer specializations in the *facultés* and to award chairs on the basis of merit alone (*chaire à titre personnel*) to outstanding scientists whose specialties may not be tied to the undergraduate degree.

[1] OECD, *Reviews of National Science Policy—France*, 1966, p. 56.

343

TABLE 19.

Trend of Teaching Staff in the Faculties of Science[a]

	1928	1960-61	1962-63	1963-64
Professors occupying chairs, and individual professors	192	394	468	498
Senior lecturers	76	674	796	878
Lecturers, assistants, etc.	246	2,564	3,961	4,731
Total	514	3,632	5,225	6,107

[a] Adapted from OECD, *Reviews of National Science Policy—France,* 1966, p. 56.

The shape of the scientist's career within the university is being transformed. With the increase in the number of teaching posts, especially at the level of the assistant and senior lecturer (*maître de conférence*), a hierarchy of academic positions similar to that of American universities is taking shape. For the first time in France it is becoming possible to have a teaching-research career wholly within the system of higher education, starting at the level of assistant and working up to the rank of professor.[2]

Also, the *agrégation* is becoming less important as a prerequisite for a university career in the natural sciences. Its demise began in the 1950s with the refusal of CEA and CNRS to use it as a screening device for their fellowship holders. While the *agrégation* is still necessary to becoming a *professeur de faculté*, the tradition which saw the *agrégation* as a defense of a broad culture against narrow specialization is passing.[3]

Along with these favorable trends in CNRS and the university potentially far-reaching steps are being taken to channel graduates of the *grandes écoles* into research careers. Beginning in 1958 a series of reforms has been undertaken to facilitate the

[2] Raymond Aron, "La Crise de l'Université," *Preuves,* May 1964, p. 18.

[3] *Ibid.*

entry of graduates of the *École Polytechnique* into CNRS where they can prepare themselves as researchers. Research positions have also been created for graduates of the school within the traditional corps, such as the *Corps des Ponts et Chaussées* and in the military services themselves. By a decree of July 4, 1959 a new concept—*la botte recherche*—was put into practice, permitting highly qualified graduates to prepare for the doctor's degree. In effect, this is a significant step toward the recognition of scientific research as a career for *Polytechniciens*.[4] In addition, several important industries in the nationalized sector, such as *Électricité de France*, now require that new engineers on their payrolls spend several years as researchers prior to entering administration. Symptomatic of these changes is the fact that by 1963, 45 of the 300 graduates of the *Polytechnique* had forgone the traditional career pattern in favor of doing research at CNRS. Perhaps of greater importance than the number is the point that the students who graduate at the top of the class are beginning to choose research.

The changes are significant, indeed, if they mean that scientific research will become one stage in the careers of France's technical and administrative elite. In any society the qualified brainpower capable of doing scientific research is limited and its optimum use requires that those members of the society capable of doing research should spend their early and creative years in research before moving on to administrative and other positions. This has become an established career pattern in the United States, and the perceptible shift in the career choice of the *Polytechnicien* may indicate or trigger a wider movement in this direction in France. If so, it would do much to increase the quantity *and* quality of French scientists and enhance still more the attractiveness of research as a career.

[4] R. Cheradame, "La Recherche Scientifique et Technique," *L'École Polytechnique en 1960*, 1960, pp. 89-91.

THE PRODUCTION OF SCIENTISTS AND ENGINEERS[5]

A task of French science policy is to balance the supply of and demand for scientific and technical personnel. France's hopes soared in the early sixties as it appeared France would soon outstrip all other European nations in the production of scientists and engineers. But as the decade has worn on France's great expectations have turned to anxiety that she would not have enough scientists or engineers to meet her rapidly growing demand or to overcome her inferiority relative to other industrial countries.[6]

The supply of scientists and engineers in France is largely dependent on the number of secondary school science graduates (*bacheliers*), that is, those students who under the present system elect to take their *baccalauréat* in "Mathematics," "Mathematics and Technology," or "Experimental Sciences." Only the former two groups of *bacheliers*, however, can prepare for entry into one of the *grandes écoles* or can qualify for higher education in mathematics and the physical sciences. The *bacheliers* in "Experimental Sciences" concentrate on the biological and medical sciences.

Beginning in 1950, and for the eight succeeding years, the number of science *bacheliers*—"Mathematics" and "Mathematics and Technology"—increased at a remarkable rate. The *bacheliers* increased from 8,000, or 25 percent of the total, to 20,000 in 1960, 34 percent of the total.[7] If one added experimental sciences, over 60 percent of French youth were then taking their *baccalauréats* in science and mathematics. Projecting the trend, the Education Commission of the Fourth Plan foresaw that by 1970 over 40 percent of the *bacheliers* would be in "Mathematics" and "Mathematics and Technology." Unfortu-

[5] This section is based primarily on OECD, *Reviews of National Science Policy—France.*

[6] "Où Vont les Ingénieurs?" *Entreprise*, Jan. 7, 1961, pp. 35-36.

[7] OECD, *Reviews of National Science Policy—France*, p. 50.

nately this rate of growth suddenly fell off after 1960, and by 1964 only 23 percent sat for the *baccalauréat* in the two fields and only 29 percent in the "Experimental Sciences."[8] While the reasons for this reversal are not altogether clear, the inadequacy of mathematics training in the *lycée* and the extreme difficulty of the former two fields, in contrast to the philosophy *baccalauréat*, were important factors. In 1966, for example, 56.8 percent of the students who took the mathematics *baccalauréat* failed.[9] These two figures—the reduced number of students who take the science *baccalauréat* and the high failure rate—have dealt a severe blow to the expectation of French science planners in the early 1960s that France would soon greatly outdistance Great Britain and West Germany in the production of engineers and scientists.

Despite its ups and downs the general rise in the number of science *bacheliers* has been reflected in increased university enrollments. In 1900 the number of science students in the *facultés* was about 4,000. In 1945 this figure had increased to 16,000, and in 1966, 100,500. While projections for 1970 will not meet earlier expectations, the total number of science students in higher education at the undergraduate level is expected to increase substantially by the end of the decade.[10]

What is more important, however, is the number of science students who actually complete their undergraduate studies and the number who then go on to take higher degrees in science. (With respect to the former, the attrition rate is nothing less than appalling. During the first year of university studies approximately one-fourth drop out, and over 70 percent never pass the *licence* in its entirety; most of these failing students have no place else to go and their potential is lost to the French economy.) Between 1950 and 1960 the number of graduates

[8] *Ibid.*
[9] *Le Monde*, Oct. 13, 1966.
[10] OECD, *Reviews of National Science Policy—France*, p. 54.

TABLE 20.

Higher Education—Trend in Numbers of Science Students and Graduates[a]

	1954-55[b]	1959-60[b]	1960-61	1961-62	1962-63
Total students:					
University (includes students attending establishments attached to Universities or Faculties)	150,631	194,763	203,375	232,610	270,906
			+11,297	+12,204	+11,434
Higher ed. & higher tech. ed. establishments (includes students in other establishments)	32,163	39,979	41,497	51,294	57,534
		13,670	13,421	20,992	22,529
total students	182,794[c]	221,072	242,748	275,116	317,345
pop. aged 19 to 24	3,682,955	3,409,171	3,303,473	3,420,676	3,502,800
percentage of age group	4.96	6.48	7.35	8.04	9.06
Science students:					
Faculties of science (enrolled)	35,248	65,506	68,062	75,282	88,603
(nonenrolled)			+ 3,040	+ 1,171	+ 1,287
Higher scientific ed. & industrial tech. ed. (public & private) (includes enrolled in other schools)	11,154	18,658	21,864	22,209	23,487
		6,403	7,001	8,095	8,472
total students	46,402[c]	77,761	85,965	90,567	104,905
percentage of age group (19 to 24)	1.26	2.28	2.60	2.65	3.0

$$\text{Table 20. (continued)}$$

Diplomas in science:	1954-55[b]	1959-60[b]	1960-61	1961-62	1962-63
Higher scientific ed. & industrial tech. ed. graduates	3,376	4,781	5,497	5,584	5,925
Licenses (total)	1,594	n.a.	3,580[d]	4,875[e]	n.a.
(teaching *licences*)	862	n.a.	2,693	2,874	n.a.
State doctorates	242	n.a.	237	339	n.a.
Third-cycle doctorates	n.a.	n.a.	358	508	n.a.
University doctorates	n.a.	n.a.	n.a.	114	n.a.
Diplomas of engineer-doctor	n.a.	n.a.	146	135	n.a.

[a] Adapted from OECD, *Reviews of National Science Policy—France*, p. 55.

[b] Includes students and graduates of Algiers University and higher educational establishments in Algiers. Total enrollments in the universities and higher educational establishments. It is not possible to obtain a breakdown of unregistered students before 1960-61. This also applies to duplicate enrollments.

[d] The figure of 3,580 is for *licences libres* only.

[e] The figure of 4,875 represents the total number of students who obtained their 5th certificate during this year.

in science increased from 2,000 to 4,700.[11] In 1962, 4,875 science degrees were awarded, but only 2,874 were teaching degrees which enabled their holders to teach in the secondary schools.[12]

With respect to postgraduate, or third-cycle education, the situation over the past several years has been equally disappointing. At this level students have three courses open to them. They can prepare for a secondary school teaching career through studying for the Secondary School Teaching Certificate (CAPES) or the *agrégation*. In 1961, 310 students passed the *agrégation* and 898 the CAPES in science subjects.[13] A second alternative is to work for the third-cycle doctorate which was established in 1954 to meet the need for more researchers. In 1962, 508 third-cycle doctorates were awarded (see TABLE 20).[14] Finally, and most important, the student can prepare for the state doctorate (the *doctorat d'État*) and, in most cases, the *agrégation* along with it. As TABLE 21 shows, the number of state doctorates awarded has been increasing very slowly and has been far below expectations.[15]

France's inability to increase substantially the number of state doctorates presents a serious problem for the future. Since

TABLE 21.

State Doctorates in Science[a]

Year	Forecast	Actual number
1961	400	237
1962	510	339
1963	660	342
1964	820	n.a.
1969	1,900	n.a.

[a] Adapted from OECD, *Reviews of National Science Policy—France*, p. 58.

[11] Aron, "Crise de l'Université," p. 20.
[12] OECD, *Reviews of National Science Policy—France*, p. 58.
[13] *Ibid.*   [14] *Ibid.*   [15] *Ibid.*

one must have the *doctorat d'État* to hold a university chair, the expansion of the university system, and with it the over-all production of scientists and engineers, depends on the number of *doctorats d'État* awarded. This poor performance imposes a severe limitation on France's long-term educational objectives; overcoming it will require an overhaul of the degree and a revision of the prerequisites for awarding university chairs.

If France has a serious scientific manpower problem she has a national crisis in the shortage of engineers and highly skilled technicians.[16] The gap between supply and demand both in terms of total numbers and especially in advanced fields such as space, atomic energy, and automation is immense and there is little immediate prospect for its alleviation. The French are making a determined effort to increase their output of engineers and technicians. The *grandes écoles* have continued to enjoy high prestige in France, but their monopoly over engineering and advanced technical education has been broken through the development of additional routes to an engineering career. While avoiding a discussion of the complicated structure of engineering education in France, I should mention several of the most important newer programs for training engineers and highly skilled technicians. First, there are the National Institutes of Applied Sciences (INSA), located at Toulouse and Lyons, and the National Higher Schools of Engi-

---

[16] There are several formal programs which train technicians, in contrast to engineers, but their output is small. As this study is concerned specifically with research and development and not the whole range of problems affecting France's industrial modernization, the matter of technician training will be only briefly discussed here. On the other hand, the distinction between engineers and technicians is not a clear one and Americans might quibble with Frenchmen over whether a particular individual is an engineer or higher technician. Actually the French situation is more acute with respect to "technicians" than "engineers." Germany, for example, produces about three times as many technicians per year as does France. *Le Monde Entreprise*, Nov. 4, 1964, p. 17.

neers (ENSI), which are run by the universities. On the basis of recent legislation (post-1954), the science *facultés* now award several advanced engineering and applied sciences degrees, including a doctorate of engineering (135 in 1962) and a doctorate in applied science.[17] Several other institutions, such as the *Conservatoire des Arts et Métiers* and the *Écoles Centrales*, also give special courses and award engineering degrees. Lastly, there was the creation in 1966 of the University Institutes of Technology which will train engineers and technicians. In all, there are about 140 institutions which can award engineering or higher technician degrees.

With the development of these new institutions since the end of World War II the number of engineering students in France has increased considerably. In general, most of the expansion has taken place outside the *grandes écoles* and in the INSA's and the ENSI's; in the future the role of these latter two types of schools will continue to grow. The *grandes écoles*, on the other hand, have not expanded very much. By 1970 their proportion of the total output of engineers is expected to recede somewhat, to about 33 percent of the total. On the basis of the present growth rate of the number of engineering students, the forecast is that France will reach a rate of 9,000 engineering degrees per year by 1970, a quarter less than the objective of the Fourth Plan (12,300;[18] see TABLE 22).

The increases in the output of natural scientists and engineers are indeed impressive from the perspective of the past, and represent substantial changes in the attitudes of Frenchmen toward science and engineering as careers. France may yet take the lead in western Europe in the production of sci-

[17] The training of engineers in the science *facultés* is a major issue of controversy. See *L'Expansion Scientifique*, Oct. 1962, and *Le Monde*, Feb. 18, 1961.

[18] OECD, *Reviews of National Science Policy—France*, p. 61; *Le Monde*, Apr. 21, 1965.

TABLE 22.[a]

Trend in Number of Degrees Awarded by Engineering Schools,[b] 1961-71

Schools	Actual number of graduates				Number of degrees forecast						
					very probable				possible		
	1961	1962	1963	1964	1965	1966	1967	1968	1969	1970	1971
Ministry of Education											
ENSI and assimilated	1,444	1,545	1,714	1,854	2,330	2,580	2,740	3,100	3,450	3,740	4,140
other schools	1,018	1,063	1,064	1,141	1,240	1,310	1,270	1,440	1,440	1,510	1,590
Other Ministries	1,226	1,236	1,263	1,193	1,320	1,390	1,390	1,440	1,485	1,530	1,570
Private Schools	1,796	1,587	1,837	1,924	1,700	1,860	1,810	2,000	2,080	2,170	2,290
Total	5,484	5,431	5,878	6,112	6,590	7,140	7,210	7,980	8,455	8,950	9,590

[a] Adapted from OECD, Reviews of National Policy—France, p. 62.
[b] Excluding postgraduate practical schools, which take only students who already hold an engineering diploma or degree, and certain other schools with their own entrance system.

entists, engineers, and higher technicians.[19] But, on the other hand, the demand for scientists and engineers has expanded greatly as France has endeavored to accomplish several ambitious goals at the same time. The task of balancing supply and demand is becoming onerous and the prospects for success, according to an OECD report, are not encouraging.[20]

Before leaving this discussion of the production of scientists and technicians in France, mention should be made of two types of professionals who are essential in a modern scientific society, the social scientists and the corporate managers, who occupy the middle ground between the traditional literary culture and the "hard" sciences and technologies of the natural scientist and engineer. With respect to these categories of professionals, France remains essentially at the nineteenth-century level. Although productive of a few brilliant individuals such as a Raymond Aron or a Louis Armand, France has not undertaken the production of the great number and variety of social scientists and trained administrators required by an advanced society. There are no social sciences in the curriculums of the secondary schools. At the level of higher education, in the *faculté* of law, economics now shares at least an equal place with traditional legal studies and in the sixth section of the *École Pratique* very distinguished work in social science takes place. But no equivalent of the Harvard Business School has been created to teach management as an applied social science; the spirit of modern management has hardly penetrated the *grandes écoles* and industry. While the founding (1945) of the *École Nationale d'Administration* is an important step, it can be asserted that France may one day discover that her backwardness in the social sciences and consequent failure to adopt the techniques of decision, management,

[19] Raymond Poignant, *L'Enseignement Dans les Pays du Marché Commun*, Institut Pédagogique National, Paris, 1965.
[20] OECD, *Reviews of National Science Policy—France*, pp. 71-72.

and control to which the social sciences are giving rise is one of the major obstacles to her full social and economic development.

THE REFORM OF SCIENTIFIC AND TECHNICAL EDUCATION

The solution of France's scientific and technical manpower problems will require a radical reform of her educational system. The complex nature of this task is attested by the fact that France had seven Ministers of National Education in the first seven years of the Fifth Republic, and the *baccalauréat* has undergone five major reforms in less than six years.[21]

While any attempt to deal here in a detailed fashion with the problems of French education or to evaluate the success of recent reforms would take us into an area where too much is in flux, the reforms of February 24, 1966 reveal more clearly than anything else the educational objectives of the Fifth Republic and the influence of scientists whose thinking was anticipated in part by the Resistance, the Wallon-Langevin Report, and Pierre Auger's proposals for three cycles in higher education.[22]

Among the most important features of the reforms are:

1. The establishment of many two-year university-affiliated Institutes of Technology to train middle-level engineers and higher technicians. It is hoped that by 1972 these institutes will absorb 125,000 of the 750,000 French students (25 percent) who will then be in institutions of higher education; this will necessitate not only an ambitious building program but the rechanneling of immense numbers of students from the more prestigious *facultés* into the less prestigious technical institutes. In associating these institutes with the university science *facultés* the intention is to give the future engineers and technicians

---

[21] *Le Monde*, Sept. 11, 1964. Cf. J.-L. Crémieux-Brilhac, *L'Éducation Nationale*, Presses Universitaires de France, 1965.

[22] For a summary of the text see *Le Progrès Scientifique*, No. 95, Apr. 1966, 28-29. See also *Le Monde*, Feb. 25, 1966.

355

an understanding of the basic sciences and thus bridge the current gap between theoretical knowledge and engineering practice. The first University Institutes of Technology were opened in October 1966.

2. In order to restrict somewhat the ever growing student population of the science *facultés* and raise the quality of entrants, students will be admitted to the first cycle of the science *facultés* only if they possess the appropriate *baccalauréat.*[23] (This regulation, to which there are some exceptions, does not apply to the letters and medical faculties.) In the *faculté* the students will "specialize" for two years (the first cycle) in a greater diversity of areas. They will receive much more individual attention and have more electives than has been the case in the past.

3. At the end of the second year of the first cycle, the students will be examined and if successful awarded a diploma. In addition, each student will be evaluated and oriented toward a future program corresponding to his aptitudes. First, he may be advised to leave the *faculté* and enter University Institutes of Technology. Or, second, he will be admitted to the second cycle of higher education. Here two courses are open to him. The first is to take a one-year course leading to the *licence* and a teaching career in secondary education; this is a shortening of the usual length of training for secondary school teachers. The second is to take a two-year course leading to the *maîtrise* (equivalent to a Master's Degree), and a career in research and higher education. Whereas the education for the *licence* will be geared to the needs of secondary education teaching, the *maîtrise* program will

[23] Originally it was proposed that there be an entrance examination to the science *faculté*, but this was considered too radical a step. *Le Monde*, Feb. 25, 1966.

emphasize specialization in one of 12 disciplines and preparation for advanced degrees and research. As a consequence, future scientists will specialize and enter on their research careers at a much earlier date.

4. A potentially important feature is the construction of two-way bridges between the science *facultés* and the *grandes écoles*: a graduate of one of the *grandes écoles* interested in research or teaching can enter directly into the second cycle of the *faculté*, and a graduate of the first cycle of the *faculté* can transfer under certain conditions to an engineering school. Through a diminishing of the historic cleavage between the *facultés* and the *grandes écoles*, students will have an opportunity to change careers and need not have to live with decisions made too early in life.

5. At the level of postgraduate studies, while the *agrégation* kept its privileged position, the principle was established that non-*agrégés* could be recruited as *assistants* (instructors) in the *facultés*.

These reforms reveal several important trends. The first is to attract better students, including graduates of the *grandes écoles*, into the science *facultés*. Second, an effort is commencing to direct students with high ambitions and low scientific aptitude away from the overcrowded science *facultés* into technical fields where they are needed. Finally, the reforms represent a victory, minor though it may be, for the scientists who favor emphasis on specialization rather than general culture in higher education and who place the needs of higher education and research above those of secondary education. Nonetheless, it should be appreciated, in French education literary culture and traditional attitudes still predominate over scientific culture and reform.

357

The Balance Sheet of Modernization:

If France is to break the resistance to change and preserve the present momentum in the areas of science and technology, a vital ingredient is money and ever more money. Creating a large scientific infrastructure, effecting ambitious educational reforms, and financing costly research and development projects impose a tremendous burden on France. Here, as elsewhere in the record of present-day France, one cannot help but be impressed both by the prodigious effort which is being made and also by the distance yet to be travelled.

According to official French Government publications budget appropriations for scientific and technical research (excluding atomic energy and military research) more than quintupled in the first five years of the Fifth Republic, from $46.6 million in 1959 to $268 million in 1964.[24] If one includes atomic energy, space, and military research and development, the rate of growth is even more impressive (see TABLE 23). In addition, the money spent by private industry on research has also begun to climb; between 1959 and 1963 the amount expended by private industry increased from 492 million to over 2 billion francs.[25]

Despite these increases, however, the French still lag far behind the United States, Great Britain, and the Soviet Union, both in absolute and relative terms. Whereas the U.S. devoted in 1962, 3.1 percent of *GNP* to research and development and Great Britain 2.2 percent, France invested but 1.5 percent.[26] With respect to industrial research the French in 1962 spent 2.6 billion francs compared with 5.4 billion francs in Great

[24] Ambassade de France, New York, "The First Five Years of the Fifth Republic of France, January 1959–January 1964," n.d., p. 16.

[25] Monique Pinson, "Science and Technology in Economic Development—France," *International Social Science Journal*, XVIII, No. 3, 1966, 390.

[26] OECD, *Reviews of National Science Policy—France*, p. 82.

TABLE 23.

Trend of Public Financing of R and D[a]
(in millions of francs)

	1959	1960	1961	1962	1963	1964	1965
State budget:							
Research envelope appropriations	248	402	463	579	719	975	1,073
Nonenvelope research expenditure of bodies included in the envelope vote	150	135	157	377	472	——	——
Space research	——	——	16	86	148	209	280
Defense	886	1,130	1,477	1,519	1,453	——	——
CEA	328	328	381	1,073[b]	1,274	——	——
Other bodies	134	166	182	407	509	——	——
Total state financing	1,746	2,161	2,676	4,041	4,575	——	——
Percentage of state budget	2.24	2.67	3.04	4.23	4.55	——	——
Own resources of: administrations and public establishments	——	——	——	70	50	——	——
Financed by local authorities	——	——	——	——	28	——	——
Total a + b + c	——	——	——	4,111	4,653	——	——

Adapted from OECD, *Reviews of National Science Policy—France*, p. 38. The figures 1959, 1960, and 1961 are very rough estimates, and the results are certainly "calculated difference." Furthermore, these estimates are not in accordance with the OECD Manual, oposed Standard Practice for Surveys of Research and Development Activity." From 2 on, the figures are in line with the definitions in the manual, but the method of ulation differs from that used in 1963. Finally, it should be noted that the financing rded includes appropriations to the social sciences.
The increase is accounted for by the inclusion of "development" in the financing data.
e figures before 1962 relate essentially to fundamental research.

Britain and 56 billion in the United States—a ratio of 1 :2 :20.[27]
In short, while France's position as measured by gross expenditure and support for research and development has improved, a greater effort is required if she is to reach the announced

[27] *Ibid.* This is at the official exchange rate.

goal of the Fifth Plan—achieving by 1970 Great Britain's 1963 level.[28]

Whether the French will reach this goal is difficult to judge because of the vacillating level of the science budget, especially that allocated for basic research. After a rapid rise in the funds for basic research during the initial years of the Fifth Republic, less money was available for civil science after 1964 because of the stabilization plan of Finance Minister d'Estaing;[29] funds for research in the military sector continued to increase, however. The Government set the goals for both the Fourth and Fifth Plans well below the recommendations of the Commission on Scientific Research. Even so, only 72 percent of the credits for research proposed by the Fourth Plan were actually distributed.[30]

With the replacement of d'Estaing by Debré in 1966 France had a Minister of Finance more understanding of and sympathetic to the needs of science. The research budget for 1967 was augmented by 52 percent over the 1966 figure,[31] a figure still well below the amount desired by the science planners. Furthermore, funds for education were far inferior to the expenditures projected as required for fulfillment of France's ambitious program of reform of scientific and technical education.[32]

The level of financial support for basic research, education, and especially CNRS will have implications for French science and technology not just for the next decade or so but for the latter part of this century. At this early date, one cannot assess what the outcome of present decisions will be. Nevertheless, there are grounds for concern that France is not making a sufficient financial effort to overcome her yet considerable

[28] Statement of Science Minister Peyrefitte, *Le Monde,* May 29-30, 1966.
[29] *Le Monde,* Nov. 10, 1964.   [30] *Le Monde,* May 2, 1966.
[31] *Le Monde,* Sept. 22, 1966.   [32] *Le Monde,* July 13, 1966.

backwardness in basic research and scientific-technical man-power.

The Governance of Science

The change in the nature of the scientific enterprise and its role in society are transforming what I have labeled the "governance of science" (see Chapter 4). By this term I mean the sets of individuals and institutions that make the broad decisions affecting the rate and direction of scientific progress. This is not to deny that in the last analysis scientific advance and discovery are dependent on individual creative scientists. But, increasingly, the "bench scientist" is dependent on the leadership of science and on formal institutions for the funds, equipment, and assistants he requires. The decisions which have to be made regarding the allocation of resources rest with the government of science.

THE MECHANISM FOR POLICY-MAKING

The innovation of the national plan, the employment of the research contract by the CEA, the DRME, and the DGRST, and the creation of a superstructure of policy-making organs are all mechanisms with which the state is seeking to redirect and coordinate the national scientific effort in terms of national priorities. Together these changes in the national organization of decision-making for science represent a significant movement away from the traditional science system of France. They do not, however, signal its demise and the reformers of French scientific institutions are more preoccupied with the immense distance they have yet to go to formulate a coherent science policy than with the magnitude of their successes.[33] Both within the structures for civil science and those for military science there abound problems of coordination, gaps in communication, and interagency competition.[34] The power of decision

[33] *Nouvelle Frontière*, No. 8, Oct.-Nov. 1964, 32.
[34] OECD, *Reviews of National Science Policy—France*, pp. 94-95.

remains highly decentralized and fragmented. With respect to the coordination of civil and military research, cooperation between the two hierarchies is complicated by the problem of military secrecy[35] and the fact that important decisions affecting the welfare of science such as the construction of Pierrelatte or Concorde are made without consulting the science policy officials.[36] Finally, planning and the flexible use of resources in response to changing needs is difficult due to the cumbersome budgeting and accounting system which the Minister of Finance has imposed upon all agencies but the CEA.

The effective coordination and development of a coherent French policy for science and technology require a much greater centralization of authority than is presently the case in France. Policy cannot be made, nor activities coordinated by committees or officials with little power to establish priorities.[37] It is no doubt in response to this need, for example, that the French Government is shifting a part of its support for basic research from the CNRS to the DRME. As TABLE 5 reveals, the funds for military research including the DRME have increased much faster than those for civil science. In contrast to the CNRS, the DRME can establish research priorities and implement them through the award of research grants and contracts to university, industrial, and other laboratories. In addition, the programs of concerted action of the DGRST have been increasingly employed as a means to stimulate research of interest to the state, particularly the military.[38] If one includes the research contracts of the CEA (140 million francs in 1962)[39] and the CNES (80 million francs in 1963), one can see that the proportion of the total research effort being oriented toward national

[35] *Ibid.*, p. 94.   [36] *Ibid.*, pp. 116-18.   [37] *Ibid.*, pp. 116-18.
[38] Albert Boyer, "Aspects Scientifiques et Économiques de la Construction d'une Armement Nucléaire Par la France," *Revue de Défense Nationale*, Oct. 1963, pp. 1,540-41.
[39] Sixty percent of the CEA's budget comes from the military. Ambassade de France, New York, "First Five Years," p. 36.

security has increased substantially over the past several years.[40] In the name of national security and independence, therefore, one can see emerging in France a more coherent national policy toward science and technology.

THE LEADERSHIP OF SCIENCE

Along with these changes in the organization of the government of science in France, there is a corresponding change in the style and composition of scientific leadership. In the 1930s and as late as 1950, the leadership of French science was divided between scientists of the Left and Right. The Right, composed of such scientists as Louis Leprince-Ringuet and Louis de Broglie, were relatively passive toward the social role of science. The Left, on the other hand, represented by Jean Perrin, Paul Langevin and Frédéric Joliot-Curie, believed in a national science policy (as they understood the term) and argued for the social responsibility of scientists.

Until the dismissal of Joliot-Curie as High Commissioner of the CEA in 1950 the leadership of French science was largely dominated by the students of Perrin, Langevin, and others of the Left. They had learned Marxism as well as physics at the *Institut du Radium*, and at the time of Joliot's removal 65 percent of the CEA's personnel were, by one estimate, Communist.[41] In addition to the CEA, the CNRS was also under the scientific leadership of a Communist, Georges Teissier, and a number of other important research agencies had Communists in key positions.[42]

Between 1949 (the signing of the Atlantic Pact by France) and 1952 Communist scientists were removed from important positions in the CEA, the CNRS, and other agencies. Their places

[40] OECD, *Reviews of National Science Policy—France*, p. 33.

[41] Dorothy Pickles, "The Communist Problem in France," *International Affairs*, Apr. 1952, pp. 167-68.

[42] Lawrence Scheinman, *Atomic Energy Policy in France under the Fourth Republic*, Princeton University Press, 1965, p. 45.

were taken in some cases by men of the conservative tradition, but in general, and increasingly with the passage of time, the leadership in important scientific institutions has passed to a new style of scientific leadership. Labeled by their critics as "technocrats," such scientist-administrators as Pierre Aigrain lack the ideological commitments of their predecessors. Like their counterparts in the leadership of American and Russian science, they see as inevitable an alliance between science and the state, a symbiotic relationship which is to the benefit of both.

In France, as elsewhere in the West, scientists are ceasing to be revolutionary, alienated intellectuals and are becoming part of the technocratic elite on which the modern scientific state depends. A new leadership of young scientists (Aigrain, for example, was made Director of Higher Education at age 39) is rising. It is composed of the deans of the science *facultés*, administrators of public research agencies, and individual scientists of great prestige who are leaving aside the traditional Leftist political orientation of French scientists and devoting themselves fully to the development of science. For the first time since the Dreyfus episode, scientists are rising *au-dessus de la mêlée* and making their peace with the state.[43]

As a consequence of this situation scientists in France and the United States have become important social reformers.[44] In the past scientists of the French Left *talked* of social reform and proposed vast transformations of traditional French society; today technocratic scientists are actually *leading* in the piecemeal reform of French institutions. The change that has

[43] Henry Guerlac, "Science and French National Strength," in Edward Earle, ed., *Modern France*, Princeton University Press, 1951, pp. 81-105.

[44] For the American situation see Don K. Price, *The Scientific Estate*, Harvard University Press, 1965; Robert Gilpin and Christopher Wright, eds., *Scientists and National Policy-Making*, Columbia University Press, 1964.

taken place is readily apparent if one contrasts the sweeping but largely unlegislated educational reforms proposed by Paul Langevin and Henri Wallon in their report of 1945 and the more successful reforms of higher education being engineered largely by scientists. Today men of both scientific and administrative competence, such as Dean Marc Zamansky of the Science *Faculté* at Paris and Dean Louis Weil of the Science *Faculté* at Grenoble, are building strong centers of scientific research and training. Throughout France, in fact, scientist-administrators in seeking to make a greater place for science in national life are helping to refashion educational, political, and economic institutions.[45]

SCIENTIFIC LEADERSHIP AND POLICY-MAKING

The new political role of the scientist in France has been made necessary by the increasing liaison between science and the Government. If this is to be an effective working partnership a scientific leadership must emerge which performs three essential tasks in a society where science has become both an end and a means of state policy. First, scientific leadership must assert and defend the interests of science in political circles. Though science in France has nearly always been a creature of the state, the scale of modern industrialized science and the demands of the state on science mean that the welfare of science is increasingly determined by events in the external political world. If science is to grow and its interests are to be defended, then the leadership of science must undertake a much greater part in national political life than has traditionally been the case.

Another task of scientific leadership is to exercise a more positive role in the governance of the scientific community.

[45] In effect, scientists are joining the traditional administrative class. See F. Ridley and J. Blondel, *Public Administration in France*, Routledge and Kegan Paul, 1964, pp. 57-65.

Traditional leadership of French science has been, and still is, essentially a conservative one, which resists the establishment of priorities and institutional reorganization. This laissez-faire tradition in science—that the government should give support to scientists and then leave them alone in determining how the money is to be spent—is becoming increasingly intolerable. The excess of demand for financial support over the supply of funds available, the rapid increase in new specializations, and the fact that society looks to science for answers to its problems make research priorities imperative.

The third task of scientific leadership is an outgrowth of the new importance of scientific research for technological innovation. It is now recognized that one must know the state of scientific and technical research in order to make other policy decisions, especially with respect to investment in huge technologies; the government must know which technology is the best and whether it will soon be obsolete. Furthermore, if society is to control and adjust to the accelerating pace of technical evolution scientists and technologists must advise political leaders on the technological implications of scientific advance.

France has taken some steps toward the realization of these three tasks. The appointment of a Minister for Science has no doubt been beneficial in providing a spokesman for the interests of science in a situation where the welfare of science is increasingly affected by political decisions. On the other hand, in contrast to the U.S. where the President has a personal science advisor with a large staff, the President and the Prime Minister of France do not. While the Interministerial Committee does advise the Prime Minister, it meets in general only once a year when it considers the annual research budget. As for the Committee for Scientific Action for Defense, it advises the Prime Minister on specific areas where science and defense policy meet, but it does not satisfy the over-all need.[46]

[46] OECD, *Reviews of National Science Policy—France*, p. 21.

Such institutions as the Planning Commissariat and the General Delegation have been necessary in France because of the relatively small amount of planning that takes place at the ministerial level and the absence of extensive communications among the ministries. While this situation is still the general case in France, some important changes are underway in the area of research and development at the ministerial level as scientists are coming to play a greater role in the making of public policy.

The most conspicuous example of this change is in the Ministry of Defense where the DRME's significant role in the military establishment has already been discussed. In the Ministry of Health the 1964 reform of the INH and the establishment of a scientific advisory committee to the minister are also important steps in the right direction. In the Ministry of National Education, the Coordinating Committee for Scientific Research and the office of Secretary General have been recently established to plan educational and research policy.

A further development is that for the first time ministers, in accordance with recent directives, are appointing members of their personal cabinets who will have the responsibility for overseeing the research activities or needs of the ministry. This is a potentially important development, not only in terms of the internal research activities of the ministry but because it will facilitate intragovernmental coordination of research at the working level. At the present time, for example, there is frequently little contact between the heads of the research agencies of a ministry and the minister. In terms of general government policy the General Delegation has difficulty in establishing a liaison with most ministries because there is no official at the ministerial level responsible for a ministry's overall research program.

This relative absence of scientists as advisors and administrators at the ministerial level is one of the most important contrasts between the American and French governmental organizations for science. In the U.S. it is essentially on this level that most science planning and coordination take place. Nearly every department of the U.S. Government now has a high official specifically to oversee its research programs, and there are numerous scientific advisory committees which serve a valuable communications function. Through a vast array of committees and informal contacts these officials and scientists seek to coordinate their various and often overlapping scientific activities. One may draw from this the conclusion that if the French are to break down the cleavages hindering the efficient use of their scarce scientific resources, they will require greater scientific leadership at the ministerial level.

THE CHANGING RELATIONSHIP OF SCIENCE AND STATE

The increasingly important role of science in French life is slowly eroding the strong tradition of disengagement of scientists and universitarians from the affairs of state. The French professor has tended to view himself as committed to pure research, with no responsibility to society for the social consequences of his discoveries. While many scientists are slowly realizing that a change is taking place in the relationship of science and society because of the decreasing lead time between discovery and application, French scientists in general remain aloof from society and its problems. For them in contrast to American scientists there was no Hiroshima to shock them out of their complacency and to make them aware of their social responsibilities. Instead atomic research programs in France evolved rather slowly from a civilian to a military emphasis, while in the United States scientists after 1945 were forced to engage in politics to turn a military program into a civilian one.[47] Also, in the United States the controversies over nuclear

[47] Robert Gilpin, *American Scientists and Nuclear Weapons Policy*, Princeton University Press, 1962, Chap. 2.

368

weapons and the experience of McCarthyism jarred American scientists into political activity. Although the careers and tribulations of Robert Oppenheimer and Frédéric Joliot-Curie were somewhat similar, in France there was no "security trial" which intensified the political awareness of scientists.

In general, insofar as they have been concerned about politics, French scientists like all Frenchmen have been more engaged with the national political struggle and ideological issues rather than with concrete political action.[48] The social responsibility of scientists has meant association with one of the major ideological traditions, usually that of the Left. The scientist's political participation has tended to be through the party which expresses for him certain political views. When he does take a stand on policy issues, he does so on those issues which stir the country at large such as Algeria or the *force de frappe*, and he joins with other groups of intellectuals in making his protest. There is, for example, relatively little opposition by scientists as scientists to de Gaulle's *force de frappe*; this is remarkable given the intensity of most scientists' feelings about it. A cynic might add, however, that some of the loudest protestors gladly accept research funds from the military.

Even with respect to matters affecting the welfare of science, French scientists have been slow to organize on a professional basis. For example, French scientists did not found their association for the advancement of science until a much later date (1872) than did German, American, and British scientists.[49] Founded by such men as Claude Bernard and Louis Pasteur to focus national attention on the needs of science after the defeat of France in the Franco-Prussian War, the French as-

[48] For a valuable comparison of the political behavior of French and American scientists see Scheinman, *Atomic Energy Policy*, pp. 211ff.

[49] Everett Mendelsohn, "The Professionalization of Science," in Karl Hill, *The Management of Scientists*, Beacon Press, 1963, p. 58. John Merz, *A History of European Thought in the Nineteenth Century*, Dover Publications, I, 1964, 298.

sociation has never provided leadership on matters affecting science as have the American or British associations.

The American scientist, on the other hand, tends to be concerned with specific issues of public policy and prides himself on being a political independent. What is most significant to him, in contrast to the French scientist, are issues which affect the welfare of science such as governmental policies toward science, or issues which he believes he has a special competence to help resolve because they involve the impact of science on society such as that of the control of nuclear weapons. There is nothing in France comparable to the *Bulletin of the Atomic Scientists* which is devoted to social problems for which science must bear some responsibility;[50] nor are there broad political action groups such as the Federation of American Scientists whose membership is predominantly scientific.

The reason for the absence among scientists of a strong sense of political identity is embedded in the nature of French intellectual life. The French intellectual traditionally has been primarily literary rather than technical and scientific.[51] Though there is a strong utilitarian strain in French culture with which one associates the *Encyclopédistes*, the Polytechnicians, and the Saint Simonians, honor and prestige are rewarded most often to men of broad culture and literary excellence.[52] Too often what counts in France is not what you say but how you say it and one gains public recognition only if one is a man of letters (*littérateur*). Great scientists like Louis Pasteur and Claude Bernard reflect this influence and have sought literary style in their writing and were as proud of their membership in the literary section of the *Institut de France* as of their election to the scientific section, the *Acadé-*

[50] The journal, *Atomes*, originally founded by Jean Perrin and refashioned in 1966, comes closest.

[51] Merz, *History of European Thought*, Chap. 1.

[52] The story is told that Bernard turned to science after failing as a writer.

mie des Sciences. Bernard's *Introduction to the Study of Experimental Medicine* was not only a scientific landmark but a literary one as well.

The political behavior of the French scientist reflects his image of himself as a part of the larger intellectual and literary class. His tendency has been to defer to these men of culture and to permit them to speak for him as a fellow intellectual. Increasingly, however, the French scientist is awaking to the realization that his interests as a scientist and those of the *littérateur* may conflict, or at least differ. There *are* two cultures and the scientist must take it upon himself to defend his own. The successful resistance of the professors of letters to the types of educational reforms that would benefit science bear this out.

The political and industrial elite of France, for their part, continue to resist the intrusion of the representatives of science and technology into their company. Whereas the leadership of American and Russian industry and government is largely composed of scientists, economists, and professional managers sensitive to the importance of science, the elite of France have a humanistic formation and, even in the case of the *Polytechniciens*, have an insufficient appreciation of modern natural and social science.

It is doubtful that this traditional relationship can long endure in an era when the state is increasingly influencing the research of French scientists and when the social impact of scientific discovery is almost immediate. Many French scientists in addition to the scientists actively participating in government are being forced to undertake a general appraisal of the change occurring in the relationship between the scientific community and the state and to determine whether this situation calls for specific actions by the French scientific community. And the state for its part is beginning to do more to involve scientists in the formulation of public policy toward issues affecting the welfare of science or involving the impact of scientific-technical advances upon society.

If one makes his vantage point the traditional structure of French science founded by the Revolution and Napoleon, he can only marvel at the magnitude of the change that has taken place since the end of World War II.

Judged, on the other hand, from the perspective of France's ambitions and the distance she has yet to travel to fulfill them, the picture is different. The reform of traditional structures has not proceeded so far that the quotation from the frustrated science reformer which opens this chapter is unwarranted. Nor has France begun to provide support to scientific research commensurate with her economic and political objectives. In short—to paraphrase Winston Churchill—the reforms which have thus far taken place represent the end of the beginning and not the beginning of the end.

The issue for many Frenchmen, however, is not whether the reform of scientific and related institutions is taking place fast enough, but rather that of whether reform is moving in the right direction. There is concern over the growing influence of the state, and especially the military, over French science.[53] Many scientists are worried that the present policies of the French government will have disastrous long-term consequences: "The power of the state over research, if it is effective, is not without danger, for science searches for the truth while the state searches for power. A state entirely master of research must orient it toward the ways that it judges most politically returnable but where they are scientifically harmful."[54]

---

[53] This view was expressed in a long article in *Le Monde*, July 23, 1964, by Louis Leprince-Rinquet, one of the most distinguished living French scientists.

[54] M. Baiseas, "La Force de Frappe et la Recherche Scientifique," *Esprit*, Dec. 1963, p. 803.

The fundamental challenge facing French science is to reconcile the long and noble tradition of the *liberté de l'Université française* and the necessity of making the French university more responsive to the needs of contemporary France. In a political system where scientists are servants of the state and there are few strong, autonomous institutions interposed between the state and the individual scientist to protect him, there are real threats to scientific freedom as the role of the government in the governance of science increases and as an effort is made to make more coherent national policy toward science. The achievement of a balance between liberty and responsiveness depends in part on the character of institutional and procedural reforms. The coming into existence of multiple sources of financial support—CNRS, DRME, CNES, INSERN, CEA—has greatly increased the opportunities for scientists, especially the younger ones. The fact that these agencies are frequently in competition enhances the freedom of scientists; too much interagency coordination and a unified science policy would pose dangers for French science. Similarly, the expansion of the university system and the increasing autonomy of provincial universities also contribute to the institutional defenses of science. To safeguard the freedom of science, as Monod has commented, "one must have disorder in the administration of research."[55]

What will be most important is the foresight and sensitivity to the needs of science displayed by officials responsible for the administration of the national science program. The problem is to have a centralization of authority strong enough to influence but not sufficiently powerful to dominate science. In this connection, an interchange on science and state in France, sponsored by the Marxist journal, *La Nouvelle Critique,* may be significant. Seeking confirmation of his own view that the *force de frappe* was destroying French science the moderator

[55] *Le Monde,* Nov. 23, 1965.

put the matter to Alfred Kastler, who won the Nobel Prize for physics in 1966 and is one of the strongest critics of the *force de frappe*. Kastler took exception with the moderator's position and responded: "I believe one can say that the individuals who are actually at the head of this type of research are university people and these are broad-minded people. They do not finance research of immediate interest but, to the contrary, long-term university research."[56]

Nonetheless, the issue posed by the increasing role of the state in the governance of French science remains: the advancement of knowledge as a goal, or as a means of state policy. These two objectives are related and should be complementary, but they may also conflict. The emphasis on the solution of immediate problems may cause science to bring forth technological feats for a brief period, but it can weaken science in the long run, as has happened before in French history. In the seventeenth century the emphasis on practical results such as the layout of the foundations at Versailles was certainly one cause of the decline of the Academy after the death of Colbert. During the Revolution the militarization by Napoleon of the *École Polytechnique* contributed to its demise as an important center of research. Today, many French scientists fear that the *force de frappe* is their Versailles—a prestige project of little use to science or France. There is a concern that applied research and spectaculars are being emphasized at the expense of basic and theoretical work which might not bear fruit before the latter part of the century.

The never-ending task of a nation's science policy is to maintain a proper balance between the exploitation of existing scientific resources and the creation of new ones for the future. This means a judicious distribution of the current supply of scientists and the allocation of funds between research and

[56] "L'Avenir de la Recherche Scientifique," *La Nouvelle Critique*, No. 155, May 1964, p. 85.

teaching, and between applied research on immediate problems and the basic research which will show results in decades to come. The available evidence suggests to many Frenchmen that the emphasis on military, space, and other applied research projects is diverting too many resources away from teaching and basic research. Whether this is the case or whether these so-called glamorous projects are the price to be paid for rejuvenating French science, as their defenders claim, must await an answer in the future.

France's technological situation is already clear. From a position of technological strength and even leadership in western Europe in the first decade after World War II, France's position seems to have rapidly deteriorated. What is even more significant, her international position has begun to slip in those scientific technologies to which she has committed such a large fraction of her total research and development effort and which she regards as essential for her long-term economic and political ambitions, namely aeronautics, atomic energy, chemistry, and electronics.

The problem is that France is simply too small a state to compete with the scientific giants across the broad front of contemporary science and technology so important for an advanced industrial economy. The magnitude of the task is borne out by the following statement from the OECD report on France:

> Although the United States spends 54 times as much as France on aeronautics, it should not be forgotten that it also spends 135 times as much on electrical engineering (excluding electronics). Great Britain spends 1.4 times as much as France on electronics, but three times more on mechanical engineering and 3.6 times as much on electrical engineering.[57]

[57] OECD, *Reviews of National Science Policy—France*, p. 82.

The serious condition of France's scientific-technological situation has forced on the French Government the realization that France, as a small state in a world of scientific-economic giants, cannot alone meet the challenge of the contemporary scientific-technological revolution. Increasingly Frenchmen have come to appreciate that France must seek at least in part to achieve her scientific, economic, and political objectives through cooperation with other states. To this end the French Government has fashioned its international science policy.

Chapter 12 · Prospects for a European Solution to the Technology Gap

To safeguard our independence—economic, scientific, technical—we must ensure that our activities remain under French direction and administration, even though we confront the enormous wealth of certain countries and although we will not refuse to carry out all kinds of exchanges with them. Likewise, we must support, no matter what the cost, those activities which assure the value, the autonomy, the very life of all our industry, those sectors which require the most research, experiment, and sophisticated tools or which need the largest team of scientists, technicians, and workers of the highest quality. Finally, when it is opportune in a selected branch to join our inventions and money and skills with those of another country, we must choose the country nearest to us and whose weight could not crush us.

—Charles de Gaulle, *April 27, 1965*

In the mid-1960s there is widespread agreement in France that the threat of American domination and the solution to French scientific-technological problems necessitate France's cooperation with other nations and especially her European neighbors. The French are divided, however, over the emphasis to be given international cooperation in science and technology. The position of the Government is that primary emphasis must be placed on national programs supplemented by specific programs of international cooperation within the framework of the Common Market and through bilateral agreements. The opposition to de Gaulle, on the other hand, argues that the only viable alternative to American domination is greater scientific, economic, and political unification of western Europe, including (many would say) Great Britain. From the perspective of this latter position de Gaulle's policies are seen to be undermining the French ability to resist American expansionism.[1]

The International Science Policy of France

French participation in international scientific cooperation can be viewed from a number of perspectives. From one, French activities vary from basic research such as France's participation in the European Center for Nuclear Research (CERN) in Geneva to undertakings which have an immediate commercial or political character, such as the French-British supersonic aircraft project—*Concorde*. In terms of scope, organization, and magnitude they range from bilateral arrangements with her immediate neighbors to participation in large international organizations.[2]

The international science policy of de Gaulle, like all other current French policies, has been based on the assumption that the basic unit of political life remains the nation-state.[3] Thus in an international system where the interests of individual nations conflict and the final arbiter remains national power, France must depend primarily on her own resources. This necessitates a strong indigenous capability in atomic energy, electronics, and aerospace.

In the opinion of the French Government the alternative to such an emphasis on national programs and a *Europe des*

---

[1] See, for example, the comments of André Philip, in *Le Monde*, Apr. 30, 1945, or those of Gaston Defferre, "After de Gaulle What?" *Foreign Affairs*, LXIV, No. 3, Apr. 1966, 440-41, and François Mitterand, in *Le Monde*, Nov. 4, 1966.

[2] For a survey see Louis Villecourt, "Concurrence et Coopération Dans les Relations Scientifiques Internationales," *Le Progrès Scientifique*, No. 93, Feb. 1966, pp. 36-37.

[3] Two important aspects of France's international science policy which will not be discussed here are her scientific and technical assistance programs to French-speaking African states and her worldwide effort to disseminate French culture, including French science.

patries is not the development of an independent, unified Europe but a Europe dominated by the United States. A supranational Europe would be, in the Gaullist view, easily subjected to American domination and influence. The existence of a truly European federation with a will of its own which could oppose American influence is incomprehensible to these nationalists; to them a supranational Europe would be unable to define a policy of its own, and by default, the crucial decisions affecting Europe would be made by the United States acting through those European officials and states responsive to its will.[4] For example, the French point out, the policies of the European Atomic Energy Community, or Euratom—where decisions are made by majority vote and France cannot exercise a veto as in the Common Market—have been strongly influenced by the U.S. to the disadvantage of French interests. In the realm of science and technology, as in economic, military, and diplomatic spheres, international cooperation should rest, according to the view of the French Government, on the decisions and alliances of sovereign states capable of formulating and articulating a unified, national will.

De Gaulle's Government believes that only France has the capability to prevent American domination of western Europe. All other European nations except Great Britain and West Germany are too weak to oppose American policies for Europe. And the French believe Great Britain and West Germany lack the will to oppose American designs. The British, preoccupied with their special relationship with the U.S. and economically dependent upon the U.S., are much too subordinate to the United States to challenge her tendency toward hegemony. The West Germans, for their part, are too dependent on the U.S. for their military security and would do nothing to weaken the American commitment to German defense.

[4] Stanley Hoffmann, "The Fate of the Nation-state," *Daedalus*, Summer 1966, p. 885.

Under these circumstances, therefore, the defense of Europe against American hegemony and the promotion of French interests make imperative the exercise of independent French leadership within the developing European community.

Several important aspects of the international science policy of France may be discerned. First, this policy, like Gaullist foreign policy on a larger scale, has the earmarks of traditional balance of power politics. Through the forging of alliances and agreements with other states, France seeks to balance the scientific and technological power of the United States and to establish France's primacy in western Europe. While the mainstay of this policy remains cooperation with France's European neighbors, France's scientific policy in recent years has also displayed an opening to the East. France has signed scientific cooperation agreements with most of the eastern European countries, as well as Israel, Japan, China, and India.

Of potentially great significance, France has made scientific and technical cooperation with the Soviet Union a new element in her foreign policy. It was largely unappreciated by American commentators that an important part of de Gaulle's state visit to the Soviet Union in June 1966 was the formation of close ties with the world's second scientific power as a means of balancing the scientific-technical power of the world's first scientific power, the United States. French commentators were very much aware of this development, and emphasized that de Gaulle was the first Western head of state to visit the "science city" of Akademgorodok near Novosibirsk and the rocket launching base at Baikonur.[5] In his speech at the University of Moscow de Gaulle stressed the important role scientific-technical cooperation between France and the Soviet Union must play in the rebuilding of *l'Europe des Européens.*

[5] See *Le Monde*, June 23, 1966. An excellent analysis of the de Gaulle trip and its importance is provided by Victor McElheny, "Franco-Russian Collaboration in Science: de Gaulle's Visit," *Science*, Vol. 153, No. 3,731, July 1, 1966, 43-45.

In accordance with the terms of the Franco-Soviet agreement of June 22, 1966 for scientific, technical, and economic cooperation, a permanent high commission at the ministerial level, and five working subcommissions, have been established to oversee and implement cooperative projects.[6] The high commission meets twice a year under the joint chairmanship of French and Soviet Ministers.[7] The five operating subcommissions are: (1) scientific, technical, and economic cooperation; (2) color television; (3) atomic cooperation; (4) space cooperation; and (5) commercial problems. These committees are to work out projects of collaboration, including joint development projects in areas of advanced technology.

The long-term success and importance of this arrangement for permanent consultation and cooperation cannot be assessed at this early stage. For the moment, however, this cooperation will enable French physicists to have access to Russia's new Serpukhov synchrotron (potentially the world's largest particle accelerator by a factor of two) and may open the way for Russia's large rockets to launch heavy French space experiments and telecommunications satellites.[8]

In addition, the French have gained Russian backing for their color television system (SECAM developed by the CNET) as the basis of a uniform color television system for all Europe. Perhaps most important, the French can use their Russian scientific-technical alliance to pressure other western European nations to join with France on specific projects. Already the French have threatened to build an airbus with Russia if other western European countries do not cooperate with her.[9] The Russians, for their part, gain by encouraging French independ-

---

[6] *Le Monde*, Oct. 2-3, 1966.

[7] At the time of this writing the French are represented by their Minister of Finance, and the Russians by the vice president of the Council of Ministers.

[8] McElheny, "Franco-Russian Collaboration," pp. 44-45.

[9] *New York Times*, Oct. 16, 1966.

ence of the United States, thus weakening the U.S. position in Europe. But cooperation with France also offers the opportunity for the Russians to acquire western technologies such as advanced electronics that they very much need for economic and military reasons.

Another notable feature of France's international science policy is the conscious attempt to augment her limited national resources through participation in complementary international and particularly European cooperative programs. Contrary to the notion frequently expressed in the U.S. and elsewhere, that French science policy is totally chauvinistic, paradoxically her policy is the most internationalist, as well as the most nationalist, science policy pursued by any European state. Though no other nation in Europe equals France, for example, in the emphasis on national efforts in space and atomic energy the ultimate success of these undertakings is very much dependent on complementary international programs. It is for this reason that France has tenaciously resisted the attempt of Great Britain to withdraw from the *Concorde* project, has struggled to maintain but redefine the objectives of the European space effort, and has been a prime mover in the establishment in Europe (and on French soil) of an International Center for Cancer Research.[10]

The logic of the French position is that while international programs can supplement national programs they cannot replace them. If individual European states do not evolve their own scientific programs and technical industries European cooperative efforts will undoubtedly become dependent on the U.S. for their scientific and technical backing. Acknowledging that it would be possible to follow a space policy based extensively on collaboration with the United States one French space official explained the attitude of his government at a meeting of the British Interplanetary Society in April 1964:

[10] *Le Monde Diplomatique*, Nov. 1965.

Only a national space programme could bring about a significant development of our national space industry. A solution based only on bilateral collaboration with the United States, or multilateral collaboration within a European space organization would result in short-term technical dependence on another country, a policy incompatible with the general orientation of European policy.[11]

As already indicated, the French reject the concept underlying the founding of Euratom, the European Coal and Steel Community (ECSC), and the Organization for European Nuclear Research (CERN)—that functional cooperation in science and technology is the route to the eventual political unification of western Europe. The Gaullist conception of a *Europe des patries*, embodied in the so-called Fouchet Plan, accepts the need for functional cooperation with France's European neighbors but not an irrevocable commitment to the politically unified Europe envisaged by such men as Jean Monnet and officials of the U.S. Department of State. France, de Gaulle reasons, must add the resources of her neighbors to her own if France and Europe are to remain independent, but France must remain free to defend the interests of France against those same neighbors as well as against the great powers.

The aggregate scientific, technical, and economic resources of western Europe, if one includes Great Britain, nearly match those of the United States.[12] The problem for Europe in balancing American power is not, therefore, so much the magnitude of Europe's resources but their effective use. In science and technology, as in the economic sphere, high productivity in the use of resources means the concentration of scarce resources, an efficient division of labor, and skillful manage-

[11] Robert (General) Aubinière, "The French National Space Programme," *Space Flight*, VI, No. 5, Sept. 1964, 147-48.

[12] Christopher Layton, *Trans-Atlantic Investment*, The Atlantic Institute, 1966, pp. 53-54.

ment. Decisions must be made with respect to the establishment of scientific and technical priorities among competing programs of various European states in accordance with the strengths or comparative advantages of each. If France or any other European nation protects or maintains scientific and technical programs in order to enhance national independence, the effective use of Europe's resources is lessened to that extent.

Put crudely, the question to be answered in examining France's international science policy is whether France can "have it both ways." Can France achieve her scientific, economic, and political objectives, especially the crucial aim of independence of the United States, through a primary emphasis on national programs serviced by limited cooperation with other states? Or must she choose ultimately a total commitment to European unification in order for France and Europe to balance American scientific, technological, and economic power? To answer these questions, let us turn first to an examination of specific programs of scientific-technical cooperation involving France and her neighbors, and then to the more general problems of scientific-technical cooperation in Europe.

Cooperation in Advanced Technologies

Within the broad scope of European cooperation in science and technology several areas stand out as important for the achievement of France's over-all objectives. They are those spheres of advanced technology which will be increasingly vital to modern economic life and will impinge most directly on national defense—aviation, space, atomic energy, and computers. Successful cooperation in these areas with her European neighbors would enable France to counter the perceived threat of U.S. hegemony; failure would raise serious questions about the economic and political future of France as well as that of all of western Europe.

AERONAUTICS

In the field of aviation, after several ill-fated attempts to co-operate with West Germany, the French believe they have found their natural partner in Great Britain. The possessor of the second largest aeronautical industry in the western world, Britain has strength in aircraft engines, which makes a good complement to French strength in airframes. Like the French, the British fear greatly for the future of their aviation industry. A report on the British aircraft industry, prepared by a committee headed by Lord Plowden, advised the Government in December 1965 that Britain should abandon her independent national aeronautical program and collaborate wholeheartedly with other European aircraft industries in order to meet the threat of American competition.[13]

TABLE 24.

Employment in Aircraft Industries[a]

American	800,000
British	225,000
French	92,000
West German	35,000
Italian	20,000

[a] *Le Monde*, June 13-14, 1965. Other estimates of the size of the national industries vary from these figures, but the difference in magnitude is readily apparent.

The principal object of the French-British collaboration, as of 1968, is the development of the supersonic, long-distance *Concorde*. Scheduled for operation in 1971 this aircraft is in competition with an American design for the lion's share of the multibillion dollar superjet market foreseen in the near future.[14] If commercially successful, the *Concorde* would assist

[13] The Report of the Committee of Inquiry into the Aircraft Industry, Appointed by the Prime Minister, Cmnd. 2,853, 1965.

[14] "*Concorde* Production ahead of Timetable," *Aviation Week and Space Technology*, Vol. 83, No. 14, Apr. 4, 1966, pp. 40-43.

greatly, though not guarantee, the survival of the British and French aviation industries.[15]

In addition, the British and French Governments have already agreed to undertake or are discussing the advisability of undertaking other joint projects in civilian and military aviation, which include (1) several helicopter designs, (2) the Jaguar strike fighter-trainer project, and possibly (3) a 240-passenger airbus which might be developed in cooperation with Germany as a competitor to Boeing's 747.[16]

Moreover, the two countries have agreed to undertake more aggressive salesmanship in order to combat the sales offensive directed by the Pentagon's Military Export Sales Department. The world weapons market is a multibillion dollar one for the United States and will no doubt increase with the rise of new nations, each of which wants a military establishment of its own. The most lucrative market, however, is that of western Europe, and especially West Germany, which has reportedly purchased 48 percent of American overseas defense sales.[17] The capture of this market is a prime French-British concern.

In order to improve their position the British and French air forces have established a joint operations requirements team to increase collaborative ventures in the design and development of military aircraft. They have also taken the initiative in proposing the establishment of a Council of European Defense and Aerospace Ministers and a European Armaments Board. Eventually, it is hoped, Europe may develop its own armaments industry and thereby lessen its dependence on the United States.[18]

[15] *Le Monde*, May 13, 1966.

[16] "England, France Combine for Strength," *Aviation Week and Space Technology*, Vol. 83, No. 10, Mar. 7, 1966, 91; "Sud-Dassault Team Designs Galion Airbus as Caravelle Follow-on in Markets Outside U.S.," *Aviation Week and Space Technology*, Vol. 83, No. 19, May 9, 1966, 74-81.

[17] Layton, *Trans-Atlantic Investment,* p. 97.

[18] "England, France Combine," p. 91.

The history of this French-British collaboration has been marked by much controversy and disappointment. The most vexing episode for the French was the attempt in 1964-65 by the newly elected British Labor Government of Harold Wilson to scuttle the *Concorde* project altogether because of its unanticipated and mounting costs. Threatened with a breach of contract suit by the enraged French government, which would have cost Britain nearly as much as her contribution to the project itself, the Labor Government decided to remain in the project. The British attempt to withdraw from the *Concorde* project was prompted largely by a sense of the futility of any effort to compete with the U.S. in the supersonic field. As was pointed out in Chapter 10, flight at supersonic speed involves a whole new order of technology and basic knowledge. The limited British-French technical and scientific competence (as well as their more limited financial resources) has greatly constrained design work on the *Concorde*. Whereas the American entry in the supersonic transport (*SST*) competition is using highly advanced technologies and concepts such as titanium metal and radical wing designs, the *Concorde* is pushing existing technology to its limits. As a consequence, though the *Concorde* will appear first and will cost much less than the American superjet, it will become obsolete rapidly, at least for transatlantic flights. The American *SST* is designed to be far superior in speed and carrying capacity, perhaps the two prime considerations affecting commercial sales and profitability.[19] As a result of the apparent technical and commercial superiority of the American *SST* the prospects are strong that the *Concorde* may be a commercial failure.

The *Concorde's* troubles, however, have been only the most dramatic of the difficulties that have plagued French-British collaboration in aeronautics and have vexed each partner with the other. From the French perspective the British

[19] For a detailed comparison, see *Le Monde*, Jan. 31, 1967.

are morally obligated to purchase French aircraft in the interest of French-British aviation collaboration. When the Royal Air Force in 1966 and again in April, 1967 agreed to purchase the American F-111 rather than the *Mirage IV*[20] and the British Government in August 1966 authorized BOAC to purchase Boeing 747's rather than await the development of a French-British airbus,[21] the French expressed extreme disappointment with their partners for not "buying European," and observed that "Great Britain only works with France [in contrast to the United States] on minor programs."[22]

These latter examples illustrate well the problems besetting French-British collaboration in aeronautics and which will be magnified many times as attempts are made to expand aeronautical cooperation to embrace all western European states. Such an expansion of the base of cooperation has already become necessary because not even France and Great Britain combined can afford to finance the several new projects that they are contemplating in addition to *Concorde*. Furthermore, without a commanding position in the European market for civilian and military aircraft, the economic viability of French-British aeronautical collaboration is highly doubtful.[23]

For the French and British the keystone of European aeronautical cooperation should be French-British collaboration.[24] The bilateral collaboration of these two largest of the aviation industries in western Europe could provide the nucleus for larger consortia composed of other European states which would produce aircraft developed by the French and the British.

[20] *Le Monde*, May 13, 1966. The order was subsequently cancelled (January 16, 1968) because of Britain's balance of payments problem.

[21] *Le Monde*, Aug. 4, 1966.

[22] *Le Monde*, Jan. 17, 1967.

[23] See Layton, *Trans-Atlantic Investment*, p. 105.

[24] "U.K., France Sign Aircraft Engine Pact," *Aviation Week and Space Technology*, Vol. 84, No. 21, May 24, 1965, 18.

Unfortunately the other European states are no more willing to be dependent on France and Britain for their aviation technology than the latter two are on the United States. Whereas the French and the British appear to propose an unequal partnership in aviation to their European neighbors, not unlike that proposed for all of Europe by the United States, the lesser European states do "not wish merely to take part in mutual production programmes but [they seek] means whereby their technology, their science, even if in more restricted areas, could advance with the whole front."[25] Moreover, problems of commercial secrecy, classified information, and intense rivalry among European aviation companies make the development of an all European aviation industry exceptionally difficult.[26]

Consequently, unless British-French aircraft have decided advantages over American, it may be too much to expect that other European nations will buy their product simply because it is "European." For other nations, buying a less satisfactory or more costly aircraft because it had been produced in Europe would be conceivable only if they themselves were full participants in the project.[27]

In light of intense American competition and the difficulties of achieving voluntary cooperation among European aviation firms and governments, European aviation experts are moving toward the conclusion that their aeronautical industries could be saved only by an all-European policy toward aeronautics. In baldest terms this could mean discrimination against American sellers in the European market. Such was the conclusion

[25] This is the conclusion of a discussion among aviation experts representative of European countries with aeronautical industries. United Kingdom Council of the European Movement, *European Cooperation in Advanced Technology, Report of a Conference*, London, July 1965, p. 29.

[26] *Ibid.*, pp. 19-32.

[27] Cf. Layton, *Trans-Atlantic Investment*, pp. 104-105, for a discussion of these problems.

drawn by one British authority in summarizing the discussion of European experts on the plight of their aviation industry:

> . . . if there are to be pan-European civil developments then there should be a pan-European market. Again, to be frank, although the words were not used, no one could doubt what members were talking about. Questions were in people's minds, for example, as to whether nationalized airlines or airlines with considerable governmental support in this country [Great Britain], in Germany, and other countries, should or should not be free to buy outside Europe, if there were common European developments. I detected a considerable element of doubt as to whether political leadership had yet embraced this problem.[28]

Aside from the question of the wisdom of a protectionist policy, the difficulty of formulating such a European aviation policy would be great indeed. Mention has already been made of the intense rivalries among the European firms themselves. In addition, American firms have already penetrated the European industry through alliances with European firms.[29] A more basic problem preventing the elaboration of a European aeronautical policy and greater collaboration is the close relationship between the national aircraft industries and national defense.

The requirements for military aircraft (which comprise such a large portion of the production of the aviation industry) are determined by national, strategic, and foreign policies. Because the strategies and foreign policies of European nations differ it is difficult to develop a common set of requirements for military aircraft to be produced through a collaborative effort. "The failures of the past have had in them an element that

[28] United Kingdom Council, *European Cooperation Report*, p. 29.
[29] Layton, *Trans-Atlantic Investment*, p. 97.

the requirement pressed by one country differed from that pressed by another because their strategic posture in the world was different. This is the kernel of the reason for a lot of failures in the past: that nations insist on technological requirements deriving out of their particular strategic posture."[30] This situation has led one expert to conclude:

> If the air staffs of France, Germany, and Britain are to overcome their chauvinism and buy foreign aircraft in return for foreign agreement to buy their own aircraft, there must be a sense of trust and a permanent political relationship. Bilateral intergovernment cooperation on technology cannot get very far. Nor is it enough for integration to be confined to economic matters. A common weapons-buying policy means a common defense policy. Europe will not succeed in pooling its resources in technology until the European community is extended to include the defence of foreign policy, too.[31]

Given the independent military strategy of France, and the intimate ties of the military strategies and foreign policies of her two most prominent European partners, Great Britain and West Germany, to American strategy and foreign policy, the prospect for European aeronautical cooperation in military aviation is not very bright. It is precisely for this reason that the abandonment by France of the British-French project to produce by 1975 a supersonic military jet with variable geometry wings is of such great significance. Its success would have necessitated and symbolized an increasing similarity of military strategies and political outlooks. Hopefully, the British decision to withdraw from east of Suez may yet provide the basis for closer British-European perspectives on strategy and foreign policy.

[30] United Kingdom Council, *European Cooperation Report,* p. 31.
[31] Layton, *Trans-Atlantic Investment,* p. 106.

SPACE

Though the international activities of the French space program are considerably smaller than the purely national effort, the international program plays a vitally important role in the French dream of becoming a space power. This program represents a substantial investment, much greater in fact, than that expended by any other European nation (see TABLE 25). In 1966 $28.3 million of France's $72.9 million space budget went to European space programs. In the framework of the Fifth Plan (1966-70) $91 million out of the $404.9 million provided for space research will be allocated for participation in European space organizations. As this amount represents one-fourth of the space budget it reveals the importance the French place on these joint ventures, especially those undertaken with their European neighbors: the European Launcher Development Organization (ELDO), the European Space Research Or-

TABLE 25.

Western European Space Expenditures for 1964, 1965, and 1966[a]
(in millions of dollars)

Country	1964 (actual)			1965 (budgeted)			1966 (estimated)		
	Natl.	ESRO-ELDO	Tot.	Natl.	ESRO-ELDO	Tot.	Natl.	ESRO-ELDO	Tot.
France	32.70	14.30	47.00	42.10	16.50	58.60	44.30	29.90	74.20
West Ger.	14.40	23.00	37.40	19.40	17.60	37.00	19.40	17.60	37.00
U.K.	3.40	16.80	20.20	5.20	32.10	37.30	11.00	38.50	49.50
Italy	2.70	4.80	7.50	2.70	6.50	9.20	5.60	13.40	19.00
Netherlands	0.58	2.69	3.27	0.68	3.33	4.01	0.76	3.85	4.61
Sweden	0.39	0.37	0.76	0.58	0.89	1.47	0.56	1.94	2.50
Switzerland	0.00	0.85	0.85	0.00	0.69	0.69	0.00	1.42	1.42
Denmark	0.09	0.34	0.43	0.12	0.47	0.59	—	—	—
Spain	0.61	0.37	0.98	1.4	0.37	1.77	—	—	—
Norway	0.29	0.00	0.29	0.35	0.00	0.35	0.44	0.00	0.44
TOTAL			118.68			150.98			188.67

[a] Adapted from U.S. Department of State, *International Science Notes*, No. 11, October 1965, p. 13.

ganization (ESRO), and the European Conference for Tele-communications Satellites (CETS).

ELDO. The European Launcher Development Organization was founded in March 1964 by an agreement between France, Belgium, West Germany, Italy, Holland, the United Kingdom, and Australia. Characterized by *The Economist,* with some justification, as "chiefly a dump for broken down military projects"[32] (in particular, Britain's *Blue Streak* rocket), ELDO's initial purpose was to build a three-stage launcher entitled *Europa I* or *ELDO-A* for heavy satellites and scheduled to be operational by 1968. Toward the accomplishment of this goal each participant is contributing funds, technologies, or facilities according to its resources.

ELDO possesses few facilities of its own, and is essentially a coordinating and contracting organization. For the production of *ELDO-A* approximately 4,500 to 5,000 scientists, engineers, technicians, and industrial workers have been organized into scientific and technical teams, in addition to the approximately 70 engineers and scientists who work at ELDO's headquarters in Paris.[33]

ESRO. The second major European space effort in which France is a partner is the European Space Research Organization. It was established on June 14, 1962 and is composed of 10 countries—Belgium, Denmark, France, West Germany, Italy, Holland, Spain, Sweden, Switzerland, and the United Kingdom. ESRO is essentially a research and service organization. With a budget of $300 million for its initial eight-year satellite research program (of which France contributes about 19 percent), ESRO is developing: (1) a launching site at Kiruna, Sweden; (2) a European Space Technology Center at Noordwijk, Holland; and (3) a network of stations for telemetry and tracking.

[32] *The Economist,* Jan. 21-27, 1967, p. 197.
[33] Victor McElheny, "Decision Time Approaches for European Rocket Program," *Science,* Vol. 151, No. 3,716, Mar. 18, 1966, p. 1,373.

ECSC. The third European space organization is the 17-nation European Communication Satellite Conference which was organized in 1963 to represent Europe in the negotiations leading to the establishment of *Intelsat* (International Telecommunications Satellite Consortia). Though lacking facilities of its own, it has proposed a three stage program including orbital tests of experimental communications satellites in 1968 or 1969; launching of an experimental communications satellite in 1970; and construction of a satellite network capable of television broadcasting directly to community or home antennas on the earth's surface.[34] The hope of European space enthusiasts is that this program can be integrated with that of ELDO to provide Europe with an independent telecommunications satellite capability.

ELDO and Its Problems. Of these three European space organizations the most important by far is ELDO. The rocket launcher is the basic ingredient in any space program; without its own launcher an independent European space program would hardly be possible. For this reason the focusing of this discussion on ELDO and its problems reveals in essence the major hurdles which face the nascent European space effort.

The motivation underlying ELDO's founding was European fear of the long-term economic and political consequences of being left behind by the major powers in space exploration. Each European state realized it could not compete alone against the Americans and Russians. While the opportunity for scientific cooperation with the American program had been made available to them, Europeans wanted to master for themselves the technology of space activity. Even though they must follow in the giant footsteps of the United States and the Soviet Union "the experience was what was required, and it would not satisfy practical self-interest in Europe to delegate

[34] *Ibid.*

the technical jobs to the U.S."[35] What interested the Europeans was the practical exploitation of space communications, navigation, weather forecasting, etc., and for this purpose they needed to acquire the "know-how" for themselves. This purpose, however, has not proven to be a completely satisfactory rationale for the investment of millions of dollars to develop a technology already available in most instances from the United States.

ELDO was founded to give the Europeans a booster capability. Beyond this, its rocket has had no specific mission other than that of launching ESRO scientific research satellites—hardly a reason for investing huge funds, given NASA's willingness to launch satellites for ESRO. Within a relatively short period ELDO became plagued by this absence of a concrete mission. It was one thing to agree in principle that Europe should have its own launcher capability; it was quite another to invest precious resources in an international program whose long-term objective was not clear. Concern began to mount particularly as the cost of the launcher exceeded the original estimates by over 200 percent.[36] In 1961 the estimate for constructing *ELDO-A* was $200 million; in 1965 the figure was $300 million, and by 1966, $420 million.[37] Costs were running over original estimates especially in the second and third stages, which were being constructed by the French and Germans.

To the critics of ELDO it appears foolish to compete with the Americans and Russians in the practical exploitation of space when the latter two have such an immense headstart. Proponents of ELDO, such as the French, point out that there are many areas where the Europeans could establish themselves.

[35] Arnold Frutkin, *International Cooperation in Space*, Prentice-Hall, 1965, p. 133.
[36] *Aviation Week and Space Technology*, Vol. 85, No. 26, June 27, 1966, p. 73.
[37] McElheny, "Decision Time Approaches," p. 1,372.

One suggestion, for example, proposes telecommunications, navigation, and radio and television distribution satellites as feasible projects from an economic and technical standpoint.[38] Another proposal is that of a recoverable space transporter— a technology not far advanced in either the United States or the Soviet Union.[39] Despite these ambitious proposals, however, in the words of ELDO's Secretary-General, Renzo di Carrobio, there is no "long-term common policy for space activities in Europe . . . due in great measure to the high cost of space activities and to the tremendous lead of the United States and Russia, which gives rise to the belief in some quarters that we in Europe cannot expect to enter the field with the confidence that we can achieve results of comparable value, even by combining our efforts."[40]

Because of this situation ELDO has undergone several crises which have almost brought its demise. In 1964 France threatened to abandon the joint effort, and more recently Great Britain, in June 1966, announced its intention to withdraw altogether from the project because of the financial strain. After much controversy between Britain and her partners, pressure on the British by the United States, and a realignment of Britain's financial obligations for the project, the British decided to remain in the organization. Under the new arrangement Britain's share of the cost was reduced from 30 percent to 27 percent; West Germany's share was raised from 22 percent to 27 percent; France's share from 24 to 25 percent; Italy's share was set at 12 percent; the remaining nine percent was to be shared by Belgium, the Netherlands, and Australia.[41]

[38] "Eurospace Urges Spurt to Reduce U.S., Russian Space Effort Lead," *Aviation Week and Space Technology*, Vol. 84, No. 2, July 11, 1966, 109-17.

[39] "Europe Firm on Space Transporter Goals," *Aviation Week and Space Technology*, Vol. 84, No. 26, June 28, 1965, 77-79.

[40] Quoted in McElheny, "Decision Time Approaches," p. 1,374.

[41] *Le Monde*, June 12-13, 1966.

Perhaps the most important outcome of the financial crisis was that it forced ELDO members to face the issue of defining ELDO's purpose. Toward this end the member states agreed to examine the notion of a European Space Authority which could formulate, implement, and coordinate a space policy for Europe.[42] Also of importance was the agreement to construct a second generation rocket of a much more advanced and powerful design than *ELDO-A*.[43] This rocket, *ELDO/PAS*, conceived by the French firm, SEREB (builder of the *Diamant*), and to be ready in 1971 or 72, will have a capability of putting a 200-kilogram satellite (about 425 pounds) into a geostationary orbit from France's equatorial launching site in Guiana.[44] Such a satellite could have the capacity to handle 2,500 telephone conversations between a large number of ground stations and relay television between main terminal stations in various parts of the globe.

At its most ambitious the aim behind this decision is to construct the foundation for a European regional telecommunications system independent of the American sponsored global system—*Intelsat*. At the minimum a European capability in telecommunications satellites would give the Europeans a stronger bargaining position for challenging the dominance of the American *Comsat* Corporation when the *Intelsat* agreement comes up for renegotiation in 1969. In particular the Europeans would like a greater role for their own space industries in the development and maintenance of satellite telecommunications and ground stations; the Europeans' share of the developing multibillion dollar space communications industry will depend on their proven experience in building communi-

[42] G.K.C. Pardoe, "A European Space Authority," *The Financial Times*, Sept. 5, 1966.

[43] "ELDO to Provide Comsat Launcher," *Technology Week*, XIX, No. 3, July 18, 1966, 20.

[44] See *Le Monde*, Apr. 30, 1966, for a discussion of the rocket's characteristics.

cation satellites, launchers, and ground stations. If they lack an industrial capability in space technology they fear they will be reduced to a modest subcontracting and component-supplying role under the leadership of American firms. As a consequence Europeans fear their financial (about 29 percent of *Intelsat's* budget) and technical contributions to *Intelsat* would only serve to augment the capabilities of the American space industry.[45]

The French have insisted that if ELDO fails to develop the *ELDO/PAS* launcher they will build it for themselves. One French observer stated this determination in the following words: "We feel we must have a comsat booster for Europe. If the British back out of ELDO, we'll do it alone. What we really want is a T.V. satellite. It's important to have one and have one independently. And if we came two or three years after the others, what does it matter? What we are not going to do is rely on Russia or the United States for comsat boosters."[46]

The French ambition in space communications, which is embodied in Projects *Safran* and *Saros*, is to establish a satellite communications system covering French-speaking Africa, Latin America, and the Middle East. Such a system might service European needs as well.[47] Toward the accomplishment of this goal, the French have gotten their ELDO partners to agree that the new *ELDO/PAS* launcher may be purchased by any member of the consortium. Furthermore, as was pointed out in Chapter 9, the French and Germans are con-

---

[45] "Eurospace Urges Satellite Launcher Push," *Aviation Week and Space Technology*, Vol. 74, No. 12, Mar. 21, 1966, 37. The reality of this fear is borne out by the fact that Europeans receive only four percent of its contracts. *Wall Street Journal*, Sept. 12, 1967.

[46] "Britain Pressured to Stay in ELDO," *Technology Week*, XVIII, No. 25, June 20, 1966, 20. Cf. *Le Monde*, March 12, 13-14, 1966, for a series on French interest in satellite telecommunications.

[47] Cf. *Le Monde*, Mar. 13-14, 1966; Jan. 29-30, 1967.

structing an experimental geostationary communications satellite.

This European space effort, then, provides a vital complement to French space ambitions. Through their own national effort they have developed the *Diamant* which can launch small payloads into low orbits; for larger payloads and greater distances, they must depend for many years to come on international collaboration.[48] For scientific space research they can depend to a considerable extent on the use of American and Russian launch vehicles, providing of course that French collaboration with the Soviet Union in space does not jeopardize her association with the American program. But for the practical and technological exploitation of space the French are dependent on collaboration with their European neighbors.

Whether the European cooperative effort will succeed in breaking the American near monopoly of the practical exploitation of space remains very much in doubt. By 1969, when the *Intelsat* treaty is to be renegotiated, the American *Comsat* Corporation will have three satellites in place and will have established a "practically inexpugnable"[49] position in space communication. Except for the French and possibly the Germans the other European states are not entirely convinced that it is wise to invest their limited resources in space; a recent report of Eurospace, for example, deplored the fact that the total European space effort is one-thirtieth of the American effort (including the manned lunar program).[50] Concern over the cost of space research may be expected to come up repeatedly when the bills for *ELDO/PAS* start coming in.

Another source of difficulty which will plague the construction of *ELDO/PAS* is the fact that in agreeing to its initiation the European states saddled this program with a number of

[48] Victor McElheny, "France in Space: Collaboration with both U.S. and U.S.S.R.?" *Science*, Vol. 150, No. 3,704, Dec. 24, 1965, 1,700.
[49] Nicolas Vichney, in *Le Monde*, Mar. 12, 1966.
[50] "Eurospace Urges Spurt," p. 110.

restrictions including the provision that each nation's share of ELDO's contracts must be in proportion to its financial contribution to the budget; this provision places a severe limitation on the ability of ELDO to work out a division of labor among the European states that makes effective use of their total resources.[51] What appears essential for the long-term development of a meaningful European space program is the fusion of ELDO, ESRO, and ECSC into one space organization. "Only a European decision to undertake in common—and time presses—an effort in order not to abandon to the United States the monopoly of spatial telecommunications would be able to give the work of ELDO the interest which up until now it is necessary to admit, it has not had."[52] Perhaps the European Space Conference, which was established in July 1967 and has a mandate to draft a long-term European space program, is the first step in this direction.

COMPUTERS

Perhaps in no area of science and technology does European cooperation seem to be more necessary than in that of computers. American industry has pressed its advantages of immense size, huge financial resources (including government contracts), and aggressive management in this sector of scientific technology. Rather than the Europeans catching up, with the advent of the third generation of computers (integrated circuits and microminiaturization) America's lead appears to be increasing.[53] The situation has been summarized by *The Economist* in the following words:

> The onslaught has left the continent well and truly dependent on the United States for computer technology. The only country left with an independent industry is Britain.

[51] *Le Monde*, July 10-11, 1966.
[52] Quoted from an editorial in *Le Monde*, Aug. 11, 1966.
[53] *New York Times*, Mar. 19, 1967.

Even here, most computer firms still rely to some extent on some kind of American equipment, but British "independents" like International Computers and Tabulators, having gone into direct competition with the Americans, are trying to break free as quickly as possible. And now, on the continent, there are sounds of a call to arms, Europe is beginning to wonder if complete reliance on America is a wise choice.[54]

Though European computer industries and governments agree in principle on the need for cooperation in order to challenge the American position in the European computer market, the barriers to effective cooperation are formidable. Many of the technical and economic obstacles were brought out in the 1966 discussion of the Conference on European Cooperation in Advanced Technology.[55] Even more difficult, however, are the policy differences among the Europeans. The formulation of a European policy on computer development that would be the foundation for massive financial assistance from cooperating governments is delayed because the individual governments in most cases have not yet formulated their own computer requirements. In the words of one British official, intra-European cooperation and financial assistance require "very clear governmental agreement on the requirements. We in the United Kingdom are beginning to search for a standardization of government requirements for computers. This is going to take a long while. Corresponding steps are being taken in other capitals of Europe. But for those capitals then to get together in Europe will take a still longer time. It does not go up in a linear scale, but in an exponential scale."[56]

Within industry itself cooperation among Europeans is difficult because of commercial secrecy. European firms worry not only about IBM but also about their European competitors.

[54] "Aux Armes Citoyens," *The Economist,* Mar. 19-25, 1966, p. 1,149.
[55] United Kingdom Council, *European Cooperation Report,* p. 41.
[56] *Ibid.,* p. 46.

A firm with a good idea is not going to make that idea available to any competitor whatever his nationality. "We live," one British official reminded his fellows at the Conference on European Cooperation in Advanced Technology, "in a competitive economy, and quite rightly, in a competitive economy, companies and institutions attach importance to the commercial value of their know-how and their research."[57]

The consequence of these obstacles is that no solely European computer organization similar to ELDO or CERN exists to promote cooperative ventures and the rationalization of the industry. The European Computer Manufacturers' Association does little to lead the industry, and, having American corporations among its membership, it is a poor vehicle for a cooperative effort directed against American computer hegemony. Furthermore, there are no important examples of European cooperation in computer research and development; the one significant attempt was the conclusion of a technical cooperation agreement between one French and two British computer firms to construct a large computer for scientific research which would also have been useful in the French nuclear weapons program.[58] But the project never materialized.[59]

In the absence of European computer cooperation, the principal challengers to IBM's dominant position in the European computer market are international consortia headed by IBM's American competitors. One such consortium is that composed of General Electric (American), Machines Bull (French), and Olivetti (Italian). Another has been formed by RCA (American), English Electric (British), and Siemens (German).[60] Other American companies have connections with European companies through licensing and information exchange agree-

[57] *Ibid.*
[58] *Le Monde,* June 5, 1965.
[59] "Aux Armes Citoyens," p. 1,150.
[60] Layton, *Trans-Atlantic Investment,* p. 104.

ments. In fact, even the French Government's new computer firm is to produce American computers under license.

In summary, therefore, outside the operations of American firms, the European computer industry remains organized largely on a national basis. As in France, with her *Plan Calcul,* computer manufacturers are merging and developing new modes of cooperation on a national basis. Whether these firms can withstand American competition, given the U.S. edge in computer technology and especially in microminiaturization, remains highly doubtful. This situation has led some to suggest that stern measures must be taken to protect their infant computer industries against the American "invaders." While to many Europeans and especially the British, the idea of protectionism is anathema, the sentiment of many European computer experts was expressed by Maurice Ponte, of the Compagnie Générale de Télégraphie sans Fil and member of the Comité des Sages: "We must not wave an anti-American flag, but we must not wave a white flag!"[61]

ATOMIC ENERGY

In the field of atomic energy the French participate in international programs which range from the International Atomic Energy Agency to bilateral agreements with individual nations. Among these programs several point up the opportunities for and problems of international cooperation in atomic energy.

Beginning with cooperation in fundamental research, France is a member of the European Center for Nuclear Research (CERN) located at Geneva. Established in 1953 by 12 western European states and with the support of the United States, by 1960 CERN had become one of the important centers of the world for high-energy physics.[62] Outside the Soviet Union and

[61] United Kingdom Council, *European Cooperation Report,* p. 45.
[62] During its initial years, CERN was directed by an American citizen,

the United States, it has the most powerful particle accelerators in existence. Furthermore, if the Europeans can solve the problems of design and financing, CERN's proposed new *300 GeV* accelerator (provided also that the Europeans can agree where to put it) will match new Russian and American machines.[63]

In December 1957 the European Nuclear Energy Agency (ENEA) was created as part of what is now the OECD. Composed of the western European nations, with the United States, Canada, and Japan as Associate members, ENEA's functions are threefold: (1) The sponsorship of joint undertakings leading toward the commercial exploitation of atomic energy (of these programs perhaps the most significant is the Dragon high-temperature gas-cooled reactor project at Winfrith Heath in the United Kingdom, sponsored by ENEA and *Euratom*);[64] (2) The promotion of scientific and technical cooperation between member countries through the review of national programs, the exchange of personnel and information, and establishment of common centers for data collection and exchange in the field of atomic energy; and (3) The study of the economic aspects of nuclear energy and its place in Europe's overall energy balance sheet.

From the perspective of the practical application of atomic energy, the most important organization of which France is a member is the European Atomic Energy Community (*Euratom*).[65] *Euratom* was established on January 1, 1958, along

---

Victor Weisskopf, of the Massachusetts Institute of Technology. In 1965 Weisskopf's term ended and he was succeeded by Roger Gregory, a French scientist. See J. B. Adams, "CERN: The European Organization for Nuclear Research," in Sir John Cockcroft, *The Organization of Research Establishments*, Cambridge University Press, 1965.

[63] Jean-Jacques Salomon, "International Science Policy," *Minerva*, II, No. 4, Summer 1964, 430.

[64] See *Euratom*, Bulletin of the European Atomic Energy Community, III, No. 3, Sept. 1964, 20.

[65] There are several industrial and professional organizations, other

with the European Economic Community, partly as a mechanism to further the political unification of Europe through cooperation in a specific functional area and partly to meet what appeared at the time to be an impending critical shortage of energy resources in western Europe.[66] A Frenchman might add that the purpose of *Euratom* was also to prevent any European nation from acquiring an independent nuclear weapons capability and to promote American domination of the European power reactor market. In any case, the belief then prevalent that the energy situation was critical shaped the original character of *Euratom* and set it on a course which has become strongly resented by the French.[67] Additional problems have subsequently disenchanted France's partners and put the future of the organization in question.

To meet Europe's apparent pressing need for energy in the shortest possible time, *Euratom* and the U.S. entered into an Agreement of Cooperation in 1958 which provided for a joint investment of $350 million in 1,000 megawatts of electricity from nuclear power plants using enriched uranium reactors of American design. European power companies were to provide $215 million of the capital requirement of $350 million for the proposed six to eight plants. The American Export-Import Bank would supply the remaining $135 million as a long-term, low-interest loan. Furthermore, the United States would supply enriched uranium at a low interest rate, buy

---

than the ones discussed here, such as *Foratom*, which is composed of European atomic industries.

[66] Jaroslav Polach, *Euratom—Its Background, Issues, and Economic Implications*, Oceana Publications, 1964, pp. 47-61. See also Arnold Kramish, *The Peaceful Atom in Foreign Policy*, Harper and Row, 1963, pp. 155ff; Lawrence Scheinman, "Euratom: Nuclear Integration in Europe," *International Conciliation*, No. 563, May 1967.

[67] For a discussion of internal French debate over the Euratom treaty see Lawrence Scheinman, *Atomic Energy in France under the Fourth Republic*, Princeton University Press, 1965, Chap. 5.

back plutonium at favorable terms, and reprocess fuel elements. Lastly, the United States and *Euratom* entered into a $100-million Joint Research and Development program to improve the American reactor design.[68]

Though the actual accomplishments of this first phase of the *Euratom* program were negligible, its significance lay in the fact that France's *Euratom* partners were encouraged to take quite a different route than that taken by France in reactor development. France, as we have already seen, had chosen to concentrate on natural uranium fueled reactors. For her the U.S.-*Euratom* agreement "helped the penetration of Europe by the American nuclear industry without encouraging the development of genuine European solutions."[69] By the same token, the other Europeans were to become dependent on and interested in American enriched uranium reactors. This difference in interests has been the basis of many issues dividing France and her *Euratom* partners over the years.

A second problem, pointed out by Bertrand Goldschmidt, has been that of putting together a European nuclear program among partners with different levels of development. The essence of his argument is that the French, and to a lesser extent the Germans and Belgians, with the most advanced nuclear programs in Europe, have had little to gain from European cooperation. In the case of France what she did want she could not obtain because of American domination over the nuclear activities of her partners. "France," he concludes, "was relatively isolated, and alone—then as now—in showing a real wish for independence based on a large national programme, led by a strong central organization and full collaboration from industry."[70]

[68] Kramish, *Peaceful Atom*, p. 156.
[69] Bertrand Goldschmidt, *The Atomic Adventure*, Pergamon, 1964, trans. Peter Beer, p. 113.
[70] *Ibid.*, p. 109.

Furthermore, for the French and other countries as well, the history of *Euratom* bears out their fear of supranational European organizations in which decisions are taken by majority vote and individual countries cannot exercise a veto. Many of *Euratom*'s policies have been judged not only antithetical to French interests but to have favored American and British interests.[71] This issue came to a head in 1961, for example, when it was proposed that *Euratom* underwrite part of the cost of reactor construction. France objected forcefully, on the ground that French funds would be used to subsidize American and British reactors.[72] The French were outvoted on this issue but were subsequently successful in preventing the reelection of Etienne Hirsch as *Euratom* President and in having him replaced by another Frenchman, Pierre Chatenet, who did not share Hirsch's commitment to a supranational Europe.[73]

These and other conflicting interests of the *Euratom* partners have provided a source of continuous controversy. While a recounting of the many disputes which have rent *Euratom* would take us too far away from our main purpose, one set of issues illustrates the difficulties of atomic energy cooperation in Europe.[74] This matter is the content and conduct of *Euratom*'s research program. More concretely, the recurrent issue has been the relative emphasis which should be given to each of three areas: the improvement of existing designs, the development of intermediate reactors (until 1980), and research into advanced reactor designs and concepts.[75] Before proceeding to a consideration of the issues, a brief discussion of the programs may be helpful.

[71] *Ibid.*, p. 133.   [72] Polach, *Euratom*, p. 153.

[73] Goldschmidt, *Atomic Adventure*, p. 133.

[74] A concise, excellent analysis of the conflicting national interests and issues which have plagued *Euratom* is provided by Scheinman, "Euratom: Nuclear Integration."

[75] In the preparation of this section, the writer has benefited from a study by Robert K. Wood, *Euratom and Nuclear Power in Western Europe*, unpub., 1964.

In the improvement of proven designs, two types of reactors have been successful on an industrial scale. One is the graphite-gas, natural uranium reactors of French and British design; the other is the American design (boiling-water and pressurized water) using enriched uranium. Among intermediate reactors *Euratom* has concentrated on two areas to meet its energy needs by a route that does not entail dependence on the United States: the Orgel concept and high-temperature gas-cooled reactors. The former is a heavy-water-moderated, natural to slightly enriched uranium fueled reactor of French design being developed at the *Euratom* Research Center at Ispra, Italy. Of considerable interest to the French, this reactor represents *Euratom*'s most original contribution to reactor technology and is keyed to the French policy of *l'indépendance énergétique* based on natural uranium. It is intended to meet Europe's fuel needs until the 1980s and could be employed effectively in huge water-desalination projects. Among the high-temperature gas reactor projects, two are especially noteworthy—the Dragon reactor being developed by the British in cooperation with *Euratom*, and a project developed under contract by West Germany.

In the longer run, 1980 and beyond, the economic success of nuclear power rests with advanced designs, especially the perfection of a fast breeder reactor and the control of thermonuclear fusion. A breeder reactor is one which produces more fuel than it consumes through the transformation of a nonfissionable fuel such as uranium 238 into a fissionable material such as plutonium, which can then be reused as a fuel. The development of fast breeders like the French *Euratom Rapsodie* reactor is generally regarded as the most promising of all future reactor possibilities. For this reason, there is intense competition among Americans, British, French, Russians, and Germans in the development of a successful fast breeder which, in the words of Glenn Seaborg, chairman of the U.S. Atomic

Energy Commission, would solve the world's energy needs once and for all.[76]

In 1964 a crisis erupted over the priorities to be given these programs. The French took advantage of the disarray to issue a memorandum which outlined their dissatisfaction with *Euratom*'s policies and called for a revision of its programs along lines of interest to France. Germany, Italy, and Belgium responded in kind and made known their own complaints. As a result the crisis brought into the open the conflicts of national interest which continue to hinder cooperation among the European states in the exploitation of atomic power:[77]

1. The first issue, whether or not to increase *Euratom*'s budget, was fought between those partners such as the Netherlands and Belgium who have a large stake in *Euratom*, and others—notably France and West Germany—who desire to emphasize national programs. The underlying national differences are seen in the fact that the Netherlands devotes about 50 percent of her atomic energy budget to international programs, while France gives less than 10 percent and Germany about 15 percent.[78]

2. The second issue was between those countries which wanted *Euratom* to concentrate on three or four projects (for example, Orgel and fast breeders) so as to increase the efficient allocation of resources and improve Europe's nuclear independence vis-à-vis the U.S., and those that wanted no revision of *Euratom*'s ongoing programs, especially the emphasis on American reactors. In essence, this was a controversy between the countries most advanced in nuclear research (France, West

---

[76] U.S. Atomic Energy Commission, *Civilian Nuclear Power—A Report to the President*, 1962.

[77] These conflicts are spelled out by Scheinman, "Euratom: Nuclear Integration," pp. 32-35.

[78] Wood, *Euratom*, p. 31.

Germany, Belgium) and lesser advanced (especially Italy). While concentration on a few projects would benefit the nations with strong national programs, a more diversified program, including emphasis on American reactors, would assist the lesser developed to catch up,[79] and in the case of Italy enable her to meet pressing needs for increased sources of energy.

3. Another issue was the awarding of contracts. Originally France and Belgium received the lion's share of contracts because they were the most advanced nuclear countries and the mechanism for the selection of contractors favored them. West Germany was especially upset over this situation, claiming that 30 percent of *Euratom*'s research funds were provided by West Germany while only 10 percent of the contracts, in terms of monetary value, were awarded to her.

4. The last and most important source of controversy was American reactor technology and *Euratom*'s relations with the United States. From the French point of view, under the terms of the *Euratom*-United States Agreement of Cooperation, European and French funds were being used to improve American reactors which were in competition with French reactors. Furthermore, Europe was not developing an independent nuclear industry.[80] France's partners, on the other hand, have preferred American enriched uranium reactors because they are much less expensive than the natural uranium design.[81] The French retort has been that unless *Euratom*'s research program emphasized intermediate and advanced concepts of European origin, the U.S. would capture the world's power reactor market.

[79] *Ibid.*, pp. 32-34.

[80] Nicolas Vichney, "Pourquoi L'Europe se Lance-t-elle Dans des Réalisations Jugées Peu Compétitives aux États-Unis," *L'Expansion Scientifique*, No. 12, Jan. 1962, pp. 29-30. Cf. Victor McElheny, "Decisions on Nuclear Power," *Science*, Vol. 149, No. 3,682, July 23, 1965, 407-409.

[81] Wood, *Euratom*, pp. 38-39.

In truth these issues as well as others remain unresolved and continue to arise in newer areas, even though certain important decisions have been taken. It was decided after much argument, for example, to give greater priority to intermediate and advanced reactor designs.[82] In addition, *Euratom* has moved toward the distribution of contracts on a geographical basis—politically sound but not particularly conducive to an effective division of labor or to the selection of projects on the basis of technical merit. In short, as in the case of the European space program, *Euratom* has been unable to develop a sense of purpose and set of priorities.

But even if *Euratom* does succeed in overcoming these difficulties, there is a growing fear in France, and among her *Euratom* partners, that the Europeans will lose out in the competition to develop intermediate and advanced reactors. In the case of the former there is considerable concern that no one will be interested in such a reactor because of the competition of enriched uranium reactors; and even if there is a market, the United States may be selling a reactor of the Orgel type long before the Europeans.[83] *Euratom*'s two entries in the fast breeder competition may fall behind British, American, and Russian designs in this field, largely because of inadequate financial support. Moreover, even if they do prove technically successful, Europeans may not be able to employ breeders for power without purchasing at a high cost large amounts of the initial plutonium fuel from the United States or Great Britain.[84] Already the financing of this fuel has become a source of bitter controversy among the member states.

With these discouraging prospects ahead, many Europeans

[82] "Euratom's Report, Joyous and Surprising," *Common Market*, v, No. 8, Aug. 1965, 167-69.

[83] *Le Monde*, May 10, 1966.

[84] For the status of breeder research, see *Le Monde*, Mar. 3, 1966. *Euratom* has requested of the U.S. the right to purchase 1,000 kilograms of plutonium, *New York Times*, Sept. 7, 1966.

are beginning to realize that greater cooperation with the British would make sense as the solution to American competition and as a means to meet their growing atomic energy requirements.[85] In addition to their possession of a proven enriched uranium reactor (the *AGR*) and their lead over Europe in breeder technology, the British have an isotope uranium plant which could supply Europe with the needed enriched uranium. Already the British have begun to convert the plant to the production of enriched uranium for civilian power plants.[86] Compared to cooperation with the British the construction of a European plant for the production of enriched uranium would be extremely costly and the uranium produced would not be economically competitive with American fuel elements. In short, Great Britain could offer Europe enriched uranium, an economically competitive reactor, and advanced technical know-how.[87]

The trouble with the suggestion that Great Britain cooperate with Europe in nuclear technology is that the British have little incentive to do so, except perhaps as part of an agreement involving British entry into the Common Market. They are satisfied with their national program, especially in the area that interests *Euratom* the most—breeder technology. In addition, they have some regrets over the one reactor development agreement they have entered into with western Europe. As an executive of the European Nuclear Energy Agency told the U.K. Conference on European cooperation in advanced technology, "it is difficult for a variety of reasons to find proj-

[85] This was the consensus of the atomic energy experts at the U.K. Conference on European Cooperation in Advanced Technology. A more general statement of western Europe's need for British technology appears in a report of the European Parliament on a common European science policy. See Parlement Européen, *Rapport sur la Proposition de Résolution (document 63) relative à une Politique Scientifique Commune Européenne*, Document 107, Oct. 12, 1966, p. 12.

[86] Goldschmidt, *Atomic Adventure*, p. 155.

[87] *Le Monde*, Oct. 9, 1966.

ects in the advanced technology fields in which *Euratom* and the United Kingdom and other countries are willing to collaborate and spend considerable sums of money."[88]

As the prospect of commercial nuclear power comes closer the two advanced nuclear countries in *Euratom*, France and West Germany, are striking out on their own at the expense of *Euratom*; or else they are turning to lesser forms of cooperation such as the Franco-German high flux reactor to be established as part of the Paul Langevin-Max von Laue Institute at Grenoble, or the German, Belgian, and Dutch effort to build a fast breeder reactor. At best, *Euratom*, as its third five-year research program (1968-1973) reveals, has been reduced to the role of minor complement to national programs.[89] While these national programs may yet yield success, the future of *Euratom* itself is precarious. Without multinational cooperation it will be difficult for France in particular and continental Europe in general to compete in the market for nuclear power plants, or even to meet their own needs.

A European Science Policy

Europeans have been able to prove that in certain specific areas effective scientific cooperation is possible among sovereign nations on an intensive and long-term basis. CERN showed that it was feasible to transfer American high-energy experimental research to Europe.[90] Despite many difficulties and limitations *Euratom*, ELDO, and bilateral means of cooperation are making limited progress in specific areas of science and technology. This largely ad hoc, piecemeal cooperation does not, however, meet the desire of the French and other

---

[88] United Kingdom Council, *European Cooperation Report*, p. 35.

[89] *The Economist*, Feb. 11, 1967, p. 547.

[90] There was a heated debate in Europe over whether or not to go into high energy physics. Many Europeans were afraid they couldn't compete against the United States. Lew Kowarski, "The Making of CERN—An Experiment in Cooperation," *Bulletin of the Atomic Scientists*, XI, No. 10, Dec. 1955, 354-57.

Europeans for cooperation on a scale that would solve their national needs and meet the threat they see posed in the technology gap between the United States and western Europe. For this it is apparent that some larger European framework is necessary.

The Treaty of Rome establishing the European Economic Community in 1957 did not deal with the subject of scientific research.[91] At the time, the importance of scientific research to economic growth and the future of the Common Market was largely unappreciated. Research in general was considered solely a national concern. Those areas of scientific research and development which were recognized as of common concern were the responsibilities of the EEC's sister organizations, the European Coal and Steel Community (ECSC) and *Euratom*. However, as American competition and European appreciation of the importance of research have grown, this initial attitude has changed. Increasingly Europeans have begun to realize that "the degree of integration achieved by the member countries requires that the Communities act to provide a coordination of research no longer limited to particular fields. . . . If this combined action for research is not expanded, the economic development of the community risks being shackled."[92]

The initial neglect of a common science policy by the EEC reflected also a more general division between its two most powerful members. On one side were the French who favored a strong role for the state in the economy and advocated economic planning on a European basis. Opposed to such economic *étatisme* were the Germans, committed to laissez-faire

[91] The following discussion is based principally on two sources: Parlement Européen, *Rapport sur le Progrès Technologique et la Recherche Scientifique Dans le Cadre de la Communauté Européenne*, Document 97, Sept. 23, 1966; and Parlement Européen, *Rapport sur la Proposition de Résolution (document 63)*."

[92] *Communauté Européenne*, Mar. 1965.

and opposed to anything which approached state planning even on a national, much less European, basis. This difference has made it difficult to work out a European science policy between West Germany, which has yet to develop even a national science policy, and France, which has highly developed institutions for making science policy.[93] Nevertheless, the French have continued to press the Germans on the need for greater planning on a European basis.

THE MOVEMENT FOR A EUROPEAN SCIENCE POLICY

In response to French and European pressure for greater planning on a community-wide basis, the EEC established in April 1964 the Committee on Medium-Term Economic Policy with the responsibility of drafting an "overall economy policy programme for the five-year period 1966 to 1970."[94] Included among its tasks was that of "developing a comprehensive scheme for the advancement of scientific and technical research and development."[95] Carrying out this responsibility the Committee established a Working Group on Scientific and Technical Research Policy to develop common European programs of scientific research and development.

The first report of the Working Group, which was completed in 1966, proposed little for implementation. Lack of time, the crisis over the future of the EEC, and divergences among member states and the executives themselves, made it impossible to develop any new initiatives for European cooperation in scientific research. Nevertheless, attention was focused on a serious problem for Europe; it was agreed that "the development of scientific and technical research must be consid-

[93] Layton, *Trans-Atlantic Investment*, p. 101.

[94] Cf. European Economic Community, Report of the Committee, "Politique Économique à Moyen Terme de la Communauté," July 25, 1963. This title was chosen because of the German objection to the term "planning."

[95] EEC, "Draft of the First Medium-Term Economic Policy Programme (1966 to 1970)," May 1966.

ered as one of the three priority objectives of the Community for the next five years."[96]

In the meantime, the French proposed in March 1965 that the Common Market move more aggressively to implement a European science policy.[97] This initiative was supported immediately by the Action Committee for a United States of Europe—the organization founded by Jean Monnet to work toward a true political union of the European states. The theme of the subsequent declarations was expressed by the French Minister for Science: "Europe will be made by the atom, space, aeronautical construction, and computers, or it will not be made."[98]

What the French have in mind in calling for a European science policy is not merely cooperation in science and technology but eventually a common policy toward American economic policies and—especially—investments. After a short-lived attempt to meet this problem on their own the French had to concede failure. Other members of the Six, not sharing France's opposition to American investment, permitted and actually encouraged American investment. When France, for example, prevented Phillips Petroleum from going into Bordeaux, B. F. Goodrich from buying into Kléber-Colombes, and General Motors from building a $100-million automobile assembly plant in France, these American companies went to Belgium and West Germany.[99] The next time General Motors wanted to build a plant in France, it met no resistance.

[96] Parlement Européen, *Rapport Sur le Progrès Technologique*, p. 41.
[97] See "Suggestions Françaises Pour l'Étude d'une Politique Scientifique et Industrielle Communautaire," *Europe Documents*, No. 309, Mar. 16, 1965. The growing interest in a European science policy was signified by the devotion of the March 1965 issue of *Communauté Européenne* to this subject.
[98] *Le Monde*, May 6, 1966. The first meeting of the European science ministers to work out a European science was held on October 30, 1967. *Le Monde*, Nov. 1, 1967.
[99] *The Economist*, Apr. 16, 1966, p. 269.

American industry can in effect employ a divide-and-conquer strategy toward France and Europe. If France rejects the bid of an American company to invest in a French firm or to establish a European subsidiary in France, the company can threaten to establish itself elsewhere in the Six. Through the Common Market the company still has access to the French market. The French economy meanwhile has lost a valuable input of capital and know-how. Under these circumstances France has no choice but to admit American investment under less than the most favorable conditions. The alternatives, as an editorial in *Le Monde* pointed out in a clever play on words, was either to have American industry invest *in* France (investir en France) or else have it *envelop* France (investir la France).[100]

From this perspective France and the rest of Europe are in an entirely different situation from Japan. It is incorrect to dismiss French fears of American investment and the technology gap with the observation that Japan has no such concerns and has effectively exploited advanced technologies such as the transistor through the purchase of American licenses. This is all very true and no doubt France and the other European countries could learn much from Japan. But the argument overlooks the fact that the Japanese Government can and does control foreign investment in its economy. Furthermore, even Japan is becoming concerned over its dependence on American licenses and is rapidly expanding its own scientific research and developing indigenous technologies in order to lessen its dependence on the U.S.[101]

To overcome Europe's weakness relative to American investors the French believe the Six must show a united front to American corporate investment. The formulation of a common policy toward American investments has long been a theme of

[100] *Le Monde*, Jan. 5, 1967.
[101] *The Economist*, June 3, 1967, p. xxiv.

de Gaulle's conversations with German leadership within the framework of the Franco-German Friendship Treaty of January 22, 1963. Unfortunately for France, though they are also concerned over American investment, neither the Germans nor France's other EEC partners share the French "protectionist" policy.[102]

As European reaction to U.S. restriction on corporate investment revealed, the Europeans are caught on the horns of the dilemma mentioned earlier: to prevent American investment is to fall farther behind technologically; to permit it is to risk American domination of important industrial sectors. The European situation has been summed up by Pierre Dieterlen, Director of the French Center of Economic Studies:

> Americans are sometimes too American, but this is not really important. In the field of scientific research, they are so much ahead of us that we shall never catch up, if only for what is commonly called the phenomenon of acceleration. We need these techniques and the only alternative for Europe is either to welcome American capital with liberalism, or to refuse it. In the first case, we shall have some chance to remain in the running; in the second, we shall constitute a terribly weak bloc between the two others. Europe is so dependent on the outside world for supplies and raw materials that any policy aimed at breaking links with the U.S. would weaken Europe beyond repair.[103]

The French desire for a European policy directed against American domination and technological superiority was the underlying theme of their statement of March 1965, which proposed two studies as a first step toward "a common policy on scientific and technical research." The first was to be a comparison of public and private civilian scientific research pro-

[102] Layton, *Trans-Atlantic Investment*, p. 44.
[103] "U.S. Investment in Europe," *Fortune*, Aug. 1965, p. 235.

grams already being carried out by members of the EEC. Presumably, such an inventory would provide the basis for a European division of scientific labor. Secondly, the French proposed that there should be a determination of which industrial sectors of the EEC countries were most "vulnerable" to foreign competition or takeover, due to the inadequacy of their research effort vis-à-vis that of outside countries, namely the United States.[104] Eventually the French no doubt would like to see the establishment of a European science fund and the planning of research priorities on a European level.

The following statement from a French official document reveals clearly the association in the French mind of European cooperation in science and technology with the threat of American economic competition and domination.

> The Community has in fact demonstrated its desire to open itself up to international trade, notably in the context of the multilateral tariff negotiations which started in Geneva last year [1964]. A liberal attitude with regard to third countries necessarily implies that the member countries of the European Economic Community should undertake an investment policy designed to enable the industry of the Community to remain competitive, particularly vis-à-vis the industries of certain major countries which receive considerable aid from the state, for example, by means of research contracts.[105]

In response to these sentiments and the preparatory reports, the first conference of the science ministers of the Six was held in Luxembourg on October 30, 1967. There the unprecedented step was taken of selecting six areas where European cooperation would be most significant: information and telecommunication; transportation; oceanography; metallurgy; en-

[104] "Suggestions Françaises," pp. 3-4.
[105] Cf. quotation from U.S. Department of State, *International Science Notes*, No. 9, Apr. 1965, p. 5.

vironmental studies (e.g., air and water pollution); and meteorology. Of equal importance, it was agreed that concrete steps should be taken at the technical and eventually political level to develop a science policy for the European Economic Community.[106]

PROBLEMS OF A EUROPEAN SCIENCE POLICY

To be successful a European science policy must go beyond mere short-range, bilateral cooperation; it must fulfill certain conditions. First, sustained cooperation in science and technology necessitates a common institutional framework in the political, economic, and educational spheres. Second, there must be a willingness on the part of Europeans to concentrate their limited resources and develop a division of labor that fosters specialization, the elimination of unnecessary duplication, and the efficient use of resources. Third, as a prerequisite to the achievement of these first two requirements there must be agreement on economic, military, and political objectives. Unfortunately, weighing against all three of these requirements is the attractiveness to Europeans of cooperation with the United States and the conflicts of interest and perspective which continue to divide the Europeans among themselves.

In a facetious proposal for the solution of the "technology gap," Professor H.G.B. Casimir, Director of Philips Research Laboratory in the Netherlands, pinpointed the major obstacle to the articulation of a common European science policy.

Abolish the Federal Government of the United States. Divide the country into its several states and make sure each has a wildly different system of taxation, a different currency, different banking and insurance laws, different cus-

[106] See *Le Monde*, Nov. 1 and 3, 1967. An excellent analysis of this subject is Jacques Houssiaux, "Vers une Politique Européenne de la Recherche Scientifique," *Revue Économique*, No. 2, Mar. 1964, pp. 177-208.

toms regulations. Re-group American minorities into as many distinct language areas as possible and in any case not less than 15, and try to make sure that whenever possible there is at least one competing minority language requiring dual language schools. Oh yes, you will need 40 or 50 distinct patent systems. Do this and the technology gap between the U.S. and Europe will fill up rapidly.[107]

What this quip brings out is that 20 years of talk about European unification has obfuscated the profound cleavages which continue to make the formulation of a common policy toward science and technology nearly an impossibility. If it is difficult enough, as we have seen, to overcome the divisions which separate Frenchmen from one another and hinder the development of a French science policy, how much more difficult will it be to overcome the several hundred years of differing national heritages? From the political to university research and teaching levels the development of common institutions within Europe is yet in its infancy.

The separation which exists among European nations in research and education can be illustrated in many ways. It is a fact, for example, that only French citizens can hold professorships in French universities, and prior to the founding of CERN in 1952 there were no European centers for scientific research.[108] Students and scientists of different nationalities studied and carried out research in the laboratories of other European nations but fundamental research has been organized solely on a national basis.[109]

[107] Quoted in *European Community*, No. 101, Mar. 1967, p. 20.

[108] Foreigners can hold temporary professorships. Only two non-Frenchmen have held professorships, both at the Sorbonne: Jean Piaget, a Swiss authority on child development and Otto Klineberg, an American social psychologist.

[109] The nature of the international community of nuclear scientists in the pre-World War II period is effectively presented by Robert Jungk, *Brighter Than a Thousand Suns*, Harcourt, Brace, 1958.

The larger and more significant effort required is the creation of what the French Minister for Science has called "a common market for brains." If Europeans are to build strong centers of research on the many frontiers of modern science, they must pool their scattered manpower and financial resources. Though specialized organizations such as CERN are an important step in this direction, the barriers to the free flow of scientists and ideas must come down and a framework for European collaboration on a broader basis must be established. "Among these barriers," a recent OECD Conference of Ministers of Science brought out, "are rigid structures in universities, poor interchange between universities and industries, lack of equivalence between various countries' pay scales and university degrees, and lack of provision for travel and postdoctoral fellowships."[110] In short, effective cooperation in basic research may very well necessitate the creation of a truly European system of higher education.

In industrial research and development on a European scale, one witnesses the same pattern of institutional weakness. Though there are the efforts such as *Euratom*, ELDO, and the *Concorde* project, in the long run and across the broad front of technology, the type of technical collaboration required is that which can only be provided by competitive industries. Here the elaboration of a European science policy faces a double obstacle. Great Britain, which has the most to contribute to a united European effort in the areas of advanced technologies, is outside the framework of the emerging European economic community. And, among the Six themselves the economic and political foundations for extensive scientific and technical cooperation have not developed.

One train of reasoning which has provided a basis for the EEC is the belief that a common market would lead logically

[110] Victor McElheny, "How quickly will Europe close the science spending Gap? *Science*, Vol. 151, No. 3,713, Feb. 25, 1966, p. 977.

to the formation of European corporations jointly owned and controlled by Europeans of different nationalities. "In particular," Charles Kindleberger has written, "to make substantial progress toward economic integration probably necessitates the development of corporations that are equally at home in the various political entities party to the integration attempt."[111] This linkage and merger of corporations across national boundaries was expected by some to eliminate national economic rivalries and create binding, transnational economic interests. It followed that the growth and meshing of these many vested interests would slowly break down the significance of national borders, and political unification would evolve on the basis of common economic interests.[112]

The expectation that a European common market would lead to European ownership of industry has not materialized. On the contrary, the forces set into motion by the Common Market appear to be moving Europe in a direction not foreseen by the signers of the Treaty of Rome. For a number of reasons the rationalization of the European economic system is taking place along national and Atlantic lines, not European. The corporate merger movement in western Europe is taking place almost entirely either within national boundaries or else between European and American firms. In contrast to the flood tide of mergers *within* European countries and the growth of American-European ties, by 1967 there had been only one major corporate merger across European frontiers, and then it was only a partial one.[113] There have been, one should add, a number of joint ventures and agreements of

[111] Kindleberger, *Europe and the Dollar*, MIT Press, 1966, p. 27.

[112] These ideas are examined in Ernst Haas, *The Uniting of Europe—Political, Social, and Economic Forces, 1950-57*, Stanford University Press, 1958.

[113] Layton, *Trans-Atlantic Investment*, p. 59. The merger was between Agfa (Belgium) and Gevaert (Germany). Even this merger has run into trouble with the anti-cartel laws.

cooperation. As Kindleberger points out, Europeans like agreements and not mergers.[114]

As a result of this situation the international corporations operating in Europe tend to be American. Through the establishment of new subsidiaries throughout Europe, mergers with European firms, and outright purchase of European firms, American companies are reorganizing and integrating the European economy. According to Kindleberger, "it looks as though the international corporation, typically that with headquarters in the United States, is the leading prospect for the effective instrument of European integration."[115] As Pierre Drouin observed in *Le Monde*, "actually the Common Market benefits American industry more than European"—because only the Americans have the resources and managerial experience to take advantage of it.[116]

It appears that the economic forces being set in motion by the Common Market run counter to the reorganization of the European economy on the basis of European corporations. The lowering of tariff barriers among the Six has encouraged the transatlantic rush of American corporations into Europe. In response to this corporate invasion European corporations are either linking with the invaders or are mobilizing to meet the challenge on a national basis rather than through the pooling of their scattered resources and talents in large Europe-based corporations.[117] The French have even prevented the merger of French with other European firms; it would appear that they are less interested in having their firms controlled by other large European firms than they are concerned over American domination.[118]

The reasons for the absence of a "European" response to the

---

[114] Kindleberger, *Europe and the Dollar*, p. 33.
[115] *Ibid.*, p. 27.   [116] *Le Monde*, Sept. 23, 1966.
[117] Layton, *Trans-Atlantic Investment*, p. 59.
[118] *Ibid.*

challenge posed by the Common Market and the American corporate expansion are many: the absence of a European legal framework within which mergers can take place; the weakness of the European capital market; the legacy of corporate rivalry and pride; differences among economic systems ranging from the West German commitment to laissez-faire to the French emphasis on planning and nationalized industries.[119] At the same time, mergers taking place entirely within a nation and especially the formation of an alliance with an American corporation suffer no such inhibitions. "What happens," Raymond Aron has explained, "is that when a European firm is in trouble it always goes to an American firm, because its European sister firms will not come forward and provide true security, size, technology, and financial means."[120]

Furthermore, the structure of existing national laws greatly inhibits mergers among European firms of different nationalities. Belgian law provides that "in a merger with a foreign company, the Belgian owner must first legally wind up his own company and pay a capital tax on the difference between his theoretical assets on the balance sheet and the actual value of these assets."[121] Similar encumbrances exist in other European countries, providing strong disincentives for the emergence of European industries.

To counter these natural tendencies mitigating against transnational mergers the Six have given high priority to the drafting of a European law for corporations, the formulation of common taxation policies, and the removal of other limitations on the creation of multinational corporations of a European character. The obstacles to the success of this effort are formidable. One American writer illuminated the magnitude of the task in the following words:

[119] *Le Monde*, Oct. 9, 1965.
[120] Raymond Aron, in *Réalités*, Oct. 1965, p. 19.
[121] *New York Times*, Feb. 3, 1967.

It would be fine for U.S. relations with Europe in general if somehow the natural play of economic forces could control the level and pace of our business penetration. *But it will take years for the Europeans to develop countervailing power of the magnitude required. Monetary union, the sine qua non of a strong European capital market, would require surrenders of sovereignty so sweeping as to be only a step removed from political unification.* Similarly, the creation of multinational "European" companies of giant size will be a slow process at best. Though the Common Market organization has undertaken a crash program to create the legal framework for them, the E.E.C. must reconcile six kinds of corporate law, six different tax systems, a wide variety of merger statutes and bankruptcy regulations. On top of this, generations of corporate rivalry, prickly matters of prestige and self-interest militate against a big company giving up its "sovereignty" to submerge itself in a European enterprise.[122]

Embedded in all the technical factors involved in formulating a European corporate law or a common tax policy are profound political issues and conflicting national interests. Given the French insistence that uniformity among national practices be achieved through the enactment of parallel national laws and policies ("parallelism") rather than through the emergence of a European legal structure, it will take a very long time to work out differences among the Six. Drawing on American experience, Anthony Lewis of the *New York Times* commented on the French theory of European cooperation through "parallelism" that "the Continent-wide scale of industry and the market in the United States has been achieved only by dedicated and rededicated devotion to the politics of union."[123]

[122] "U.S. Investment in Europe," *Fortune*, Aug. 1965, p. 235.
[123] *New York Times*, Feb. 3, 1967.

426

The formulation of a European science and technical policy requires not only the creation of a common institutional framework but the elaboration of an extensive division of labor and concentration of resources. Given Europe's limited scientific resources, not every European country can hope to have "centers of excellence" in every important and promising area of science and technology. Unnecessary duplication must be avoided and priorities established within individual countries as part of a larger European division of scientific and technical labor.

The cost of unnecessary duplication may be observed in the case of nuclear power technology. Though all Europe could benefit from a cooperative program in breeder technology, France, West Germany, and Great Britain are developing breeders of similar design. Each costs approximately $120 million, a sum which could be effectively used in other areas.[124] But as we have already seen, all three countries want to be at the forefront of and independent in this important and advanced technology.

Unfortunately the same fears and ambitions that cause Europeans to be wary of overdependence on the U.S. for science and technology operate also as barriers to effective intra-European cooperation. From basic research through technological development and production, each nation wants to maximize its own self-sufficiency and minimize dependence on other nations. Few nations, for example, want to be dependent on another for basic research in potentially important areas. Basic research is believed to be not only a source of useful inventions but an attraction to the best scientific minds. Without a strong basic research program a nation runs the risk of a "brain drain."

Similarly, with respect to collaboration in technological development, the same tendency toward self-sufficiency obtains. In areas of considerable commercial or military importance,

[124] *The Economist,* Feb. 11, 1967, p. 547.

industries and nations are reluctant to collaborate. Even where equitable arrangements for the sharing of benefits can be worked out in advance, nations fear for the atrophy of their own industries especially in areas of technology with potential military significance. As we have already seen, rather than have its advanced technological industries link up with those of other European countries, each member of the Six, through research contracts, purchasing policies, and other inducements is encouraging the merger of local companies into essentially nationalized industries in these areas.

This tendency toward self-sufficiency operates to foreclose for the time being the possibility of large European firms and the creation of a large, guaranteed European market with corresponding benefits of economies of scale. As *The Economist* has pointed out, "the combined market for electronics capital goods in Britain, France, and West Germany was less than 20 percent of the American market. Divide that into three more or less equal parts and you have indigenous firms based on national markets that are barely more than a twentieth the size of the American one. It is not surprising that American corporations have virtually taken over the computer industries of West Germany, France and Italy, and nearly knocked out the British industry in 1964."[125] The European response to the "technology gap," this article continues, "is that in a whole host of major industries, from coal and steel and aviation to nuclear energy and cars and computers, the trend is towards one or two national firms that are treated as national assets: they have become the chosen instruments of their governments."[126] As a result commercial rivalries are being accentuated through nationalization and a unified European response to the American industrial challenge cannot be mounted.

[125] *The Economist*, Jan. 21, 1967, p. 197. This observation is based on a study by Christopher Freeman published in the *National Institute's Economic Review* in Nov. 1965.

[126] *The Economist*, Jan. 21, 1967, p. 197.

Just as France or West Germany may worry about the gap between themselves and the United States, the lesser developed western European countries such as Italy worry about the gap between themselves and the more developed of their partners. In *Euratom*, ELDO, and ESRO the gap between the more and less developed nations makes cooperation and a "rational" division of labor extremely difficult. The arguments from both sides are reminiscent of those one encounters when Frenchmen and Americans talk about the Atlantic technology gap. To French eyes intra-European cooperation should maximize Europe's (read France's) existing strengths; any other course is seen to be an ineffective use of Europe's scarce resources. The Italians, on the other hand, see this practice as a means to make the rich European countries richer and the poor poorer. The purpose of European scientific and technical co-operation, according to the Italian Minister of State for Foreign Affairs, is not to enable France to compete better against America but to close the intra-European technology gap:

> Unfortunately there is a practice in ELDO and ESRO to assign most of the work on the basis of cost and technical arguments. Such practice may seem rational at first sight, but favours the more advanced nations, and increases, instead of diminishing, the gap between them and the less advanced. One must continually bear in mind that acquisition of know-how by all members is the fundamental goal of the co-operation envisaged by these institutions. This problem requires serious consideration as no country can accept being a paying member of an organization, but having only part of the economical and scientific benefits that should follow membership.[127]

A similar tendency to subordinate Community interest to national interest is seen in the distribution of research and de-

[127] United Kingdom Council, *European Cooperation Report*, p. 10.

velopment contracts. In both *Euratom* and ELDO the policy is to distribute contracts among the participating states in proportion to financial contribution, rather than on the basis of some more rational allocation criteria. As such it is difficult to concentrate resources on priority projects or to establish an effective division of labor.

The fact that international collaboration has been motivated principally by a desire to supplement national programs and has not been conceived as a steppingstone to a larger political goal has resulted in a tendency among Europeans to seek short-term gains at the expense of establishing long-term mutual confidence. The French in particular have been accused by their fellow Europeans of seeing scientific cooperation solely as a means to get other Europeans to help France compete against the United States. The Belgians point out that France asked them to participate in Saclay, but the French were unwilling to renew the contracts of Belgian scientists and to permit them to have careers at Saclay. In reactor development the same charge is made—the French want other Europeans to buy their reactors but they will not share information.

The several attempts of Europeans to collaborate in science and technology bear out these observations. As we have already noted, few of the cooperative efforts undertaken by Europeans in space, atomic energy, or electronics have been noteworthy for their success. On the contrary, the escalation of costs far beyond initial expectations, the unilateral decisions of one country or another to withdraw from projects, and the suspicions of certain countries that others see European collaboration solely as a means to enrich themselves, have made cooperation more difficult. These problems are illustrated by two examples, the establishment of a European color television network and the joint development of weaponry.

The difficulties of European collaboration in the area of commercial technology are well illustrated by the case of color

430

television. For several years a battle has raged among European color television manufacturers over which system Europe should adopt. By the spring of 1966 the field of contenders had been reduced to two—the German *PAL* system and the French *SECAM*. Behind the *PAL* system were ranged Great Britain, West Germany, Holland, and Italy. Supporting the French were the Soviet Union, eastern Europe, and the underdeveloped countries. Unless the two systems can be made compatible or some other compromise is worked out, Europe faces the prospect that her color television will be a mosaic.[128]

In one area especially, Europeans have increasingly based their hope for a breakthrough with respect to effective and long-term technical cooperation—military weaponry. Although Europeans—even the French—accept the necessity of dependence on the United States for their military security, Europeans have sought to maintain their own armaments industry. In part, this has been due to a desire not to become overly dependent on the U.S. for the defense of Europe. For France and Great Britain, in addition, the export of weaponry has long been an important means of foreign exchange; for this reason especially they have resisted a division of labor within the Atlantic Alliance which fosters "American domination of the new-weapons market."[129] Finally, the Europeans have been

---

[128] *Le Monde*, Mar. 30, 1965. *PAL* is a converted American system. *SECAM* is technically incompatible with American television, a fact which no doubt enters French, Russian, and eastern European thinking.

[129] Brig. Gen. E. Vandevanter, *Coordinated Weapons Production in NATO: A Study of Alliance Processes*, RAND RM-4169-PR, Nov. 1964, p. 6. The importance of the international armaments market should not be underestimated. The desire to have a greater share of it is one motivation behind France's military modernization. (General Lavaud, "La Délégation Ministérielle Pour l'Armement," *Revue Militaire Générale*, Dec. 1961, p. 617.) The problems and prospects of European cooperation in weapons development have been treated in an excellent series of publications by the Institute for Strategic Studies, "Defence, Technology and the Western Alliance," 1967. Unfortunately, the find-

motivated by the belief that weapons research and development has an important spinoff for the civilian, competitive economy.

Collaboration in weapons development has been made necessary because of the fantastic escalation of costs. As Britain's Minister of Aviation pointed out to the Conference on European Cooperation in Advanced Technology, whereas a *Spitfire* in World War II cost a little more than £5,000 to produce, the *Canberra* 15 years later cost £180,000 a copy in its early version. The production cost of an advanced aircraft such as the *TSR-2* would have been 15 times as much as the *Canberra*; its research and development cost alone would have been £300 million. "The plain fact is," Jenkins told the assembled delegates:

> that if countries of the size of the United Kingdom, or France, or West Germany, or Italy wish to manufacture modern weapon systems, even in this generation and still more in the future, without imposing upon themselves an insupportable burden of defence costs, they must do so upon a collaborative basis. The advantages of doing it in this way are three-fold; first, to share the very heavy research and development burden; second, to enlarge the market, and thus to keep the ratio of research and development costs to production costs within reasonable limits; and third, to pool technological knowledge.[130]

Unfortunately the experience of European collaboration in the development and production of weapons has not been a happy one. The Europeans have not been able to supplant American domination of the advanced weapons market. With the exception of three minor and partially successful proj-

---

ings of these studies were published too late to be incorporated in this book.

[130] United Kingdom Council, *European Cooperation Report*, p. 4.

ects, all communal programs for the production of weapons have used weapons perfected in America and produced in Europe under license.[131] European attempts to design and collaborate in the production of their own weapons, such as a NATO tank and a vertical take-off aircraft have foundered on the rocks of conflicting national interests, the inability of the Europeans to agree on common technical requirements, and the unwillingness of the United States to depend on European weaponry. One expert reviewing this history concluded that "the prospects today for acceptable new projects are grim, partly because nations seem unable to work out an approach for items which would be appropriate for common production, and partly because many new weapons are either technically too intricate or politically too sensitive for pooled activity."[132]

Underlying the apparent inability of the Europeans to organize scientific and technical collaboration on a broad and continuing basis is the absence of common goals and purposes. Europeans are more divided among themselves in their interests and perspectives than they are united on the objectives to be achieved through cooperation. At the present time only Great Britain and France have found a basis for extensive cooperation in a number of technical areas, but the obstacles to the ultimate success of these projects remain great because of the fundamental political questions which divide these two countries from one another and from the rest of Europe. The problem facing these two nations and the rest of Europe in responding to the need for collaboration in science and technology was put by *The Economist*:

[131] Vandevanter, *Coordinated Weapons*, p. 61. The exceptions are *Transall* (military transport), *Atlantique* (sea patrol aircraft), and the *Leopard AMX 30* tank.

[132] *Ibid.*, p. 60. For the French view of NATO as an American marketing device see *Armed Forces Management*, June 1966, pp. 59-62.

In civilian as in military procurement, it is hard to agree on the goods or arms governments want if they do not subscribe to similar economic or defence strategies. This identity of view does not exist in piecemeal co-operation because this form of joint effort basically exists to shore up national industries, not to create a new structure. In fact, Anglo-French industrial co-operation is in many ways a form of the effort of the two countries to keep ahead of the non-nuclear rank and file in Europe. Yet this tends to be self-defeating, as the costs of advanced industries mount up and multiply. For the main problem is to find a large enough market. It exists in America. It cannot exist in Europe unless Germany and Italy are given a stake in joint research, development and production. Short of that, they will remain neutral between an American industrial colossus and a struggling Anglo-French partnership, and the advantages of possible European co-operation will be lost. As a way of making Europe's advanced industries competitive with the American, co-operation "a là carte" seems likely to give mediocre results.[133]

Despite the significant attempts of OECD to get Europeans to think as one about their scientific problems the development of a common outlook and the advancement of European union have been prevented by the conflicting interests and perspectives within the Six. These differences breed suspicions and distrust, which make it difficult, among other things, for Europeans to articulate a common policy toward American investment. One highly placed Belgian expressed his view of the matter to the writer in the following words:

The attitude of Belgium toward American investment differs considerably from that of France. The Belgians feel that it is more preferable to depend upon the United States in the 20th century just as she was dependent upon Great Brit-

[133] *The Economist*, May 1966, p. xv. Italics mine.

ain in the 19th, than to be dependent upon an expansionist France or revisionist Germany. Belgium therefore favors an open Europe, in contrast to the closed Europe preferred by France. Holland, Luxembourg, and Italy prefer an open Europe dependent upon the United States. Germany, on the other hand, has very little fear of France. For the Germans, France is the Austria over which Bismarck triumphed in the 19th century in the unification of Germany. . . .

The most significant effort of Europeans to frame common purposes and objectives as a basis for extensive collaboration in foreign policy, defense, science, and economics was the French-German Treaty of Cooperation of January 22, 1963.[134] Negotiated by de Gaulle and Adenauer this treaty sought to create a Bonn-Paris axis around which European "unification" could form. To cement and further this alliance within an alliance the two nations agreed to formulate common foreign and economic policies, including, if de Gaulle had his way, a common policy toward American investments in Europe. In the military realm there was to be coordination of strategy and weapons development; the Franco-German *Institut Saint Louis* was founded for military research and development. "Concerted action programs" were to be established in appropriate areas of scientific and technical research. To strengthen their economic position vis-à-vis the United States and remove a source of conflict, the two governments were to promote mergers and cooperation between French and German corporations. In short, economic, scientific, and other types of collaboration were to be undertaken in order to serve the larger political purpose of French-German unity.[135]

[134] Ambassade de France, New York, "French-German Cooperation," *Foreign Affairs*, No. 152, Jan. 22, 1963.

[135] Olivier Giscard d'Estaing, "Coopération et Fusion des Entreprises Françaises et Allemandes," *Politique Étrangère*, No. 2, 1966, pp. 136-56.

Perhaps this effort at close French-German cooperation is fated not to be a success regardless of American behavior toward it. French and German interests are not identical and each wants something out of the treaty which the other is not prepared to give. For France the purpose of the treaty is to forge a Franco-German nucleus around which could form a European community of sovereign nations independent of the United States. Germany, on the other hand, seeks to obtain greater French cooperation in support of its demands for reunification. Far from desiring the formation of a European bloc independent of the U.S., the German Parliament (much to the annoyance of de Gaulle) in ratifying the treaty added a preamble that the treaty should also serve to reinforce the association between Europe and the United States as well as strengthen NATO and encourage British entry into Europe.

Even before the treaty was signed these differing German and French interests with respect to NATO and relations with Great Britain had come into open conflict and the long-term prospects for the success of the treaty were dimmed. But whatever might have been or may yet be, the United States unintentionally or by design (as de Gaulle contends) weakened the efficacy of the alliance through its subsequent actions.[136] In the words of Henry Kissinger, the United States reacted to the treaty by undertaking "an assiduous wooing" of the Germans.

> One motive behind the MLF was to prevent West Germany from accepting a possible French offer of nuclear cooperation. . . . In order to tie Germany to us, successful efforts were made to have German arms purchases funneled to the United States. The culmination of this process was an agreement between Secretary McNamara and Defense Minister von Hassel signed on November 14, 1964, which in affect

[136] See President de Gaulle's Press Conference, Oct. 29, 1966. *Le Monde*, Oct. 30-31, 1966.

436

made the German armed forces dependent on the United States for their military equipment.[137]

Similarly, in other areas of advanced technology—aviation, computers, atomic energy—there has developed, in effect, an American-German alliance which in turn has limited close French-German collaboration. In aviation every German aviation company except one is linked with an American company;[138] IBM dominates the German computer market;[139] and in atomic energy Germany is developing her industry through purchasing American designs and licenses. Recent proposals of the American government for joint American-European space research cooperation, and the enthusiastic German response, impress Frenchmen as yet another example of American seduction of their German partner and a device calculated to destroy intra-European space cooperation.[140]

The Germans have been easy to seduce away from the French. The U.S. has much more to offer the Germans than do the French—investment capital, advanced technology, and, most important of all, military protection. In return for the latter the Germans are obligated to purchase American and British weapons to offset the cost of stationing British and American troops in West Germany, a fact which poses a severe limitation on Franco-German cooperation in weapons development. Furthermore, in contrast to the French who have stressed independence from the United States, the German strategy of scientific and technical modernization has been that of importing and building on American technology.[141]

[137] Henry Kissinger, *The Troubled Partnership*, McGraw-Hill, 1965, p. 207.

[138] Layton, *Trans-Atlantic Investment*, p. 96; see *The Economist*, May 13, 1967, for the *Transall* story.

[139] Layton, *Trans-Atlantic Investment*, p. 95.

[140] This is the conclusion of Nicolas Vichney, in *Le Monde*, Feb. 18, 1966. Cf. Victor McElheny, "Trans-Atlantic Cooperation," pp. 190-91.

[141] Henry Wallich, *Mainsprings of the Germany Revival*, Yale, 1955.

The production in Germany of the American-developed *Starfighter* (F-104G), for example, was undertaken with the intention of refounding at a highly advanced level the German aircraft industry which had been utterly destroyed by World War II. Which strategy toward technological modernization—the German or the French—will turn out to be the more successful in the long run will no doubt have a profound consequence for the future balance of political power within western Europe itself.

The initial failure of the Franco-German Treaty of Cooperation, and even the attempt to shore it up following the coming to power of Kurt Kiesinger, illustrate a moral Henry Kissinger has frequently pointed out. It is that extensive collaboration among states in science, technology, or any other area cannot be successful unless there is a "willingness . . . to subordinate short-term advantages to a long-term conception of the future and . . . [the] ability to develop a concrete and common program."[142] In the absence of both these prerequisites, it is in the interest of the neighbors of France to emphasize their ties with the United States at the expense of independent European programs.

As in the case of the internal transformation of France, progress in European scientific and technological cooperation since the end of the Second World War has been considerable. Twenty years ago one never would have thought that such developments as CERN and *Concorde* were possible. Yet cooperation on a scale which would enable Europe to balance the Great Powers in areas of advanced science and technology is severely limited by at least three factors. In the first place, bilateral cooperation will not take France and the other European countries very far; it simply does not insure a sufficient scale of resources or a large enough guaranteed market.

[142] Kissinger, *Troubled Partnership*, p. 206.

Secondly, agreement on political, strategic, and economic goals must precede successful scientific-technical cooperation; without such agreement on long-term objectives the nations of Europe are unwilling to subordinate their immediate and parochial interests for the sake of a truly European effort. And, thirdly, in almost every area of science and technology continental Europe, if it is to balance the United States, needs the resources of Great Britain; the entry of Great Britain into the EEC could double its resources and would do much to redress the Atlantic imbalance in science, technology, and economic power. In the words of a resolution adopted by the European Parliament in October 1966, "the development of a [European] science policy must necessarily depend on the experience and support of the United Kingdom."[143]

The nations of Europe, in seeking to formulate a common response to the technology gap, appear to be caught between two poles of action, neither of which succeeds very well. On the one hand, technically sound programs approached on a multilateral basis are apt to fail because the different European countries cannot agree on what sort of computer or rocket they want, or on how they should organize their cooperation. Bilateral arrangements, on the other hand, limit the resources available and the market.

As a consequence of this situation the solution of her scientific and technological problems through European collaboration poses a dilemma for France. In the name of national independence the French reject the evolution in western Europe of a political authority and union including Great Britain which might articulate a common political purpose and lay the basis for European collaboration across a broad spectrum. But without such a united political will it is difficult to see how the Europeans can hope to maximize the utilization of their resources and avoid a growing dependence upon the

[143] Quotation from *The Economist*, Oct. 22, 1966, p. 359.

United States for their science and technology. In short, to meet the challenge of the contemporary scientific-technological revolution, France must not only cease to be France in terms of her traditional attitudes and institutions but she must become part of a larger *political* community which includes Great Britain.

Chapter 13 · The Technology Gap in Political Perspective

Research has become the principal source of the economic power and independence of a country. Secrets and patents protect the discoveries. The interests of the countries are competitive. Research oscillates between hopeful cooperation to inevitable competition as it passes from the stage of the fundamental to the stage of application.

—ALAIN PEYREFITTE, *French Minister for Science, December 1966*

For centuries it was thought that science was universal, its problems were international, and states would not draw scientists into their conflicts. In becoming political, scientific problems have become national, and modern states have sought to give themselves a powerful research potential, and to utilize it to achieve the objectives of their overall policy.

—COMMISSION ON RESEARCH FOR THE FIFTH PLAN, *1966*

From the statement of Jean-Baptiste Colbert, Louis XIV's able minister, that "commerce is the means to augment the power and grandeur of his Majesty and to lower that of his enemies and rivals"[1] to that of de Gaulle's Minister for Science, that "scientific research has become one of the means of state policy" runs a long tradition of French thinking.[2] For the Fifth Republic science has the same significance it possessed for Colbert and succeeding generations of French leaders, that

[1] Quoted in Allan Johnstone, *United States Direct Investment in France*, MIT Press, 1965, p. 3.
[2] Assemblée Nationale, Séance du 30 Octobre 1963, *Journal Officiel*, p. 6,016.

441

of an instrument for advancing the interests of France. Thus it was that in 1666 Colbert founded the *Académie des Sciences* in part to improve France's declining trade position.[3] During the wars of the Revolution the Convention established the *École Polytechnique* and revived the *Académie* in order to lessen French dependence on British technology and to mobilize science for war.[4] After defeat in the Franco-Prussian War of 1870 the Third Republic reformed education in order to "catch up" with German science and technology.[5] Then the poor performance of France in World War I and her defeat in World War II led to national crises of confidence over the poor condition of French science and technology. And today the Fifth Republic continues this tradition of "scientific Colbertism."

The underlying assumption of French policy toward scientific research is that the world is entering upon an era of intense international competition (though not necessarily military conflict) where the destiny of a nation will be increasingly determined by its scientific and technological capabilities. In contrast to the frequently expressed view of scientists that science as an international community in pursuit of truth can be a force for international harmony, the French, and increasingly other nations as well, are operating on the opposite assumption. The universalist spirit of science is not permeating politics; instead science is being nationalized and made an instrument of the nation-state.

Whereas in the eighteenth century scientific competition was solely interpersonal, in the nineteenth it became interinstitutional as well. And in the contemporary world science

[3] G. N. Clark, *Science and Social Welfare in the Age of Newton*, Oxford University Press, 1937, p. 19.

[4] John Merz, *A History of European Thought in the Nineteenth Century*, Dover Publications, 1964, p. 146.

[5] Stanley Hoffmann, ed., *In Search of France*, Harvard University Press, 1963, p. 19.

has become a major factor in inter-nation competition. The benign competition among scientists and scientific institutions for priority of scientific discovery in fundamental research is being overlaid with a competition among nations for priority of discovery of new scientific knowledge and—more important —for attainment of a leading position in the rapid exploitation of these discoveries in the innovation of novel technologies possessing commercial or military significance. In both these realms priority of scientific discovery and application have an increasingly important effect on a nation's standing in the world and therefore must be a primary concern of the contemporary statesman.

If this is the nature of the world science is bringing into existence then, reason the political leaders of the Fifth Republic, a nation like France which prizes her political independence and desires to play a significant part in international affairs, cannot afford to be dependent on other nations for her science and technology. In particular, France must not depend on the U.S. for the science and technology necessary for the security and prosperity of the French people. Frenchmen fear that failure to achieve scientific autonomy would lead to the absorption of France and Europe into what they regard as the expanding science-based American empire.

In order to meet the challenge identified as American imperialism and to reestablish the position of France in the world, the policy of the French Government is to seek scientific and technological self-sufficiency in at least those areas highly relevant to national security and the economic independence of the country. Thus France must go into space not merely for the sake of scientific curiosity, but to enhance her military security, restore her self-esteem, and advance her electronics industry.[6] Similarly, France must have her own oceanography, atomic energy, and biological research if she is to reap eco-

---

[6] *L'Expansion Scientifique*, No. 3, Dec. 1957, p. 4.

443

nomic and military benefits from knowledge of the seas, the atom, and the life sciences.

Just as the first industrial revolution gave rise to the concept of economic autarky, the second industrial revolution, based on the exploitation of scientific theory and the advent of scientific technology, is giving rise to the concept of scientific autarky. The twentieth century equivalents of economic protectionism and the desire to be economically independent appear to be scientific protectionism and self-sufficiency. In a world of national rivalries and conflicting interests the leaders of the Fifth Republic believe they must have a national capability in all those areas of science and technology which give rise to revolutionary technologies that shape the course of events. Consequently, following the lead of the United States, the Soviet Union, and Great Britain, France has emphasized those scientific technologies that carry high prestige, relate most directly to military power, and are regarded as the growth areas of the modern economy.[7]

This identification of science and national power did not begin with France nor will it end there, but the French case exemplifies the situation. For those of us who share the Western faith in man's reason, the entrance of science into economic, social, and political life is to be greeted as the beginning of a great and hopeful chapter in human history. If each nation, however, should seek to be independent of every other in the realm of science and technology the new alliance of science and power may be a force not to unite mankind but to divide it still further.

The French are not so naïve as to believe that France, given her limited resources and the limitless expanse of science and technology, can be self-sufficient in all areas of modern science and technology. But, it is believed, France can and must main-

---

[7] OECD, *Reviews of National Science Policy—France,* 1966, p. 81.

tain a presence in all those areas which have potential economic and military significance. As in the case of the *force de frappe*, such capabilities do not make France completely self-sufficient but at the least they comprise a "minimum deterrent" which increases France's freedom of action and decreases her susceptibility to blackmail by one or the other of the great powers.

In a world where science is closely tied to economic and military matters, policy regarding science and technology follows the foreign policy of the state. As a result, while other Europeans may increasingly share French concern over the Atlantic imbalance in science and technology, they lack a sufficient political incentive to pay the high price of weakening their connections with the United States and developing in concert independent European capabilities in such areas as aerospace, computers, and atomic energy.

The need for prior political agreement before effective steps can be taken to solve the technology gap must be kept in mind when one considers the prospects for two projects which are viewed by increasing numbers of Europeans as solutions to the technology gap—a technological Marshall Plan[8] and a European Technological Community including Great Britain.[9]

The most forthright expression of the "Marshall Plan" proposal was that of the Italian Foreign Minister Amintore Fanfani to the NATO Council in late 1966. Under the terms of this proposal, though the Europeans would finance scientific and technical projects, the U.S. over a 10-year period would make available to European industries and governments American technical know-how in those areas of greatest concern to Eu-

---

[8] *Le Monde*, Sept. 14, 1965.
[9] *New York Times*, Oct. 7, 1966. A number of alternative solutions to the technology gap have been analyzed by John Calmann, "European Cooperation in Defence Technology: The Political Aspect," Institute for Strategic Studies, Apr. 1967.

rope: electronic computers; aeronautics; space research; space satellites for scientific, industrial, and commercial uses; atomic energy; desalination and pollution control technology.[10]

If one compares the situation at the time of the Marshall Plan with the present, the difficulties of Fanfani's proposal are readily seen. Then, the problem was to provide Europe with huge amounts of capital to rebuild its war-devastated industry. The U.S. government provided these funds, American industry sold Europe the needed goods, and the Europeans had a strong incentive to organize the rebuilding effort through the Organization for European Economic Cooperation. Today, on the other hand, the source of the problem is the technological advantage of private American corporations over their European competitors. In effect, Fanfani is asking the U.S. to assist European industry to compete against American industry.

Needless to say, the price the U.S. Government and industry would probably exact for a technological Marshall Plan is one which the French and many other Europeans would be unwilling to pay. The French position is well known, but other Europeans also are beginning to fear America's dominant position and near monopoly of many advanced technologies. The resistance of both West Germany and Italy to signing a nuclear nonproliferation treaty demonstrates a fear that the treaty would arrest their development of atomic energy for peaceful purposes. It is wrong for the U.S. to dismiss these fears as simply nationalistic and unfounded. They reveal a disquiet over dependence on the U.S. for advanced technologies. As the British Minister for Aviation warned other Europeans, "it is only too easy for interdependence to be a polite euphemism for total dependence, and that is not what any of us want."[11]

[10] Victor McElheny, "How Quickly Can Europe Close the Science Spending Gap?" *Science*, Vol. 151, No. 3,713, Feb. 25, 1966, 978.
[11] United Kingdom Council of the European Movement, *European*

But Great Britain's rather vague proposal for a European Technological Community which could balance American scientific and technological power also faces formidable political obstacles. Though British participation in the EEC would double the Community's scientific-technological resources it would magnify all the problems of coordination that already afflict the Six. Furthermore, on the basis of experience of recent British-European cooperation, it is very difficult to believe that Prime Minister Wilson's proposal is attractive to the French. On the contrary, the entry of Britain into the Market would "saddle" the Six with Britain's grave economic problems and compound the difficulties for French industry. Britain would bring into a European market already concerned over too much competition, a huge number of large corporations, many of which are the British subsidiaries of American firms.

But even this economic problem would undoubtedly be manageable if it were not for other British-French differences. There are good reasons to believe that France for the immediate future would oppose the entry of Britain into Europe regardless of Britain's behavior toward Europe and the United States. A Britain in Europe would tend to join West Germany in supporting an open Europe with respect to the import of agricultural products and the export of industrial products. But even more important, in a sense de Gaulle is correct in his assessment that Britain is insufficiently European. One does not have to leave the area of scientific and technical affairs to illustrate this point. From the French perspective, at each decision-point since World War II Britain has taken an Atlantic (read American) rather than a European stance. Beginning with the Quebec Agreement of 1943 through the Nassau Agreement of 1962 to the two treaties on nuclear testing

Cooperation in Advanced Technology, Report of a Conference, July 1965, p. 5.

and nonproliferation, the British have sought to enhance the nuclear hegemony of the Anglo-American powers to the displeasure of western Europe. Until the day, therefore, when political relations in western Europe are drastically altered to the detriment of French interests and France needs Britain, it is difficult to believe France will permit Great Britain to enter the Common Market.

Regrettably, the inherent contradiction in American policy toward Europe makes it difficult for the United States to assist Europe in the solution of its scientific and technological problems. At the same time that the United States desires European economic unification it wants unrestricted access to the Common Market, especially for advanced technological products. Similarly, although the U.S. favors a Franco-German rapprochement and close cooperation, it opposes a Bonn-Paris axis around which an independent Europe could form. The U.S. favors British entry into Europe but not at the expense of Britain's special relationship with the U.S. and the diffusion to France, West Germany, and Italy of technologies which would advance independent nuclear capabilities in western Europe. The American goal, in short, is a united Europe which includes Great Britain and is closely tied in all spheres to the United States, yet does not have an independent nuclear capability and foreign policy.[12]

To advance this objective of "Atlantic partnership" the United States has generously assisted those European scientific-technical programs that have complemented her own efforts and have advanced close American-European ties. On the other hand, she has opposed those initiatives for European scientific and technical cooperation which run counter to America's "grand design." The U.S., for example, has refused to assist Europe in the "strategic" areas of technology, that is, to

[12] Ernst van der Beugel, *From Marshall Aid to Atlantic Partnership*, Elsevier Publishing, 1966.

provide Europe with know-how or technology in the computer, space, and atomic energy areas—which might encourage the proliferation of nuclear weapons and challenge America's dominant position in certain commercial areas such as satellite communications.[13] From the French perspective the transfer to Europe of American technology has been sufficient to thwart European cooperative efforts but not enough to overcome Europe's over-all inferiority.

At several strategic points in the evolution of French scientific policy France has sought help from her European neighbors. At these junctures American policy seemingly has sought to frustrate the French initiative and divide the other Europeans from France. From the French point of view the most cynical case of this deliberate American policy was the fate of France's proposal that *Euratom* construct an enriched uranium plant which would benefit electricity production, propulsion, and, of course, military weaponry. At first France's *Euratom* partners were interested, but this interest immediately waned when the U.S. offered to sell *Euratom* enriched uranium at a price far below that of the proposed European plant. As Scheinman points out, "the obvious conclusion was that the United States was attempting to prevent the establishment of a European enriched uranium plant by offering an economically appealing alternative."[14] The eventual French response was the construction on their own of Pierrelatte.

There is no intention here to point out Machiavellian machinations by the United States, righteousness in the French cause, or short-sightedness among other Europeans. Rather it is hoped this discussion will illuminate the fact that agreement on long-term economic, political, and military goals must precede European cooperation in science and technology. In the

[13] *Le Monde*, Mar. 12, 1966.
[14] Lawrence Scheinman, *Atomic Energy Policy in France under the Fourth Republic*, Princeton University Press, 1965, p. 177.

case at hand, the other Europeans did not share French interest in an independent nuclear capability and therefore "were not concerned about the limitations which the United States would place on the U-235 it sold to *Euratom*."[15] The U.S., for its part, surely cannot be condemned for discouraging further proliferation of national nuclear armaments or for its desire to draw Europe closer to itself in the power struggle with the Soviet Union.

How different, though, might things be in the late 1960s if the United States had supported an integrated European uranium industry and discouraged the building of Pierrelatte? One may further ask if the United States is not today pursuing a similar policy by encouraging European and especially German participation in the American space program at the sacrifice of an independent European space program?[16] Without its own programs in areas of advanced science and technology a strong, united, and independent Europe is impossible. And without a European alternative to balance what the French perceive as the American imperial impulse, there can be little hope that France will one day reorient her highly nationalistic scientific, technological, and military programs.

Consequently, just as the technology gap cannot be solved on a European basis in the absence of prior political agreement, it cannot be solved on an Atlantic level without fundamental agreement on the purpose of the cooperation. Unfortunately, for Washington the technology gap is an official nonissue. When Europeans bring it up, as they frequently do, American responses normally take one of several forms. The usual official American response is to reply that the problem is not really a technology gap but a management gap or an education gap; or, as former Commerce Secretary John Conner put it, it is

[15] *Ibid.*, p. 178.
[16] See text of Joint Communique of President Lyndon Johnson and Chancellor Ludwig Erhard, Sept. 27, 1966.

an "industrial disparity." On other occasions, American officials will grant that a technology gap of some sort exists but then go on to point out to the Europeans that that is their problem. Most ingenuous of all is a response which goes like this: "Look! You Europeans do what you're good at, and we'll do what we're good at. You French stick to your wine-making and perfumes; leave the computers and high-performance aircraft to us." American academic economists, who tend to share the official position on the technology gap, phrase this in more sophisticated terms. Committed to the doctrine of free trade and the principle of comparative advantage, they point out that the technology gap represents a rational division of labor among the members of an emerging Atlantic economic system.

Both European and American attitudes are in a sense correct. Europe, as we have already suggested, benefits enormously from American technological advance and from this perspective has little reason to complain. Correct, too, is the argument that the problem is largely managerial; as the experience of ELDO, *Euratom*, and the *Concorde* project reveal—with huge cost overruns, poor coordination, and time delays—Europe lacks managerial competence to deal with huge technological systems. These observations, however, do not lessen the European distress over the Atlantic imbalance in science and technology.

In short, it is an oversimplification to say that the problem facing France and other European countries is a technology gap; in most cases American technology is available to European industries through licensing. But it is equally oversimplified to say that the problem is merely managerial, i.e., the capacity for efficient and effective utilization of resources. The term "technology gap" is really a symbolic representation of the whole spectrum of challenges posed by a dynamic, expanding, and socially democratic society for conservative societies ruled

451

by traditional elites wanting the power that science and technology can bring, but unwilling to pay the price of a profound social-economic transformation.

The intensity of the European reaction to the technology gap must be understood in the context of the profound economic and political developments which have engulfed western Europe since the end of World War II. The European socio-economic political structure has been buffeted and the European economy has been greatly stimulated by a number of converging forces. First, there has been the trauma for France, Great Britain, and several other European countries of decolonization; seldom in history have proud and ruling peoples been reduced to second-class status so fast. Second, for the first time in history, the political and industrial leaders of western Europe have experienced and must come to terms with a full-employment market economy; this fact has set in motion a series of economic consequences which are transforming the traditional ways of European life. Labor is now able to make its wage demands effective; high wages in turn have put a squeeze on profit margins, and industrialists are forced to learn new ways in order to become efficient and competitive.

On top of these developments, western European businesses face the challenge of increased competition from their neighbors as trade barriers are lowered among the Common Market countries, and, in response to the emergence of a mass market in Europe, large American corporations have entered the economic fray. In part, because they seem to aggravate an already difficult situation; in part, because they accept the market economy and cartelization is not in their interests; and in part, because nationalistic sentiments can easily be stirred up against them, American corporations operating in Europe can easily serve as a scapegoat for Europe's social and economic problems. In short, the "technology gap" provides a simple explanation of the very complex and far-reaching set of forces shaking the foundations of traditional Europe.

Tracing the source of European concerns over the technology gap and U.S. economic penetration of Europe to its psychological roots, however, is no substitute for an examination of the validity of the European fears. If they are forced to specify their fears, thoughtful Europeans identify three dangers in the present trends. In the first place, these Europeans fear that American direct investment in Europe in all economic sectors could reach such a level that the essential decisions affecting the European economy are made in the United States. Secondly, they fear that American control of the defense-related industries may become of such a scale that individual European countries will lose their freedom of diplomatic action. And, thirdly, they see developing an Atlantic division of labor and continual brain drain which will deprive European countries of their capacity for autonomous innovation.

Even for the French these dangers, except in a few sectors such as computers, were not of serious proportions in the 1960s. Though U.S. firms in Europe have on several occasions taken unpopular decisions, they are frequently more responsive to the policies of host governments than are indigenous firms, and with a few exceptions in the defense-related areas American firms in Europe have conducted their business independently of the foreign policy of the United States. It is rather the long-term consequences of present trends that disturb French and other European leaders.

To meet this long-term challenge on a national basis, there are available the three strategies discussed in Chapter 5. All three, unfortunately, present difficult problems for various European nations. As this book has sought to show, the strategy of following in the footsteps of the large scientific states poses

453

an overwhelming challenge for the medium-sized nations of western Europe. It means a scattering of scarce resources across a broad front of scientific research and development, with little prospect of an economic (in contrast to a political or military) return. The effort to overcome this size problem through European cooperation comes apart on the rocks of the conflicting national interests and the differing ambitions of the European states themselves.

The alternative that each European nation pursue the strategy adopted by Sweden and concentrate on specific scientific-technical areas selected on the basis of commercial criteria would appear to be a wise course from an economic standpoint. Certainly it is the direction in which countries such as Holland, Belgium, and Italy have moved. But this strategy doubtless necessitates an abandonment of any pretensions to exercising an important political role in the world, and for western Europe it undoubtedly means acceptance of a large measure of political, economic, and of course military dependence on the United States. As a nation with memories of greatness and fears of abandonment, France has rejected this strategy. The two former great powers of Europe, Great Britain and West Germany, have yet to decide whether they will accept the role of another Sweden.

The strategy perfected by Japan, of building an industrial base and export trade utilizing American licenses, is not seriously entertained in Europe. Though West Germany has relied heavily on American technology, this was part of a strategy of revival and cannot be presumed to be a long-term commitment. The strength of the German scientific-technical traditions, the new openness of Germany to outside competition, and the dormant yet unquenched longing for national reunification lead one to conclude that Germany has yet to decide which strategy to follow eventually.

Whichever strategy individual European states may seek to

454

follow, the choice for the Europe of the Six is either to create the conditions to achieve competitive efficiency in European industries or to revert to protectionism. Only in choosing the first course can European governments meet the American challenge through the achievement of efficient economies of scale—a large market, large corporations, and a large volume of goods—which would satisfy the rising expectations of the European peoples and keep Europe competitive in world markets. Equally significant, Europe needs American capital, management, and technology if it is to meet these demands. From this perspective the movement of American industry into Europe is in part a technological Marshall Plan which has stimulated the European economy and has actually operated to lessen the long-standing American technical advantage over Europe in many areas of international trade.[17] The task of Europe is to take advantage of the opportunities provided by American investment and create a modern industrial society based on efficiency and economies of scale. Unfortunately, as we have seen, the trend throughout Europe is toward restrictive practices that limit the achievement of economies of scale. The "nationalization" of advanced technological industries through government contracts and purchasing policies, the concentration of industry and organization of markets along national lines, and the reappearance of the cartel mentality in response to "gluts" in various commodity sectors—electronic components, steel, man-made fibers, automobiles, chemicals, and petroleum—are indicative of this move toward economic nationalism.

But whether protection or efficiency is the course of action

[17] Hal Lary, *Problems of the United States as World Trader and Banker*, National Bureau of Economic Research, Woodhaven Press, 1963, p. 54. On the other hand, the gap which continues to exist, or even widen, is in certain advanced technologies; and Europeans have become more sensitive to the problem because of the great role of these technologies in economic and military affairs.

chosen, neither course will succeed without political unity, not necessarily the creation of a supranational state but a unity of political wills. In practice, this means the political cooperation of France and West Germany. Together they could impose their wills on the lesser countries of the Six. Without their agreement the Common Market cannot formulate a common response to the technology gap. But again, as we have seen, there is little basis to expect French-German cooperation over the long run. On many of the economic and political issues facing western Europe, French and German interests conflict. France is an economically self-sufficient and politically self-satisfied power interested in a closed Europe and the preservation of the territorial status quo. West Germany, on the other hand, must export outside the Six to survive and desires reunification with the Germans under communist rule in eastern Europe.

In the Kennedy Round of tariff negotiations and the establishment of a European agricultural policy, these conflicting interests arose but were subordinated to the desire to preserve the Common Market, and the two nations were able to compromise their differences. Cooperation between the two has also been facilitated by reason of West Germany's exposed position vis-à-vis the Soviet Union, her commitment to integration in the democratic West, and her sensitivity over stirring memories of the Hitlerian past among her European neighbors.

One must ask whether this relatively passive stance will continue to characterize West Germany if French "obstructionism" and American "domination" reach a point where they threaten West Germany's economic and political interests. If this day should arrive we may witness in the twentieth century the repetition on a European scale of a process which took place in the nineteenth. We have tended to visualize European unification much as the German liberals visualized German unification prior to 1848: a horizontal and cooperative effort of equal states. Instead, western Europe may one day be unified as was Germany in 1871 by an act of will by one state. West Germany, in defense of its interests, may play the Prussia of European unification while France plays Austria. What may yet appear is a Bismarck willing to take the leading role.

To forestall this, or some other undesirable event, can one reasonably hope for U.S. initiatives which could resolve the issues symbolized by the technology gap? There are unfortunately few examples in history of an expanding power deliberately limiting itself. The large American corporations operating in Europe can not easily limit themselves in the competition for efficiency and markets; to do so they would risk being undone by their American and European competitors. Any efforts of the U.S. government through licensing, purchasing, or financial policies to even the balance between American and European corporations would be greatly resisted by American corporations.

Moreover, the encouragement by the United States government of the emergence of a united Europe capable of meeting the challenge of the many dimensions of the technology gap might pose over the long term a serious threat to American interests. Such a European entity would have not only the power to drive American corporations and exports out of the European market, but could seek to develop a foreign policy (especially toward German reunification and Soviet Union) and a military force independent of the United States. It is because of these huge political issues embedded in the technology gap that anyone surveying the present course of events and the helplessness of anyone to act to save the situation is tempted to repeat the words of de Gaulle, "*Les choses étant ce qu'elles sont . . .*" and shrug his shoulders.

Contrary to the often expressed view of America's European critics, the difficulty lies not with the presence of an

American political will to expand or an economic will to dominate, but in the absence of countervailing power from the Europeans. As long as Europe's political problems (especially the future of West Germany and western Europe's relations with the Soviet Union) remain unsettled and the Common Market provides American corporations with unparalleled commercial opportunities, the U.S. Government and American corporations cannot act very differently from the way they do if their interests are to be secured. And the Europeans, for their own part, are too divided among themselves and too dependent on the United States to counter what they regard as the long-term consequences of American economic expansionism. But however unsinister America's basic motives may be and however much Europeans must share responsibility for what is happening, these facts do not lessen Europe's profound apprehensions over its future.

The challenge facing Europe was expressed in the opening address to the Conference on European Cooperation in Advanced Technology held in 1966:

> Modern industrial research programmes call for material and human resources hitherto undreamed of, and resources which are beyond the capacity of even the leading European nations, with populations of fifty millions or so. The conclusion forced upon us is that the European countries must pool their efforts if they wish to play a continuing part in world economic development. Otherwise, it will not be many years before they are so far behind the United States and the Soviet Union in advanced industrial fields that relatively, they will have fallen to the level of underdeveloped countries.[18]

In the last analysis, therefore, we come back to the issue posed at the beginning by *Recherche Scientifique et Indépen-*

[18] United Kingdom Council, *European Cooperation Report*, p. 4.

dance: What is to be the political destiny of France and, one must add, of Europe in an age where scientific research and development have become primary ingredients of national power? As I have sought to show, the answer to this question cannot be provided by Paris alone. It probably cannot even be determined by the Europeans alone. Without political unity Europe (including Great Britain) cannot articulate a common policy toward the United States and a common response toward the contemporary scientific-technological revolution. Nor is there much reason to believe that the problem (as the Europeans see it) can be "solved" under present conditions on an Atlantic basis through some sort of technological Marshall Plan.

Unless the present course of developments is drastically altered, one must conclude, along with the EEC Committee on Medium Term Economic Policy, that, "if the Six countries remain, as they probably have done for a generation, the main world importers of discoveries and exporters of brains, they will be condemning themselves to a cumulative underdevelopment which will soon render their decline irremediable."[19] The possibility is real that Europe will become increasingly dependent on the United States, importing from her the science and technology required for economic growth and national security. Perhaps, as France would have it, European concern over American hegemony may yet generate common European policies toward science, technology, and the United States. If not, Europe will become ever more irrelevant as an independent power in a world whose affairs are dominated by scientific nation-states of continental dimensions.

[19] Quoted in speech by Robert Marjolin to the European Parliament, Oct. 18, 1966.

459

INDEX

Index

Other books published for
The Center of International Studies
Princeton University

Gabriel A. Almond, *The Appeals of Communism*
Gabriel A. Almond and James S. Coleman, editors, *The Politics of the Developing Areas*
Gabriel A. Almond and Sidney Verba, *The Civic Culture: Political Attitudes and Democracy in Five Nations*
Richard J. Barnet and Richard A. Falk, *Security in Disarmament*
Cyril E. Black and Thomas P. Thornton, editors, *Communism and Revolution: The Strategic Uses of Political Violence*
Robert J. C. Butow, *Tojo and the Coming of the War*
Miriam Camps, *Britain and the European Community, 1955-1963*
Bernard C. Cohen, *The Political Process and Foreign Policy: The Making of the Japanese Peace Settlement*
Bernard C. Cohen, *The Press and Foreign Policy*
Charles De Visscher, *Theory and Reality in Public International Law*, translated by P. E. Corbett
Frederick S. Dunn, *Peace-making and the Settlement with Japan*
Richard F. Hamilton, *Affluence and the French Worker in the Fourth Republic*
Harry Eckstein, *Division and Cohesion in Democracy: a Study of Norway*
Herman Kahn, *On Thermonuclear War*
W. W. Kaufmann, editor, *Military Policy and National Security*
Klaus Knorr, *On the Uses of Military Power in the Nuclear Age*
Klaus Knorr, *The War Potential of Nations*
Klaus Knorr, editor, *NATO and American Security*
Klaus Knorr and Sidney Verba, editors, *The International System: Theoretical Essays*
Peter Kunstadter, editor, *Southeast Asian Tribes, Minorities, and Nations*
Sidney J. Ploss, *Conflict and Decision-making in Soviet Russia*
Lucian W. Pye, *Guerrilla Communism in Malaya*
James N. Rosenau, editor, *International Aspects of Civil Strife*
James N. Rosenau, *National Leadership and Foreign Policy: A Case Study in the Mobilization of Public Support*
Rolf Sannwald and Jacques Stohler, *Economic Integration: Theoretical Assumptions and Consequences of European Unification*. Translated by Herman F. Karreman
Richard L. Sklar, *Nigerian Political Parties: Power in an Emergent African Nation*
Glenn H. Snyder, *Deterrence and Defense*
Harold and Margaret Sprout, *The Ecological Perspective on Human Affairs, With Special Reference to International Politics*
Thomas P. Thornton, *The Third World in Soviet Perspective: Studies by Soviet Writers on the Developing Areas*
Sidney Verba, *Small Groups and Political Behavior: A Study of Leadership*
Karl von Vorys, *Political Development in Pakistan*
Myron Weiner, *Party Politics in India*
E. Victor Wolfenstein, *The Revolutionary Personality: Lenin, Trotsky, Gandhi*
Oran R. Young, *The Intermediaries: Third Parties in International Crises*